Psychology Applied to Nursing

By

LAWRENCE AUGUSTUS AVERILL, Ph. D.

Formerly Professor of Psychology, Massachusetts State Teachers College, Worcester, Massachusetts

And

FLORENCE C. KEMPF, R. N., B. S., A. M.

Professor of Nursing Education and Head of the Department of Nursing Education, College of Science and Arts, Michigan State University, East Lansing, Michigan

Fifth Edition

Illustrated

W. B. Saunders Company
Philadelphia and London

Reprinted, October, 1956

© 1956, BY W. B. SAUNDERS COMPANY

Copyright, 1938, 1942, 1946 and 1951 by W. B. Saunders Company

COPYRIGHT UNDER THE INTERNATIONAL COPYRIGHT UNION

All Rights Reserved
This book is protected by copyright.
No part of it may be duplicated or reproduced
in any manner without written permission from the publisher.

Made in the United States of America
Press of W. B. Saunders Company, Philadelphia

LIBRARY OF CONGRESS CATALOG CARD NUMBER: 56–5826

PREFACE TO THE FIFTH EDITION

THE AUTHORS OF *Psychology Applied to Nursing* have been flattered by the continuing role which this text is playing in the general field of nursing education. They have striven in the present revision to bring the book thoroughly up to date in all particulars and to adapt it still more closely to the needs and capacities of student nurses. With the steady increase in our population, the growing number of older people in it, and the advance in our knowledge of the care and nursing of the handicapped, the abnormal and the aging, along with the demands for ever more nurses in our general hospitals, clinics, schools and private families, the contributions made by nurses trained in the psychological backgrounds of their profession are becoming constantly more significant. It is our ambition and hope to implement this growing army of nursing practitioners to meet more skillfully and understandingly the demands of the age.

In the mechanical rearrangement of the text, the authors have deemed it logical to include in Unit 1, along with the original Chapter 1 on "Psychology, Adjustment, and the Student Nurse," old Chapters 17 and 18, "Psychology in Nursing" and "Psychology at Work in Today's World," which now become Chapters 3 and 2, respectively. In this way, it is felt that the student will become oriented to the prominent place occupied by modern psychology in the complex modern age. With the building in of this background at the outset, she will be equipped to proceed into the specialized study of psychology as it is related to her own field of nursing. In this arrangement, old Chapter 2, "Self Guidance In Study," becomes a new Unit 2, remaining in the early part of the book, as it logically should, with its helpful materials on economical and effective ways of studying the specialized units that make up the body of the text.

Pursuant to the now almost universal tendency among psychologists to place little or no emphasis upon "instinct," the authors have in this edition of *Psychology Applied to Nursing* eliminated the term completely, and have omitted their earlier presentation of "ego projection" as being of little help to the young student. In its stead has been developed a psychology of man's basal wants and his drives for emotional satisfaction.

A number of new sections have been added, in the interest of keeping the text in line with developing trends in psychology as they apply definitely to problems and practices of nursing. In them will be found new material on the mentally ill; psychology in the ministry; delinquency; slum clearance and housing projects; old age assistance; public and private housing for the elderly; vocational rehabilitation; child and adolescent psychology; narcotic addiction; alcoholism; and problems of nursing as they relate to certain specific modern diseases and conditions, including cancer, cardiac diseases, epilepsy, cerebral palsy, multiple sclerosis and muscular dystrophy.

All factual and statistical materials have been brought up to date. The style and terminology throughout have been simplified and the general vocabulary has been scrutinized with the purpose of making the whole text more comprehensible to the young student.

The Suggested Readings at the ends of chapters have been reduced in number and out-of-date titles discarded. We have felt that too many references tend to bewilder students and that, while schools of nursing libraries have reasonably adequate supplementary books and professional periodicals, few of them possess the comprehensive list of reading references that we had appended to our chapters in the earlier editions. In the present edition, we have limited these materials to a few but important titles at the conclusion of each chapter, selected with care for their practical worth as well as for their availability in most modern nursing libraries.

As heretofore, we have stressed mental health throughout, and we have striven to present a workable and challenging psychology gauged to ensure that the student nurse shall build into her personality and her resources a usable fund of psychological knowledge and skill that will make her not only a wholesome personality herself but also a sympathetic practitioner of the art of ministering to those who stand in need of her good services. This dual philosophy will be found to obtain in every section of the book.

The authors are grateful to the student nurses at Michigan State University, and to Miss Hilda Helmke, for permission to use their photographs.

LAWRENCE A. AVERILL
FLORENCE C. KEMPF

CONTENTS

UNIT I

THE DRAMATIC ROLE OF PSYCHOLOGY IN ALL MAJOR HUMAN ENTERPRISE

Chapter 1
Psychology, Adjustment, and the Student Nurse — 2
Psychology and Its Methods, 9; Thought Problems for the Student, 11; Suggested Readings, 12.

Chapter 2
Psychology at Work in Today's World — 14
The Psychological Field, 14; Psychology Applied to Areas of Human Living, 18; Thought Problems for the Student, 33; Suggested Readings, 34.

Chapter 3
Psychology in Nursing — 35
The Patient, the Nurse's First Concern, 35; Principles in Practice, 42; The Guidance of Health, 43; The Hospital Situation, 48; Thought Problems for the Student, 54; Suggested Readings, 55.

UNIT 2

How to Study Effectively

Chapter 4

Self Guidance in Study   58

Some Rules for Self Guidance in Study, 59; The Wider Meaning of Study, 71; Thought Problems for the Student, 72; Suggested Readings, 73.

UNIT 3

Why People Behave as They Do

Chapter 5

The Original Foundations of Behavior   76

Man's First Basal Want: Bodily Comfort, 78; The Drive for Emotional Satisfaction, 86; Thought Problems for the Student, 94; Suggested Readings, 96.

Chapter 6

Habits, Attitudes, and Other Determiners of Behavior   97

Learned and Unlearned Behavior, 97; Habit as Motive, 100; Attitudes as Motives, 104; Interests as Motives, 106; Success and Failure as Motives, 108; Emotional Dependence as Motive, 111; Thought Problems for the Student, 113; Suggested Readings, 114.

Chapter 7

The Neuromuscular Mechanism as Motivator   115

The Sense Organs as Gateways to the Brain, 115; The Nervous Processes, 124; Responding Muscular and Glandular Processes, 130; Thought Problems for the Student, 140; Suggested Readings, 141.

CONTENTS

UNIT 4

HOW WE LEARN

Chapter 8

Learning: Stages and Procedures 144

The First Stage in Learning: Acquiring the Information, 144; The Second Stage in Learning: Retaining the Data, 151; The Third Stage in Learning: Recalling the Data, 155; The Motivation of Learning, 158; Thought Problems for the Student, 166; Suggested Readings, 167.

Chapter 9

Learning: Some Comparisons and Principles 168

Experimenting with Animal Learning, 168; Trial and Error in Human Learning, 171; Learning and Insight: Gestalt, 172; Animal Learning as Conditioning, 174; Some Important Principles of Human Learning, 177; Thought Problems for the Student, 188; Suggested Readings, 190.

Chapter 10

The Individual Learner 191

The Progression of Learning, 191; The Place of Intelligence in Learning, 198; The Individual Thinker, 206; Certain Physiological Factors Determining Learning, 209; Effects of Certain Extraneous Factors Upon Learning, 212; Thought Problems for the Student, 216; Suggested Readings, 218.

UNIT 5

THE PROCESS OF GROWING UP

Chapter 11

Psychology of Childhood and Adolescence 220

Physical Growth of the Child, 220; Motor Development and Control, 223; Mental and Emotional Growth: Habits, 225; The Problem Child, 230; The Onset of Puberty, 231; Pubescent and Adolescent Growth, 233; Adolescent Interests, 235; Adolescent Delinquency and Misdemeanors, 240; Church and Religious Interests, 244; Community Influences Needful for Youth, 245; Relationship of Nursing to Childhood, 247; Thought Problems for the Student, 250; Suggested Readings, 252.

Chapter 12

Achieving Adulthood 253

    Thought Problems for the Student, 268; Suggested Readings, 269.

UNIT 6

CONFLICTS AND TENSIONS

Chapter 13

Conflict, Tension and Frustration 272

    Mental Conflict, 272; Adjustment and Maladjustment, 276; The Meaning of Integration, 286; The Nurse and Introversion, 287; Thought Problems for the Student, 289; Suggested Readings, 290.

Chapter 14

Emotional States and Tensions 291

    The Psychologic Concept of Feeling, 291; The Emotions, 295; Mood and Temperament, 315; Thought Problems for the Student, 316; Suggested Readings, 317.

UNIT 7

IN PURSUIT OF MENTAL HEALTH

Chapter 15

Mental Hygiene of the Family 320

    The Adequate Home, 320; Education for Family Life and Homemaking, 322; The Disharmonious Home and Its Effects, 323; The Broken Home and Its Effects, 329; Ignorant Homes, 330; The Problem of Discipline, 332; Importance of the Early Years, 334; The Nurse and the Family, 335; Thought Problems for the Student, 337; Suggested Readings, 339.

Chapter 16

Mental Health in Succeeding Life Stages 340

    Mental Health in Infancy and the Preschool Age, 340; Mental Health of the School Child, 344; Mental Health of the Adolescent,

347; *Mental Health of the Adult, 351; Mental Health of Senescence, 354; Thought Problems for the Student, 355; Suggested Readings, 356.*

UNIT 8

SPECIAL PROBLEMS OF ADJUSTMENT

Chapter 17

The Psychology of the Aging and Aged   358

Some Problems of Aging and the Aged, 359; Nursing Problems, 369; Thought Problems for the Student, 373; Suggested Readings, 374.

Chapter 18

Nursing the Physically Handicapped   375

The Handicapped Adult, 375; Nursing Problems in Certain Specific Modern Diseases and Conditions, 387; The Handicapped Child, 394; The Nurse in the School, 401; Thought Problems for the Student, 403; Suggested Readings, 404.

BIBLIOGRAPHY   405

INDEX   409

Unit I

The Dramatic Role of Psychology in All Major Human Enterprise

Chapter 1

The knowledge which a man can use is the only real knowledge which has life and growth in it and converts into practical power.

FROUDE

Science of the mind

PSYCHOLOGY, ADJUSTMENT, AND THE STUDENT NURSE

What Values May the Student Nurse Derive from the Study of Psychology? Wherever people work together, play together, live together, there they influence each other's behavior and there too arises the need for understanding people so that the maximum good in personal relations may be achieved. Psychology has contributed to the discovery of the bases which underlie universal urges and drives, feelings and fears, as well as to the discovery of the varied strengths, weaknesses and ambitions of individuals. Through the study of this subject, principles have been derived by which human behavior may be understood, influenced and guided.

The student nurse is entering a vocation which deals with all kinds of people. Before she can develop an understanding of other people, however, she must first seek insight into her own behavior and what lies behind it. She needs to recognize that behind every act of her own there is a motivating force which must be examined before self insight can follow, before guidance of others may even be considered.

An understanding of origins, an appreciation of values, and a constantly increasing power of self-discipline may result from the study and application of psychology. Self-discipline is, we recognize, an aim never fully attained; but the more we understand about our natures and the more we learn of the intelligent directing of forces underlying them, the greater is the degree of possible self mastery. When the student nurse, realizing this, has learned why people behave as they do, she will be able to guide others, as well as herself, and control situations.

What Makes an Effective Student Nurse? It is a well established practice for schools of nursing to require a personal interview with applicants for admission. Many students will recall the question: "What makes you think that you would make a good nurse?" Some had not explored their reasons for interest in nursing, and found it a difficult question to answer. Yet, probably all will agree that every prospective member of the profession should not only know herself, but should strive to match that self with the qualifications which we seek in the nurse when we bring her to the bedside of the sick, to the homes in our communities. Suppose, then, we examine some of the attributes which contribute to success in nursing.

Mental and Physical Well-being. We require that a young woman who has the right kind and degree of aptitude shall not only master subject matter but shall think through its relationship to life, its connection with the procedures which she practices daily, and that she shall recognize when changes in behavior, based on more knowledge, are indicated. Important too are a wholesome, cheerful approach to each day's activities, cordial relations with people, the ability to keep going with a smile when the average individual would be inclined to give up. This ties up closely with sound physical health. Therefore, schools of nursing try to ensure this quality by a thorough physical check-up and necessary corrections prior to acceptance into the school.

A problem which faces the student is how, when she is surrounded by illness, she can safeguard her own health. Early in her program of study are included lessons on personal hygiene and the reasons, based on physiological and psychological principles, for developing regular habits of self care. The charm of the American girl is sometimes credited to her meticulous cleanliness, her appearance of wholesomeness. It is an essential for the nurse, who, in her spotless white uniform, symbolizes health. It is achieved only when the student nurse makes application of the learnings in this area which are made available to her. To develop a program of self care, based on scientific knowledge, is important; to follow such a program faithfully requires the belief that positive health is of the greatest value. It is easy to be casual and careless in such practices, but neglect constitutes a hazard to well-being. Such indifference in the student nurse disqualifies her as a teacher of health.

Spiritual Sense of Security. The student nurse who is in a school of nursing too far from her own home to continue attendance at the church of her affiliation is encouraged to seek the church of the same denomination or of a similar creed in the community where she now is. When hours of duty interfere with church attendance in the morning, she may be able to attend an afternoon or an evening service.

It is a definite asset when a student nurse is adusting to new situations and people to continue the familiar practice of meditation, prayer and worship which contributed to her serenity and security while at home. It does require some effort to fit her religious program into the busy schedule of school and hospital but it can be managed to the benefit of the individual.

Fig. 1. Regular thoughtful *study* is important.

Usually churches have programs of activities for young people which provide an opportunity for newcomers to meet and become acquainted with both young men and women in that community. Since nurses are expected to be both well informed people and well rounded personalities, it is desirable for them to know their contemporaries who are engaged in the various fields of work in the community and not to confine their companionship to people in their own professional group. The church is one of the institutions which offer this opportunity as well as the important center for worship which answers a need felt by many people.

<u>Good Habits of Study and Work.</u> The program of study demands sincere interest and eagerness to learn, as well as specific habits of application to work. An early chapter in this book concerns itself with the guidance of study. Insight and skill will result only when the individual has the persistence to keep trying; when she frequently examines her progress in learning and its relations to what she is doing; when she gauges her skills in practice and is willing to profit

from constructive criticism; and when she voluntarily seeks the guidance of supervision from those qualified, so that her errors and weaknesses may be discovered and corrected. It is a great morale builder for the student nurse to become aware of her own daily progress, to derive satisfaction from the little things, and to take pride in doing well whatever she does. She needs to understand that growth is inevitable if she brings to each class and each task a willingness to learn, that she may begin each day anew with the advantage of the knowledge gained yesterday, that there are always desirable goals left for the future, and that deferred satisfactions are inherent in the social professions.

Effective Behavior in New Situations. It is important for the nurse to maintain emotional balance and serenity when others cannot. This requires a nervous system stable by inheritance. Very important, too, are the emotional habits which have functioned through the early years of life. If she has indulged in frequent fits of anger, or yielded to moods of elation and depression, with their characteristic behaviors, the development of self control will present a problem; if tears have been the usual response to trying situations, the changing of this response will be difficult. Shyness, self consciousness, extreme sensitiveness to the opinions of others present handicaps, although probably not such serious ones as excessive self assurance, without either comprehensive knowledge or experience as a basis. It is exceedingly important, then, to determine what measure of self control the nurse, as an individual, can develop. Faith, knowledge, experience and a sense of humor contribute to that inner strength which enables people to meet the unexpected with poise and to maintain a sense of perspective. Nursing is a field for individuals who are developing the self control basic to that unified behavior through which the nurse may devote her thoughts and energies to her patients' needs in all situations.

Commendable Attitudes Expressed in Action. The social adaptability of the prospective nurse is also an important factor in her success. She will come in contact with persons of all levels of social origin and security and in all vocational fields. She needs to have respect for the dignity of all individuals, regardless of race, religion, education, occupation or appearance. Attitudes and consequent behavior of young people reflect their home training and backgrounds. Has she, in the give and take of family life, learned the practice of consideration of others, the daily courtesies which one associates with good breeding? Have her parents encouraged her to make choices and decisions which her growing maturity qualifies her to make, or has she continued dependent on parental decisions? Does she respect parental authority and respond obediently to it, or does she resent and evade such guidance as may be attempted?

Difficulties in adustment to home life, unless examined and corrected, may well lead to residence problems for a student nurse. In dormitories where large numbers live together, some rules and regulations make for greater comfort and security for all residents; they do so, however, only in so far as each resident upholds them. Willingness to compromise on privileges and on matters of minor consequence, and cooperation toward the greater satisfaction of the majority are exceedingly important where people of many varying personalities live together.

The trend is more and more toward various forms of student cooperative associations. Here students and faculty share in determining rules and privileges, the students, however, carrying the major part of organization, development and administration. This cooperation is an important step in assisting students to learn by practice, self-discipline and good citizenship. It requires more time than the old-fashioned way, but usually results in happier students who enjoy the responsibilities of adulthood in their personal as well as in their professional lives. It is one more experiment in the democratic way of living. In the words of Poincaré, "Experiment is the sole source of truth. It alone can teach us anything new; it alone can give us certainty. But to observe is not enough. Science is built up with facts as a house is with stones. But a collection of facts is no more science than a heap of stones is a house."

If living arrangements are such that two nurses share a room, this is a chance to show that the shared life can be fun. A nurse sharing a room with another should observe the following rules: She should keep her belongings in her own space and make it a neat dwelling place; she should not borrow cosmetics, clothes or money; and by the same token, she should not lend; she should waste no one's time—there is never quite enough as it is; when the roommate is studying, neither conversation nor radio music should obstruct the effort; she should avoid boasting about her popularity, possessions, exploits, family prestige or cleverness—it is far better to be discovered than to be found out; she should observe the "hear not, see not, speak not" adage when it comes to gossip, which has a corrosive effect on all it touches. She should be a good companion, a real friend without inviting dependence or expecting her roommate to carry responsibility for her or her possessions. It is an art to live in such close proximity with another person, maintaining cordial relations and without one of the participants imposing on the other—but it can be done.

Continuing Previous Interests and Activities. The educational opportunities and cultural advantages which a nurse has had contribute to an interesting personality. Appreciation of the things which make life richer, more beautiful and more wonderful is a definite asset; a nurse well rounded in her interests and activities has resources to draw from in leisure moments, as well as in the care of her patients. This circumstance is no small factor in the patients' mental recovery.

The student nurse should acquaint herself with the recreational and cultural facilities which exist in her new surroundings. There are usually programs, concerts and lectures which may be enjoyed at relatively small cost. Since there is so much that is new in her environment, it might be preferable for her to continue developing a previous interest in her leisure time program. An interesting illustration which came to the author's attention is cited:

Every morning at 7:15 as the author passed through the living room of the nurses' residence, she observed that a graduate nurse was playing the piano. She played beautifully and it was a temptation to linger and enjoy the music. Curiosity finally led to the question: "How does it happen that we are favored with such a pleasant concert at this hour of the day?" This nurse, as a child, had always practiced her music lesson every morning immediately after breakfast. She continued this practice through high school. When she entered a school of nursing she found that she felt better about things and the day went more smoothly whenever she could spend a period of time, although brief, with her music. She decided that if she got up in the morning fifteen minutes earlier than her classmates and spent that amount of time at the piano, she would be satisfied. She followed this schedule during her three years as a student nurse; since she graduated, she has been in one hospital where it was not possible for her to continue this practice. When she changed her position, she made sure that she could continue to grow in her avocation as well as in her chosen profession. She is now taking music lessons, since her nursing classes and study no longer demand so much of her time. Thus, while preparing for her profession, she did not permit herself to forget the skill which she had developed in a special field, but rather grew in this aptitude. From her music she secured satisfaction, enjoyment and release for tensions when there were difficult days in her regular line of duty.

The information was not secured whether she attended concerts and operas as opportunities arose during her student days, but from the quality of her morning selections, one would conclude that she has extended her appreciation in this area beyond her own performance. Her music will be an asset as a topic for conversation with hospital patients, in the care of psychiatric patients, or in home nursing, and it represents a social accomplishment of great value.

Each person has aptitudes which are waiting to be developed and expressed. The nurse must consider the activities in her experience which represented her outstanding satisfactions, and must explore the possibilities for continuing growth in the aptitudes which she has already discovered are part of her heritage and in the skills in which she has achieved some proficiency. They will serve to broaden her

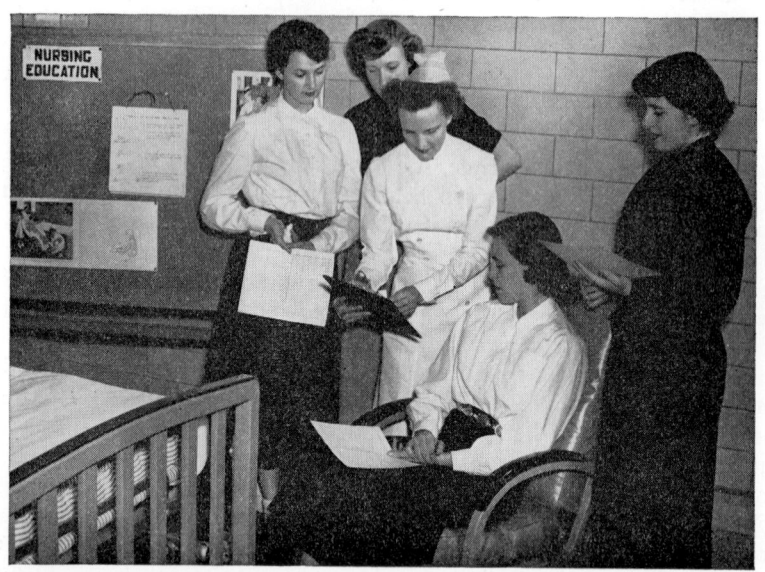

Fig. 2. Seek and use teacher guidance whenever help is needed.

point of view in daily living and they may contribute an ingredient to nursing care which will be refreshing and interesting to the patient.

By now it is surely apparent to the reader that to become a good nurse presents a challenge which is not for the half-hearted, the indifferent, the lazy, nor for the young woman who wishes merely to please a parent or aunt. It is a field for young women of fine intellect, who are willing to work to secure preparation which will make for effectiveness in their professional as well as personal lives. In the pages that follow, the prospective nurse will find much information, many explanations and illustrations which will make for better understanding of herself and of others and of the motives which underlie behavior patterns of all people. The purpose of this book is to give her guidance for her best growth and development as a person and as a nurse. To read is not enough. She should think over and discuss what she finds here with classmates and instructors, investigate suggested references as time permits, and compare the points of view of the various authorities. In her daily work, she should look for applications of this subject matter so that she may reach her own conclusions and recognize generalizations which underlie good adjustments in her personal as well as in her professional life.

The opportunities in the profession of nursing have never been greater. The earnest student may visualize for herself a vocation in which growth and satisfaction are limitless. As she learns to apply sound principles of psychology, she may extend her personal happiness and her professional effectiveness.

PSYCHOLOGY AND ITS METHODS

Psychology is that field of study which concerns itself with our human behavior and the motives that underlie it. While strictly speaking the term suggests study of the mind, or "psyche," psychologists have long since realized the futility of attempting to study mind as such. What they are interested to find out is how we react to situations that confront us and why we think, feel and behave as we do. In other words, psychological science seeks to study and account for the product, or the expression, of mind rather than to study "mind" *per se*. In following through this program which he has set for himself, the psychologist finds it possible to help us to understand, first, ourselves and our own behavior, and then the behavior and the motives of the society around and beyond us. In the achievement of such a dual goal, psychology contributes to the happiness and the effectiveness of men in their personal and social relationships, and so aids in establishing a better human environment and a happier world.

Among the many methods that psychologists employ in their study of behavior, three stand out most prominently; they are: (1) the observational method, (2) the experimental method and (3) the clinical method. In the first of these—the method of observation—the psychologist *observes* the behavior of individuals or of groups. Without attempting to control or standardize the details of his study, he records human behavior as he encounters it. Thus, a psychologist watching and recording the behavior of a group of children in a free play situation would be employing the method of observation. While subject to grave limitations and a margin of error, and hence not too scientific, this method is available to any student, simple to use, and almost limitless in the scope of the problems that may be attacked.

All that is needful is, in the first instance, a careful observer, and, in the second, a reacting subject or group.

The experimental method requires, in addition to observer and subject, a rigorously controlled technique in which all the factors affecting the behavior or performance of the subject are held constant, with the single important exception of the specific one (called

Fig. 3. We learn by serving.

the *independent variable*) that has been singled out to be examined. Thus, if a psychologist were to study the day-by-day influence of room temperature upon a learning group, he would have to use the same group at the same hour, with an exactly equivalent task to be done, and with the same conditions of motivation, seating, lighting, freedom from distraction and direction giving, but with varying room temperature, from sitting to sitting. It would be possible, after a prolonged and careful experiment of this sort, to state with confidence that the most efficient mental work is accomplished, at least for the particular subjects studied, with room temperature at—say—68° F. This method of establishing psychological knowledge is one that requires careful planning, consistent execution and faithful recording. It requires also careful interpretation.

The clinical method of studying behavior is one of the most challenging as well as the most recent of all the psychological methods. It is employed primarily by psychological consultants and by psychiatric practitioners as a means of understanding the causes of people's fears, worries, obsessions, and of their personal, social or vocational maladjustments. Many of the ills from which mankind suffers and which keep individuals from achieving their goals and purposes are psychological in origin rather than organic or medical. If the clinical psychologist can determine the factors that are producing problem behavior in a child, or unrest, failure, frustration or aberration in an adult, he can often assist the individuals involved to better adjustment and more satisfying life experience. This method is employed commonly, as its name suggests, by a trained psychologist acting as clinician in his own office or consulting room, with his subject before him, in a *face-to-face* effort to search out the sources and nature of the patient's mental or emotional difficulty as the basis for prescribing a new approach to his problems or an altered regimen for his life.

Before turning again specifically to the problems of nursing, we pause in the next chapter to consider some of the broader applications of psychology as employed today by specialists in widely different areas of the world's work. Our purpose in so doing is to orient the young student to the prominent place occupied by modern psychology in the present complex age.

THOUGHT PROBLEMS FOR THE STUDENT

1. Illustrate from your experience how a lowered level of physical well-being has affected your ability to get along with people.
2. Confirm by newspaper clippings the statement that the nurse in spotless white is used to symbolize positive health.
3. What would represent little things from which the young nurse might derive satisfactions?
4. In a brief paragraph write an account of an embarrassing experience which you recall. Now write in detail how you would meet the situation with poise if it were possible to relive that experience.
5. What are some attitudes and behaviors your home training has made a part of you that will serve as a sound foundation for nursing?
6. List four rules which you believe would be desirable in dormitory living.
7. Examine the cultural facilities which exist in your community and select three which appeal to you for leisure enjoyment.
8. Develop a daily program of self care which incorporates the physiological

principles of personal hygiene which you now know. Add principles of mental hygiene as you discover them in reading the pages that follow.
9. What do you believe may be the dangers associated with "excessive self assurance without knowledge or experience as a basis"?
10. Write an essay of 300 words discussing the characteristics which you think qualify you as a potential good nurse.

SUGGESTED READINGS

1. Crawley, Mildred: A Mental Health Approach to Nursing Arts. *Nursing Outlook*, August 1953, pp. 454–455.
   "A faculty group reorganizes the basic course in nursing arts to emphasize the development of skills in human relations."
2. Gault, Alma E.: Nursing's Professional Reach. *Nursing Outlook*, July 1954, pp. 375–377.
   The potential of nursing as a profession is extended as we continue to develop the inherent art and science.
3. Goodnow, M.: *Nursing History*. 9th ed. Philadelphia, W. B. Saunders Company, 1953.
   In this well known book will be found something of the background in nursing history that ought to be a part of the mental equipment of all professional nurses of the present day.
4. Gregg, Alan: The Opportunities Before Us. *Nursing Outlook*, August 1953, pp. 448–450.
   A brief view of where nurses are, where they may choose to go.
5. Hearn, Gordon: A Social-Psychological View of Nursing Service. *Nursing Outlook*, November 1953, pp. 632–634.
   "Helping people to get well and stay well is, in large part, a social psychological problem."
6. Kempf, F. C.: *The Person as a Nurse*. New York, The Macmillan Company, 1950.
   A book which enables students to understand the selective process which operates when applicants present their credentials for admission to schools of nursing. Discussion then follows on the explorative thinking which should underlie students' adjustments as they come to identify themselves with their profession.
7. Lindemann, E., and Greer, I. M.: Emotional Maturity. *The Journal of Pastoral Care, Fall-Winter*, 1949, Cambridge, Massachusetts.
   A discussion with meaningful illustrations of how effective, creative, productive and constructive individuals may grow. Criteria denoting maturity are simply stated.
8. Murphy, Gardner: Professional Progress through Personal Growth. *American Journal of Nursing*, December 1954, pp. 1464–1467.
   "Nurses, who constantly grow themselves, have a better understanding of their patients as persons and consequently give better nursing care."
9. Porter, Elizabeth K.: What it Means to be a Professional Nurse. *American Journal of Nursing*, August 1953, pp. 948–950.
   The responsibilities confronting the modern nurse may be understood by careful reading of this article.
10. Tatum, J. R.: Changing Roles of Professional Personnel in the Field of Medical Care. *Nursing Outlook*, December 1953, pp. 694–696.

This article can assist student nurses in clarifying their concepts of the changing role of the nurse.

11. Ubbink, Mary R.: Patients for a Day. *Nursing Outlook*, April 1954, pp. 190–191.
What it means to be a patient can be better understood with a little first hand experience.

A. Related:
 1. Sociology
 2. physiology
 3. psychiatry (abnorm. behavior whereas psychology is norm. behavior)

B. psychologist — deals c̄ behavior
C. Research
 1. Isolate problem
 2. Estab. proced. to gather facts
 3. Gather facts
 4. Organize
 5. May have to repeat

Chapter 2

It should not be surprising that the problems of our rapidly changing social and economic structures have been so generally recognized to be psychological problems.

A. T. POFFENBERGER

PSYCHOLOGY AT WORK IN TODAY'S WORLD

THE PSYCHOLOGICAL FIELD

Early History of Psychology. Psychology is as old as the world itself, although its development as a scientific study falls completely within the last three-quarters of a century. Beginning with the work of Aristotle (384–322 B.C.), it remained for many centuries a field of purely speculative philosophy in which armchair scholars arrived at many improbable conclusions about the great enigma—man. It is not surprising that in its prescientific era, mysticism and dogmatism combined to make psychology—the study of the soul, as it was termed— a word to conjure with. This mystical element is still found today in the layman's usual understanding of the word. Of the significance of psychology as a modern science based upon biological principles and having its own peculiar methods, he knows little.

The history of psychology as a science is usually conceded to have begun with the opening at Leipzig University of the first psychological laboratory, under the direction of Dr. Wilhelm Wundt, in 1879. Four years later, in 1883, the first laboratory in our own country was opened at Johns Hopkins University, under the direction of the late Dr. G. Stanley Hall, who had studied under Wundt, in the years immediately preceding, at Leipzig.

Progress of psychology as a science in these two laboratories, and in others that followed them shortly, was at first slow. Nearly two decades were required to strip away the mystical and the metaphysical trappings which had been accumulating for more than two thousand years around the "science of the soul" before modern scientifically-minded students could orient themselves in the field and undertake those programs of modern research in problems of human behavior that so enrich psychology today.

Many notable names have appeared since the time of Wundt and Hall. William James (1842–1910) at Harvard became, subsequent to his appointment initially in physiology and afterwards in psychology, a leader in the science. His "Principles of Psychology" became notable throughout the entire Western world. J. McKeen Cattell (1860–1944) actually occupied the world's first professorship in psychology, in 1888, at the University of Pennsylvania. Later Professor of Psychology at Columbia University, he was elected to preside over the first American International Congress of Psychology. Sigmund Freud (1856–1939) was the first man to make use of psychology in the medical field, applying it to the understanding and treatment of insanity and nervous diseases and disorders. E. L. Thorndike (1874–1949) was among the first to apply psychological principles to the problems and methods of education, and wrote in elucidation of his extensive research in this area.

It would be impractical to extend here the list of names of notable men and women who have contributed to the evolution of psychology into the many-sided and far-reaching programs that characterize it today. It is the purpose of this chapter to list and explain the principal avenues of psychological research as they relate to the problems of improving human living, efficiency and welfare. The thousands of trained and accredited psychologists who are carrying forward this effort may remain anonymous without any detriment to our present purpose. There are upwards of 11,000 members of the American Psychological Association. These include most of the qualified psychologists in this country.

The Principal Fields of Psychology. The life and activities of men are so many-sided that psychologists have found it helpful to map out our human behavior into a number of areas, in each of which more intensive research may be carried on than could possibly be done in an undifferentiated general field. Specialists working within each of these areas strive continuously to push out the frontiers of our knowledge with particularized methods and techniques.

The American Psychological Association recognizes seventeen divisions of psychological effort. They are here enumerated, with a brief descriptive label designating the scope of each:

DIVISION	SCOPE
1. Division of General Psychology	Adult human behavior
2. Division of the Teaching of Psychology	Aims and principles involved in teaching psychology

DIVISION	SCOPE
3. Division of Experimental Psychology	Human and animal behavior subjected to laboratory or controlled techniques
4. Division of Evaluation and Measurement	Construction and administering of intelligence, aptitude, schoolroom, personality and other tests
5. Division of Childhood and Adolescence	Behavior, drives, values of children and youth
6. Division of Personality and Social Psychology	Motives, actions and traits of individuals, groups, crowds, mobs
7. Society for the Psychological Study of Social Issues	Cultural changes and organization; social control
8. Division of Esthetics	Taste, beauty, hedonic tone
9. Division of Clinical and Abnormal Psychology	Study and handling of the mentally ill, defective or exceptional; crime and delinquency
10. Division of Consulting Psychology	Professional interviewing and advising with individuals, or with persons temporarily (or permanently) uncertain or out of adjustment
11. Division of Industrial and Business Psychology	Job analysis; personnel selection; training for business and industry; human engineering; salesmanship; advertising
12. Division of Educational Psychology	Psychological principles involved in learning and teaching in general
13. Division of School Psychologists	Training and work of those who carry on psychological services in schools
14. Division of Counseling Psychology	Guidance work in schools at all levels; vocational analysis
15. Division of Psychologists in Public Service	Training and work of psychologists in hospitals, clinics, public institutions
16. Division of Military Psychology	Performance under stress; discipline; adjustment to camp life; morale; handling of the nonadjusting; readjustment and reclamation; propaganda
17. Division of Maturity and Old Age	Study of the aging and aged; adjustment in retirement, in homes and institutions

While there is obviously some overlapping in these areas, they represent well enough the varying lines of research and activity in which psychologists engage. We shall be concerned, in the present chapter, with several of these fields, as we turn our attention from time to time to a great number of problems and situations pertinent to the nurse as a personality and as a practitioner in one of the most significant arts of this century: that of caring for the ill, the disabled, the unhappy and the unadjusted.

Principal Contemporaneous Schools of Psychology. 1. *Connectionism, or Stimulus-Response Psychology*. This particular school (of which the late Dr. E. L. Thorndike was the most consistent exponent) emphasizes the relationship of the stimulating agent or force to response or reaction. Learning and the modification of original behavior result when a stimulus has been linked across intervening neural pathways with its peculiar and appropriate response. The diagram

$$S \longrightarrow R$$

is the well known symbol of the Connectionists. S (the stimulus) leads directly to R (the response to it). The stimulus may be any force arousing a sense organ, or it may be any free-rising idea that may chance to be in the mind at any given instant of time. Thus, every S incites to action, either motor, ideational or volitional. Learning becomes therefore a process of connecting the appropriate S$\longrightarrow$ bonds and exercising them through practice.

2. *Behaviorism, or Conditioned Response Psychology.* This school of psychologists, while not denying the S$\longrightarrow$ relationship, accounts for behavior largely through the operation of a new neural connection, called the *conditioning* (or *inadequate*) stimulus, and the *conditioned response*. Associations between a neutral stimulus (the inadequate one) and an adequate stimulus lead to a tendency for the former to arouse the response originally called out by the latter. We shall refer to this viewpoint in our discussion of emotional conditioning (see Chap. 8). According to the behaviorists, reflex arcs underlie all our responses. Even consciousness itself is motor, since it is subtended by reflexes of the tongue, larynx and other speech muscles. Learning and the modification of behavior proceed, according to this school, from the effects of wise or unwise conditioning, as we shall see.

3. *Gestalt Psychology, or Organismic Psychology.* The Gestalt school looks somewhat askance upon behavioral processes as the results of piecemeal and isolated joining together of unitary reflexes into chains of response. To the Gestaltist, learning and the modification of one's behavior result in a reaction of the whole organism to the situation confronting it. People respond to meaningful wholes, not to parts. In a new or problem situation the organism experiences a condition of tension, of mental suspense and uneasiness, that persists until the solution is reached. Gestalt psychology, therefore, stresses organismic totality rather than isolated partiality in all acquisitional or interpretative experience.

While most psychologists subscribe more or less to one or another of these schools, in their actual work many of them are usually ready to adopt whatever sound findings research men in any school come upon, and are glad to incorporate all psychological truths, however and by whomever discovered, into their own personal philosophy and practice. In this way, the *science* of psychology moves forward through Connectionistic, Behavioristic and Gestalt channels alike. This is, of course, as it should be, for blind adherence to any particular school in any area of human exort is likely to delay wide popular dissemination of the fruits of research.

PSYCHOLOGY APPLIED TO AREAS OF HUMAN LIVING

Psychology in Propaganda. It remained for two great world wars —and particularly for the second of them—to demonstrate how powerful propaganda can be made in influencing the opinions and the actions of people. Nazi Germany developed this weapon to its highest and most insidious degree. Based on an emotional appeal to hatred of the enemy and on glorification of the Nordic Germans, it was employed by the Ministry of Propaganda as a two-edged sword to drive the Nazis to work their will upon the world.

Other fighting nations, of course, on both sides, made effective use of this device to arouse hatred and anger in their nationals, inject iron into their blood, and enlist all-out support of and identification with the war effort.

Propaganda is not, however, limited to whipping up hatreds and lust for blood and vengeance. It is likewise a powerful force in creating or influencing public opinion in peacetime pursuits and problems. Its influence may be traced in the efforts of pressure groups of every type and variety to stimulate support for this or that legislation or reform; distrust or fear of this or that racial, political or religious group; conviction that this, that, or the other drug, toothpaste, washing powder, or brand of cigarettes is not only superior to others being advertised, but is actually a *must* for discriminating and informed purchasers.

Propaganda, if cleverly manipulated, will win popular interest in and support for anything, whether good or bad. It will defeat a man, or it will elect him. It is resorted to in order to popularize our food, drink, clothing, amusements; it fixes our standards and beliefs; it brings to our ears and eyes through pulpit, press, screen and loudspeaker the alleged "right" ways of thinking, feeling and acting. Nobody escapes its influence; only a few have the intelligence and fortitude to perceive its possible dangers and continue to regulate their lives independently of its tentacles.

The Institute for Propaganda Analysis distinguishes various propaganda techniques, among them the following: *name-calling*, with its taunt of "chiseler," "Communist," and "Puritan"; *glittering generalities*, with the glowing assurance of conformity with the "American standard," "democracy" and "freedom"; the *transfer device*, with its flattering claim of "endorsement by leading physicians," and "support of the best people"; the _testimonial_, with its intriguing approval of "movie stars," "athletes," and "prominent socialites"; the _plain folks device_, with its boast that one is "a plain dirt-farmer," "he came up through the mill," or "he rose from the ranks"; the _band-wagon technique_, with its clarion assertion that "everybody is doing it," "Uncle Sam says," or "five million people can't be wrong"; and the _card-stacking technique_, with its misrepresentation, its half truths and its whispering campaigns.

He is a hardy and self-possessed person indeed who can resist the implications that inhere in these universal techniques of the propagandist. The art of influencing people is the latest and greatest of all cultivated arts; it is also, in some circumstances, the most dangerous.

Psychology in Business and Industry. Our modern industrial and technological age, in which mass production of commodities is the index of a plant's efficiency, is far different from the age of the guilds and the family production units that preceded it. This changeover from a home economy to a factory economy has had profound repercussions upon the personality and the morale of the worker—the indispensable cog in the industrial machine—and upon the consumer, who absorbs the products. If the technological setup is to function well, therefore, those who operate it must concern themselves with such matters as intelligent selection of personnel, job analysis, operational efficiency, morale of workers, advertising, public relations, consumer relations, and the like.

Selection of Personnel. Foremost among problems of industrial psychology are those centered in selecting personnel. To choose among the applicants for a particular job that individual who will be the most competent to fill it is a matter of no small moment for all concerned. Selection of the wrong person will be expensive in money, wasteful of time, and disappointing to employer and employee alike. One of the valuable contributions of the plant psychologist or the personnel manager is the introduction of scientific methods of selecting the workers and allocating them to the particular work for which they are best suited by temperament, training or "knack."

The oldest and still most commonly used method of hiring workers is, of course, the simple interview. Relatively few employers ever hire anybody whom they have not "interviewed," the hunch being that the keen interviewer can "size up" an applicant with invariable accuracy. As a matter of fact, however, there are many slipups, many "misses," in this age-old method of hiring help; it is quite possible that interviewers are proven wrong as often as they are proven right in their judgments, as subsequent experience shows.

One must hasten to add, however, that some interviewers are more successful in predicting an applicant's ability to do a job than are others. With increasing practice, these originally good predictors may become highly efficient and valuable employment officers. To aid them, some research has been reported on standardizing the interview.

Rating scales also are widely used to check the abilities and capacities of the worker, as a means of determining more or less objectively his worth to the organization. If the rater is familiar with the day-by-day performance called for by the job, and can avoid over-leniency and the "halo effect," arising from an applicant's possession of winsome or striking traits not particularly germane to the job under study, he can be a decided asset as an employment officer.

A sample item from a rating scale follows:

COOPERATIVENESS

To rate the candidate, place a check-mark at the proper point

( )	( )	( )	( )
Is strongly opinionated and critical; uncooperative	Prefers to hold himself aloof; has little interest in the common task	Is passively cooperative; does not object to "go along" with the rest	Participates cheerfully and actively in the common task

Another aid to the personnel man in his selection of workers is the standardized aptitude or employment test. Tests of this sort have been developed in many vocational fields. In general, they are classifiable into (1) tests of general mechanical aptitude, (2) tests of clerical aptitude and (3) tests of particular aptitudes. Examples of the first include the O'Connor Finger Dexterity Test, the Minnesota Mechanical Aptitude Test and the Ziegler Rate of Manipulation Test. Tests of the second classification include the Minnesota Vocational Test for Clerical Workers, the Link Battery of Clerical Tests and the Thurstone Clerical Test.

A third group of standardized tests is used by personnel men and consultants for measuring aptitudes in specialized vocational fields. Among these are tests for typists and stenographers, policemen, mail clerks, machinists, and metal trade workers. In most of these, attention is paid to measuring such specific capacities in the subject as observational keenness, accuracy in following directions, judgment, powers of comprehension, dexterity, visual discrimination, spatial perception, technical comprehension and such other abilities as are of significance in competent workers in particularized vocations. The

Klein Sales Aptitude Test is typical of this third group of measuring instruments.

Job Analysis. In order to evaluate the effectiveness of a worker, the plant's psychologist is aided by making detailed analyses of the various types of jobs. Job analysis includes a survey of the nature of the work to be done, study of the manipulative movements required to be made for optimum performance, economical operation of the machine, and the like. In jobs in which the motor or manipulative operations are not too rapid, simple observation and recording suffice; in highly skilled, high-speed manual processes, however, it may be impractical to attempt to analyze the worker's technique in this naive way. In such types of performance, motion picture recording is found to be extremely helpful. When the film is projected on the screen in slow motion, accurate study of a man's performance becomes possible. The film may be used to analyze a worker's skill or lack of skill, the economy or lack of economy of his movements, and his coordinations. It can also be used for instructional purposes, both for habit-ridden older workers and for novices whose motor responses are still in the plastic and modifiable stage.

Further techniques used in job analysis include interviews with workers and questionnaires on job information.

Efficiency. The term "efficiency expert" has fallen somewhat into discredit in certain quarters, and for obvious reasons. In the early days of psychologists' first employment by industry, much of their work consisted in finding ways and means of speeding up production in order to reduce cost units. A great deal of research went, and is still going, into matters concerned with optimum size of load (*e.g.*, for a man wheeling bricks up an inclined plane to the mason), effect of the length of working hours upon sustained production, wasted movements, amount of work output, oxygen consumption and carbon dioxide exhalation, and the like. The goal of the psychological service in the plant was to maintain production at the highest possible peak.

The modern efficiency man, however, conceives efficiency to be a subjective, psychological factor quite as much as an objective, productive one. Not only are goods to be produced maximally, but those who work on the production line require to be kept satisfied and contented. Morale of the worker is thus an objective that looms large in industrial psychology today. Rest periods properly interspersed among work periods; rest rooms and cafeterias; provision of sick benefits, nursing and medical care; adequate safety devices; maintenance of cheerful and healthful surroundings in the work room; provision of bonuses, pensions and profit-sharing systems; support of mutually beneficial labor organizations—these things are found to help to condition and underwrite the efficiency of the employee. His work output, in other words, bears a constant relationship to his personal feelings of satisfaction, loyalty and security. These emotional attitudes are therefore deemed worthy of cultivation by efficiency men in our modern industrial plants. The term "human engineering" is now sometimes employed to designate psychological work in industry designed to assist the worker to adjust with maximal satisfaction to the requirements and opportunities of his job.

Advertising and Consumer Relations. The ultimate motive in business and industry is to sell the product or the service. Advertising becomes, therefore, one of the necessary adjuncts to the manufacturing of commodities.

Unquestionably, some advertisers are unscrupulous and are content to palm off on the buying public commodities and preparations that are inferior or downright harmful. One has but to follow the *Notices of Judgment,* published periodically by the Pure Food and Drugs Administration, to realize the knavery and dishonesty of many producers of foods, drugs, condiments and cosmetics. And one has but to read or listen to the extreme claims made for this, that or the other manufactured article by copy writers and announcers, to understand that misrepresentation of advertised products is not limited to the area of food and drugs.

On the other hand, honest advertising is not only a legitimate but a helpful device to sell reliable and standard goods to people who are in the market to buy. Avoiding the worst features of the high pressure form of salesmanship that induces people to "buy things they don't need with money they haven't got," "wholesome advertising keeps a reliable product before the public and endeavors to interest people to buy it."

The field of consumer relations is an important field for the producer to cultivate, and he is carrying forward the task vigorously. Consumer research data involving sales trends, seasonal variations in demands, appeal of advertising copy, customer taste in the matter of style of package and container, etc., enables the manufacturer to keep check upon his public and his wares. Personal interviews, questionnaires and telephone calls by field investigators provide the basis for much of this information, which is then used by the company to improve the quality of its product, the type and appeal of its advertising and the details of its distribution. Applied psychology thus plays a leading role in consumer research and consumer relations. Organizations such as the American Medical Association and Consumer's Research, Inc., conduct investigations into the relative merits of various brands or makes of commodities and the validity of the claims made for them. Published information of this sort is to the consumer's interest and often serves as a warning to the producer or the manufacturer that the public is something more than a collection of defenseless guinea pigs.

Psychology in Clinical Practice and Mental Hygiene Programs. In perhaps no field has applied psychology been more fruitfully cultivated than it has in the field of personal adjustment and mental health. The original channeling of the science into this human area was largely brought about by the inspiration of one man—Clifford W. Beers. Throughout the civilized world today, his memory is honored for his contribution to this area of mental health.

Beers became mentally ill in the early 1900's, shortly after leaving college. He was compelled to spend three years in institutions for the insane in his native state of Connecticut. In those days, insane asylums were dismal, inadequately managed and poorly staffed. Psychiatry had not developed as a branch of medicine, and the patients in mental institutions were a pitiful lot, for whom little more was done than to house them until they either recovered or died. Beers had the good fortune to recover, and resolved to devote his life and his work to the welfare of the mentally ill. In a notable book, *A Mind That Found Itself*, he recounted vividly his experiences while ill. The public was aroused by his revelations of the treatment accorded the insane, and almost overnight reforms were demanded and instituted throughout the country.

Pursuing his work, Beers founded, in 1908, the Connecticut Society for Mental Hygiene and the next year was instrumental in organizing the National Committee for Mental Hygiene, which he served as Secretary-General for the remainder of a long life. Many other states and most foreign countries followed suit, with the result that most civilized countries today are organized to promote programs of mental health and human adjustment.

At the present time, while much still remains to be desired in the care and handling of the mentally ill, it is encouraging to reflect that actual cruelty in mental hospitals has declined and, in the best of them, disappeared entirely. The greatest criticism that can be made of these institutions today arises out of the public's failure to provide adequate funds for their maintenance. In an era of mounting costs for all services, it is understandable that taxpayers should occasionally look askance upon the enormous budgets required for the support of state hospitals. In consequence, staffs and personnel are usually underpaid and overworked, and many competent persons are deterred from entering the service because of the unsatisfactory salaries offered.

Hospitals for the Mentally Ill. In a complex age such as the present, many people find problems of living and working too much for them, and become so maladjusted that hospitalization in mental institutions offers the only hope for their readjustment. There were, in 1954, almost 700,000 hospital beds in our public mental institutions and there are long waiting lists. It is a known fact that no fewer than nine million people in our country suffer from some mental or emotional disorder. More than 250,000 are admitted each year to state or public hospitals, and it is reliably estimated that one of every twelve of those who are now children will enter such an institution at some time during his lifetime for treatment of a mental illness. Even at the present unsatisfactory level of support for these hospitals, the tax outlay for their maintenance approaches one billion dollars annually. This amount, staggering as it is, provided in 1954 only $2.83 a day per person for the care and treatment of mental patients, including medical care, food, staff salaries, clothing, supplies and administration. When this is compared with the $21.09 spent for each patient daily in general hospitals, exclusive of physicians' fees, it is obvious how little real treatment of the mental patient is possible, and, still more unfortunately, how little research work can be financed to improve and increase care and knowledge of the mentally ill. Actually, only about five dollars a year per hospital case is appropriated for research in mental disease, and this mostly by the federal government. The average mental patient will spend eight years in hospital where, in too many instances, he will have done for him little more than is required to board, clothe and confine him.

Branching out from its original purpose of providing better treatment for the mentally ill, the mental hygiene movement shortly infiltrated into almost every area of human experience. Its scope today includes, in addition to the insane and psychotic, the feebleminded, the epileptic, the criminal and delinquent, the psychopathic, the psychoneurotic, the unstable, the "problem" individual, the alcoholic and all other deviating types.

Mental hygiene is also interested, on the positive side, in aiding people to adjust wisely and satisfyingly to the total life experience. Mental hygiene workers may be found in clinics, welfare organizations, charitable groups, schools, correctional institutions, hospitals, courts, churches, health departments, and most other organizations that are concerned with education or with reeducation and reclamation. In order to direct widest possible public attention to the whole problem of mental health as it affects us all, many states have in recent years set aside a Mental Health Week during which time speakers, churches, social organizations, hospitals and the public press cooperate in focusing the thinking of our people upon this highly important area of human experience and need.

The Case History. Mental hygienists and social workers who work intimately with maladjusted people find it helpful to construct as complete and reliable a case history of the individual whom they are studying as possible. Intelligent guidance and counseling presuppose a good working knowledge of the background and life history of the patient, for on no other basis than complete understanding of the factors and forces that have made him what he is can the therapist arrive at a practical plan for his readjustment.

The assembling of a case history requires skill and resourcefulness if the resulting material is to be reliable and suggestive. Ordinarily, information under such headings as the following is desired in a case history:

> Name, age, sex
> Marital status
> Family extraction
> Neighborhood and community backgrounds
> Economic status
> Health and disease history of the individual
> School status and achievement
> Social and personal traits
> Interests, hobbies
> Previous study by welfare or other agencies
> Nature of the present problem.

Aided by this picture which the social caseworker has compiled, the psychiatrist can often determine the source of the problem behavior or maladjustment of the individual, and can map out a correctional or a reeducative program which will aid him to straighten out his difficulty. Frequently in the larger clinics a case conference about a particular individual, in which several workers and therapists pool their judgments and experience, leads to the emergence of an adjustment program for the person that is superior to one that a single therapist, working independently, might be able to conceive.

Guidance. Many applied psychologists are engaged in guidance of one sort or another. Guidance is a recognized and accepted field of effort. In our schools, vocational guidance, in which the likelihood of success in a given occupational field is calculated, is coming to occupy an established place. In our schools and colleges, too, educational guidance, which advises young people on the basis of their abilities and interests what courses to pursue, what subjects to elect and what college to attend, is of importance in orienting the student. In child guidance, in which unadjusted or poorly adjusted children are aided to straighten out emotional or conduct abnormalities, psychiatrists, psychologists and social workers are able to render valuable service to discouraged or baffled parents and to bewildered or frightened children.

The last-mentioned field—child guidance—is the one in which probably the most systematic guidance work is being carried on. Originating through the efforts of the National Committee for Mental Hygiene to discover means of preventing juvenile delinquency, the first child guidance clinics were demonstration clinics, operated under grants from the Commonwealth Fund set up in five large cities in the United States, and continued over a period of five years. The work of these demonstration clinics was so successful that the idea of child guidance was adopted widely, and today there are several hundred such clinics in as many communities in this country.

Directed by a psychiatrist, who is himself assisted by psychiatric social workers, psychologists, physicians and stenographers, a clinic of this sort is equipped not only to construct complete case histories of its young patients but also to carry forward supervised correctional programs for them in home, school and community. Referrals to child guidance clinics are commonly made by parents, teachers, clergymen, physicians, the courts and social agencies. Funds for their maintenance come from state or community bureaus, local community chests, philanthropic groups, and the like. The services rendered by them are often free, or else are available for only a nominal charge. Thus children and parents from all types of homes may receive their ministrations.

Medical and Nursing Practice. Every practicing physician numbers among his patients a sizable group of men and women whose principal afflictions are emotional and functional rather than organic. Unless his training in the medical school has included courses in introductory psychiatry and mental hygiene, he will be likely to look upon the difficulties of this group of patients with scant sympathy and still less understanding.

Yet these people are desperately in need of help such as only a well rounded physician can give them. For him to dismiss the symptoms of the complaining psychoneurotic with a shrug of his shoulders is to be guilty of increasing instead of cutting down the incidence of hospitalization for mental disease. Prompt and early sympathy with and attention to the needs of these individuals are desirable in the interest of preventing the symptoms from becoming more acute. After all, the line of demarcation between mental disease and physical disease is so illusory that no physician can afford to be unconcerned over the fears, hypochondrias and emotional maladjustments of his patients.

"Nervousness" belongs quite as much in *Therapeutics* as do organic diseases of the heart or peptic ulcer; indeed, in time it may eventuate in either of these conditions.

Psychiatrists, of course, are called upon to deal professionally with the more difficult and persistent types of maladjustment, ranging all the way from problem behavior of children to the elusive psychoses that afflict patients in mental hospitals. Much of their work consists in the application of the principles of mental health to the care and treatment of their patients and in training and encouraging them to understand and practice these principles for themselves. In hundreds of institutions, including the great state hospitals and the smaller asylums, homes and "retreats," conducted both publicly and privately, psychiatrists and therapists must provide through their ministrations the ray of hope and of readjustment without which recovery can rarely take place. Professional men and women in these institutions need to be among our best and most competent applied psychologists.

In the experimental centers conducted in connection with some of these institutions, psychology is being applied also in research upon the effects of drugs, narcotics, alcohol, and sulfate stimulants; upon the relationship of the endocrines to adjustment and mental health; and upon the types, symptoms and treatment of all varieties of mental disorders and defects. In all of these and other types of research, increasing attention is devoted to the personality as it is modified by physical conditions within the organism.

By virtue of his intimate and continuing contacts with non-hospitalized fathers, mothers and their children, the general practitioner of medicine is in a promising position to influence the right thinking, feeling and acting of hosts of ordinary, everyday people. Respected for his wisdom and skill, he is called upon to practice his art from the earliest prenatal months of the individual to that distant day when he lies upon his death bed. Counselor, interpreter, adviser, he needs to be quite as definitely an applied psychologist as he does a man of medicine. Psychology and medicine are and of right ought to be forever inseparable.

The public health nurse also practices applied psychology in her work with the sick. Inasmuch as this theme will be stressed constantly throughout much of this book, we shall make no further reference to it at this point.

Consultation and Counseling. An area of psychological service that has come in recent years to command a great amount of prominence is what we may call the general field of counseling and consultation. This branch of applied psychology concerns itself with many realms of human activity, some of which we have already considered in the present chapter. The practicing consultant plays a prominent part in assisting personal adjustment in innumerable situations. To his office come men or women who are perplexed or baffled by life, and who need the inspiration of fresh hope and courage to carry on.

Problems of personal and family adjustment occupy prominence in the consultation rooms of practicing psychologists. Advice in these intricate and delicate areas frequently results in restraining a man from gravitating to the bottom of society or from resorting to actual self destruction, and in providing him with a new purpose. Broken homes, bitterness and rebellion may be avoided under a skilled consultant's influence. Discouragement over what life has brought; misery developing out of ruinous indulgence or addiction; desperation over mental or physical or spiritual ills—these stalk the rooms of the consultant day after day, year in and year out, as unhappy, frustrated human beings roll their burdens across the threshold. Into his ear are poured tales of wayward or problem children, of tottering homes, of lost faith, of physical disease and depletion, of tensions and discord and unrest, to all of which while his skill and insight may not suffice always to restore peace and resolution, he listens sympathetically and strives to find the key that may open the door to a new day for the sufferer.

In the field of vocational counseling the practicing psychologist occupies an increasingly prominent place. Already many of our junior and senior high schools maintain counseling service in this area, with the purpose of helping young people to choose wisely the occupations which they are shortly to enter. Vocational counseling in the school involves testing aptitudes, intelligence and interests; explorational analysis of the principal kinds of employment that make up the work of the world; surveying the opportunities offered by the community for absorbing the annual quota of new young workers; and some kind of actual vocational performance in various occupational fields, both in shop and special classrooms in the school and in industrial and business plants outside. The goal of all this effort is to insure better and happier vocational adjustment for every young person coming up through the schools.

Privately organized agencies outside the school also assist potential young workers to choose their careers wisely. These range all the way from plant-conducted guidance and training service in connection with industry to such elaborate organizations as the Research Foundation, Incorporated, which tests through its numerous laboratories set up in various cities the vocational promise of large numbers of youth every year. Boys' clubs, girls' clubs, Y.M.C.A.'s, Y.W.C.A.'s and other private or semiprivate organizations also frequently provide vocational counseling service.

The rich possibilities of vocational counseling and guidance have so intrigued psychologists that, as we have seen, they have devised elaborate tests to cover most of the major fields of the world's work, and equipped a considerable number of their colleagues to administer them and advise the testees accordingly. In a complex industrial age in which approximately 1,750,000 youth annually in peacetime must choose their vocational niches from among upwards of 20,000 listed occupations, the significance of this effort of applied psychology to guide them intelligently can hardly be overestimated.

Other consultational and counseling services which applied psychologists are called upon to render include the calculation of abilities and disabilities of pupils; the measurement and evaluation of personality traits; case work with inducted service men, rejected draftees and discharged veterans; occupational therapy with the injured, sick or incapacitated; work in prenatal, postnatal and pre-school clinics, outpatient departments, hospital wards and dispensaries; and counseling in the juvenile court, the penitentiary, reform school and detentional institution. In brief, wherever people are bewildered, or ill, or frightened, or insecure—there the practicing psychologist is in strategic position to assist in straightening out the tangled threads of life and experience.

Psychology in Law and Criminology. In ancient China the guilt or innocence of a suspect was frequently established by the so-called "Ordeal of rice." The prisoner was given a mouthful of dry rice to chew, and after thorough mastication of it was required to spit it out on a leaf. If the rice was found to be dry, he was adjudged guilty; if moist, he was declared innocent and was duly acquitted.

The primitive Chinese lawyers knew that fear dams up the salivary glands, and they reasoned that it was the fear of detection of his guilt that kept a suspect's mouth dry in the ordeal. Obviously, it might just as likely have been fear that his saliva would not flow! Thus, an innocent person might be condemned.

Primitive trial by ordeal was less elaborate and less reliable than the Western custom of trial by jury. The latter system of establishing the guilt or innocence of the prisoner at the bar developed widely among civilized nations. Involving witnesses, defense and prosecuting attorneys, testimony, jurymen and judge, a modern court trial becomes often a prolonged, expensive and sometimes inconclusive affair. Psychology has long been interested in the problems centering in the process of establishing innocence or guilt as it is carried forward in the courtroom, and has been instrumental in contributing significantly to many human phases of it.

The psychology of testimony has been carefully studied. The validity of the court's findings depends to a large degree upon the nature and reliability of the reports made by witnesses of an accident or crime. It does not require the confirmation given by experiments in the psychological laboratory to demonstrate the circumstance that, under stress of emotion such as commonly occurs when one witnesses an accident or crime, the observer may "see" many details that were not actually present and may misjudge such critical matters as speed, duration of time, distance, persons involved, and the like. Laboratory research, duplicating the events taking place in such moments of stress, has built up a mass of scientific evidence in these matters.

It has been established, for example, that individuals differ in visual and auditory acuity, although courts commonly take no cognizance of the fact that approximately 25 per cent of people under twenty years of age have defective vision, and that this type of deficiency climbs to more than 80 per cent among the middle-aged. Obviously, with such wide variations in sensory acuity, witnesses of the same event will disagree widely in their depositions.

If one adds to these sensory sources of error in testimony the tendency of people to "fill in" or complete partially perceived experience in order to round it out or make it consistent with their own "hunches," he realizes how inaccurate may be the account of an eyewitness, even though he is testifying under oath. Besides, an accident is over almost in the twinkling of an eye, and since it is impossible for an observer to attend to more than one thing within a single instant of time, it follows that he must of necessity miss many of the details about which he will be questioned and cross-questioned by the attorneys in the case.

Moreover, our courts of law are so crowded with cases to be tried that there is frequently a delay of weeks and even months or years between the time of the occurrence of an event and the time of the trial. During this interval the witnesses have so worked over the details, forgetting some and "filling in" others, that depositions may vary markedly and critical aspects of the case be distorted. Fidelity of report is further jeopardized by the emotionalism that attends appearing on the witness stand, by the suggestions implicit in the lawyers' skilled and sometimes purposely confusing wording of questions, by the fear that one will make a misstatement while under oath, and by the determination, once such a misstatement has been made, to stick to it subsequently in order to maintain one's consistency and integrity before the court.

Jurymen, too, who must follow all the interweaving and often conflicting claims and arguments in a trial, are subject to error. Both sides of the case build up as airtight arguments as possible; oratory mounts to impassioned heights; appeals are made to their sympathies for the culprit, on the one hand, and for those injured or bereaved, on the other. Besides, each juror is likely to have his own "hunch," his own personal opinion, his own background of prejudice. All of these considerations will have a bearing upon his capacity to reach a fair, objective conclusion. So will the newspaper accounts of the trial which he reads before and/or after he is impaneled in the jury. So will the public discussion about it in which he participates prior to its appearance on the docket. So will the opinions of other jurymen and the persuasiveness of the foreman when the twelve finally go into consultation.

After the guilt of the suspect has been duly established, the next problem confronting our judicial and penal systems is the disposition that is to be made of him. The older, classical school of criminology, stemming from Anglo-Saxon jurisprudence, took the position that the criminal was to be punished, that he must make retribution to society for what he had caused society to suffer. The modern school of criminology, stemming from psychological and sociological concepts, often looks upon the criminal as an individual to be reformed, re-educated, readjusted. The function of the court becomes, from this viewpoint, not the "sentencing" of the culprit to "sixty days," or "ten years," for his crime; rather, it becomes the reclamation of the individual through finding the roots that are nurturing his asocial behavior, severing them, and giving him a chance to redeem himself thereafter.

In the modern field of criminology, the psychiatrist, the psychologist and the social case worker play the dominant roles, roles formerly held by the judge, the jailer and the warden. To get at the motives, conflicts and frustrations that underlie a man's errant behavior; to test his intelligence, diagnose his personality, measure his attitudes; and then to estimate the chances of his reclamation and to supervise its process—these are skills and functions that reside in the mental hygienist and the applied psychologist, not primarily in the lawyer or the juryman, or yet in the jailer.

In the various types of detentional and correctional institutions, psychological service likewise is commonly maintained. Institutions of this sort include reform schools, training schools, prisons, penitentiaries and asylums maintained for the defective delinquent and for the criminally insane. Resident psychologists devote much time to classifying the inmates for therapy and for vocational rehabilitation, making individual case histories, initiating and overseeing therapeutic activities, determining eligibility for parole, helping the individual when released to ease his way back into free society. In many other ways psychologists aid the penal administrator to handle his colony as effectively as possible from the viewpoint of understanding and reeducating as many persons as are susceptible to reclamation and amenable to making a new start in the world from which their abnormal behavior has temporarily excluded them.

Psychology in the Ministry. The mid-twentieth century, in considerable measure because of the turbulence of international relations and the frightening spectre of total war, becomes increasingly a time to try men's souls. In an age of uncertainty, suspense and insecurity, our social problems become exaggerated as men struggle, often blindly, for assurance and inner peace. In spite of the obstacles to serenity, many men achieve an adjustment that enables them to ride out the storms that buffet them. Others try to escape their difficulties by indulgence in extravagant conduct, with the inevitable results of waywardness and crime, of physical and moral disaster, of self indictment for sin, of consuming remorse and guilt.

In such situations, based in part on external insecurity, and in part on internal inadequacy, the spiritual advisers of a people are faced with the obligation of ministering to the emotional upheavals of their constituents caught in the storms and stresses of human existence. The pastor's study often becomes, in consequence, a consultation room in which the minister strives to reassure, to help a human being to bear his grief, to aid and counsel him in his psychosexual problems, to win him graciously back from moral collapse, to encourage him to recover lost ideals, to lead him into a faith that can hold him against the pressures of a seething and disconcerting age.

Pastors, then, need all the wisdom and the fortifications that psychology can give them in counseling with their people. Most of the better theological schools now provide courses for young ministers-in-training in the field of human relations and mental hygiene. Hand in hand with their education in theological subjects, church management and history, they need guidance in the understanding of human nature, human emotions, human problems and motivation. Ministers in the modern age who are preachers only may strangely overlook the existence and poignancy of the deep social and personality problems that afflict humanity in times of crisis.

While clergymen are clergymen, not psychiatrists, and should not delve into emotional pathology nor attempt to manipulate subconscious mechanisms, the fact remains that they stand in unique and intimate relationship with far more troubled people than can ever hope to have the assistance of psychiatrists. For this reason, and because they enjoy not only the respect but the spiritual confidence of their people, they are in peculiar position to counsel with them at every age and at every crisis. This opportunity becomes a mandate in our modern society, and applied psychology becomes a handmaiden to theology in the pulpit, the consultation room and the parish. The psychologically-minded minister may stand as a first line of defense against the inroads of conflict, bewilderment and despair that harrass people. He must, however, be wise enough to limit his consultation efforts to the less subtle personal problems and to call in the professional psychiatrist for the deeper and more profound or abnormal ones.

THOUGHT PROBLEMS FOR THE STUDENT

1. Cite evidence from personal observation or experience that the term "psychology" is still, at least in the popular mind, a term to conjure with.
2. Find the names of several other notable men and women that appeared on the psychological roster in the late nineteenth and early twentieth centuries. Specify the particular contributions of each of them to the new science.
3. Can you find in the source books reference to any additional fields of psychology beyond those enumerated in the chapter? If so, determine the scope of each.
4. Search out the names of several of the leading exponents of the three schools of psychology mentioned in the text.
5. List as many examples of propaganda at work in some phase or other of the current scene as you are able.
6. Look up in some standard book in applied psychology a discussion of the technique of interviewing.
7. Make an elementary job analysis of some phase of your present daily routine as a nurse. From the standpoint of efficiency, what aspects of it appear still improvable?
8. Write to the Food and Drugs Administration, Washington, D.C., for free copies of the *Notices of Judgment* which it publishes. Analyze the principal reasons for seizure of the various products.
9. Write a reliable and accurate case history of one of your patients, checking all data as carefully as possible.
10. Visit a child guidance clinic and/or confer with the social worker concerning the scope of the work done by such an agency.
11. Think over some of the ways in which the knowledge and practice of the principles of mental hygiene can aid the nurse to be more effective and successful in her work with the sick. Write a paper on this theme.
12. Cite evidence to show that the reports of eyewitnesses or observers of the same event disagree considerably in details. How can you account for this phenomenon?
13. From the standpoint of probable correction and readjustment of the offender, what are some of the weaknesses of our courts?

14. Suggest how a clergyman and a psychiatrist might cooperate effectively in handling a specific problem of adjustment in a seriously troubled parishioner.
15. Make a list of services in our modern society performed by psychologists. Try to add several to those outlined in this chapter.

SUGGESTED READINGS

1. Blair, G. M., Jones, R. S., and Simpson, R. H.: *Educational Psychology*. New York, The Macmillan Co., 1954.

    A comprehensive treatment of the field of educational psychology.

2. Fidler, G. S., and Fidler, J. W., Jr.: *Introduction to Psychiatric Occupational Therapy*. New York, The Macmillan Company, 1954.

    This book will be of value to all professional people concerned with the adjustment of psychiatric patients.

3. Lehner, G., and Kube, E.: *Dynamics of Personal Adjustment*. New York, Prentice-Hall, Inc., 1955.

    An excellent general book dealing with all phases of adjustment.

4. Outler, Albert C.: *Psychotherapy and the Christian Message*. New York, Harper & Brothers, 1954.

    Of particular value to those interested in helping persons to better religious adjustment through the insight offered by the major schools of psychotherapy.

5. Ruch, F. L.: *Psychology and Life*. 4th ed. Chicago, Scott, Foresman and Company, 1953.

    Part IV of this well known book will be especially suggestive in helping the young student to visualize the contributions of psychology in the major areas of human experience.

6. Weiss, M. O.: *Attitudes in Psychiatric Nursing Care*. New York, G. P. Putnam's Sons, 1954.

    A work warmly sympathetic to the nursing needs of mentally ill patients. Excellent reading in the field.

Chapter 3

In theory there is nothing to hinder our following what we are taught; but in life there are many things to draw us aside.

EPICTETUS

PSYCHOLOGY IN NURSING

THE PATIENT, THE NURSE'S FIRST CONCERN

As THE nurse approaches the patient's bedside, what can she do to lessen the obviousness of her amateur status and at the same time contribute to the mental ease of the sick person who is meeting her for the first time? She is by now familiar with the often repeated advice that the nurse should imagine herself in the place of the patient so that she may prove more helpful. If she has had experience as a sick person, it may prove to be of assistance. But she will find among her patients all types, and in some instances the widest range of her imagination would never enable her to put herself in the place of the patient.

The nurse should approach each patient with the realization that here is an opportunity to meet an interesting person, as well as one requiring the skilled care she has been taught to give. This presupposes that she has developed skill in the procedures and is acquainted with their underlying principles. If she feels unsure of herself, review and repractice should come next, because self assurance must be built on knowing that she knows how and why.

A manner of dignified kindliness, consideration without undue concern, and conversation on impersonal topics will serve to lessen self consciousness and to inspire the confidence of the patient. The nurse is taught to consider all parts of the human body as accessories of the whole person, any part of which may be affected by disease, so that the person-to-person approach must never come second to attention to the part affected. When patients are markedly modest, diverting attention to impersonal topics will be helpful; when patients seem to lack all sense of modesty or tend to exhibitionism, it is advisable for the student who has not yet learned to cope with extreme behaviors to have present a graduate or an older student whose presence as chaperon is likely to have a restraining influence; the older nurse may also be able to contribute some guiding principles of management based on her own experience.

When the nurse is troubled by feelings of inadequacy on first assignment to patients who have just been operated upon or are very ill, her cue again is to seek help from the head nurse or from her instructors. Patients' questions for which she is not yet adequately prepared she should also refer to her head nurse or the doctor. It is safer to postpone an answer than to give misinformation; when the answer is never provided, however, an opportunity to teach is lost.

Occasionally the student may be assigned to patients whose diagnoses shock or arouse fear in her. The discussions in the foregoing pages should have led to a realization that nursing is not a place for the easily shocked or the self righteous individual. The willingness to understand the person who has the disease, to help and not to judge, must always be uppermost in the nurse's mind. Those diseases which are communicable can be prevented by meticulous attention to the practice of medical aseptic techniques. Moreover, there is increased security in full knowledge of the nature and characteristics of the causative micro-organism.

Because nursing care is of such a personal, intimate nature, the nurse's first approach should aim for complete rapport. *She is the hostess in the hospital establishment;* her guest must be put at ease; and the mere civility of a meeting between strangers has no place here.

Approach to and Care of the Patient. The principle of likenesses in all people must serve as the basis for understanding—differences in degree should be expected. Introduction of the nurse and of other employes who enter the unit, as well as those who are bed neighbors, is important. Orientation of the person to her new surroundings should include a demonstration of physical facilities necessary in care, something about how they work, assurance of their harmlessness, or cautions about using them if there are related hazards.

It is unlikely that the nurse, on first meeting the patient, will have all the knowledge about the person that is desirable. However, just as her observations about illness must be accompanied by a knowledge of what to look for, so in her developing acquaintance with the person she must have the sensitivity to recognize, interpret, use and report the personal findings.

Adjustments of the Patient. Many persons are reluctant to have physical examinations. If the nurse interprets the physical examination so that the patient understands that it is carried out to determine not only what is wrong but also what is right and stresses prevention as well as correction, the patient may feel reassured. Explanation of technical terms when possible is desirable; if inadvisable, then avoidance of the use of them in the presence of the patient is a kindness. Procedures and the purpose of treatments should be explained before they are initiated; if there will be pain associated with them, the patient should be told, but without undue emphasis, and she should be assured that the nurse will be careful and gentle. The patient who has something to hold or watch may find this diverting so that discomfort becomes more endurable. When surgical intervention is necessary, the patient should be told about the cooperation that will be needed from her postoperatively for best results.

All patients have fears. Through her knowledge of the *person* and her past experience, the nurse can determine what will be most helpful in reassuring her patient. Associated with the fear of the diagnosis are many other apprehensions that may haunt the person in bed: fear of "needles," of "cutting," of deformity, of crippling and helplessness, of unemployability and becoming a burden, of suffering and pain, of incurable disease which may be interpreted as personal or family disgrace, of losing loved ones, and of death. The nurse must be a person who encourages and merits confidence so that the patient may put her fears into words; sharing them may bring some relief. Some of these fears should be relayed to the head nurse, and some to the physician. Social service personnel and occupational therapists are available in many hospitals and are most helpful. Religious advisers may bring comfort and sustain courage. Guiding the family to the understanding and attitudes that are comforting to the patient may produce relief. The knowledge that loved ones care and need her may encourage effort and hope for recovery by the patient when all else fails.

When the sick person's condition permits, it is advisable to provide her with interests and diversions so that she can be helped to forget herself in them. If there is something she can do for others, so much the better, and the nurse should give guidance in such projects. The patient's faith must be built up—and sustained—in the nurses, the doctors and the hospital. As her fears are relieved by knowledge and as her security is assured by understanding and love, physical recovery will also be accelerated.

How can the nurse become acquainted with the personality which represents the individual whose care has now become her responsibility? Whenever possible, she should read the patient's social and medical history before she introduces herself.

Knowing the Patient's Name. It is important to the patient that the nurse pronounce his or her name correctly; that she know how to spell it in order to avoid mistakes in medications and treatment; it is also important to the individual. When the nurse addresses the person in bed as Mr. Cohen or Miss Cox, it increases the individual's feelings of security; "She knows who I am and I will therefore get the care my doctor knows I require," might express the patient's thinking. First names or nicknames may be used with children because such names have a familiar sound which helps to lessen the barrier of strangeness for the child—there is so much that is new and unfamiliar in the hospital surroundings.

Noting the Patient's Appearance. The reaction of the nurse to the patient when she meets her for the first time may be much like the reaction of other people to her for years. Perhaps she has developed feelings of shyness because of a plain appearance; or she may have learned to use her attractiveness as a means of getting her own way. The nurse must learn, however, to register much more than casual observations; a person's attractiveness or unattractiveness should not determine her response. She will, of course, note color of eyes, skin and hair, regularity of features, whether she is thin or plump. Even more important is the expression of eyes and face. Does she look tense or relaxed? Are her eyes clear and does she look directly at one? Does her posture suggest dejection and weariness, Does the color or texture of her skin suggest physical needs which should be reported? The nurse's keen observations, paralleled by a manner of sincere pleasure in meeting and serving the person, build feelings of confidence in the patient; they contribute to the information which the nurse requires. Nurses and doctors have learned to use their eyes as windows, but to see with their minds. Keen sensory perception with careful interpretation of everything that she sees will guide the nurse's response to and care of the patient.

The Effect of Heredity and Environment. *What Hereditary Characteristics Are Important in this Situation?* In reading the medical history, the nurse may discover something of the patient's nervous stability or instability; her intellectual aptitudes and limitations; her aggressiveness or passivity in adjusting to people and life. The history provides the background; it is a helpful record to which the nurse has access. She will now, in contact with the person, have the opportunity for hour-by-hour and day-by-day observations. These should have value in understanding the patient's behavior; they may have direct relationship to the patient's diagnosis; they may reveal patient needs which have not been satisfied. Recall, at this time, of the native drives which are common to all human beings, should enable the nurse to recognize not only the usually anticipated responses but also when compensation is being made because a native characteristic has been ignored or a native urge has been blocked. Hereditary characteristics may be increasingly better understood, as we have indicated above, when one considers the *principle of likenesses* as basic and then keeps in mind that the differences in individuals exist in degree. The range of nervous stability, intelligence and the urge to dominate is a wide one. The nurse who will be successful in the management of patients will need to give constant attention and study to these aspects of the whole person.

The Environment Helps To Make the Person. The nurse will probably also read the social history of her patient so that she is informed of her marital status, size of family and occupation. The history may include mention of education and church affiliation. It probably will not tell much about her home and the community from which she comes. This is the area in which acquaintance will probably grow most readily in the daily conversations which accompany the giving of nursing care. Sometimes being an interested listener will give insight to the forces which have served to mold the person. At other times, an occasional question from the nurse will be indicated in order to acquire the information necessary to be helpful to the patient. If she has had only an eighth grade education, the words the nurse will choose to explain a treatment will need to be quite different from those used for a specialist in physiology. If she is a salesgirl in the dime store, guidance on equipment for use in self administration of insulin may be different from that given if she is a chief buyer in the household department of a large store. If she lives in the heart of the city in a fifth floor apartment without an elevator, suggestions for outdoor exercise will be different from those offered if she lives in the country. Environment—physical, social, economic, occupational, educational and religious—from the earliest years to the present, has helped to determine patterns of behavior that the patient reflects. Now that the hospital is added as an environmental influence, the nurse is one of the key persons who can help make it a constructive influence for recovery as well as for better standards of health in the future, if she first learns and then interprets wisely that which would be helpful for her patient to know.

The Patient's Illness. *Illness Brought Her to the Hospital.* This person with "all that she is and hopes to be" has developed signs and symptoms of disease which have brought her to the hospital—this is the nurse's patient. What can she do to help her adjust satisfactorily to the discomforts, inconveniences, fears and pain which confront her? Previous experience and knowledge of nurses, doctors and hospitals, as well as existing habit patterns, will determine the ease or difficulty with which she will accept, cooperate in or resist the plans for medical care. It is important to begin at her level of knowledge and understanding as well as to consider the degree of illness in assisting her in hospital adjustment. The hospital gown and bed, strange surroundings and people are all factors in lessening feelings of adequacy and security; the warmth and sincerity of personal interest which the nurse brings can be one of the therapeutic influences which will enable her

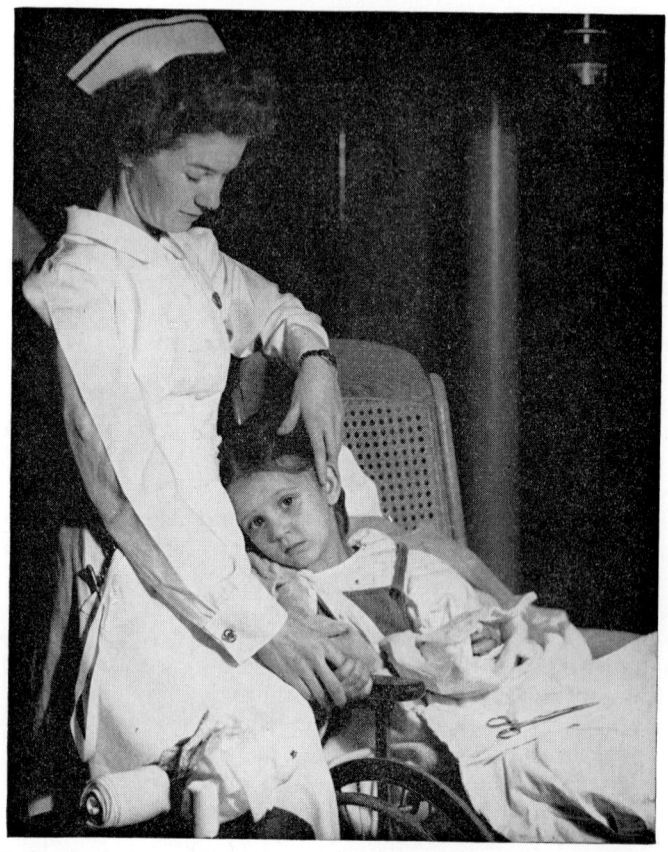

Fig. 4. Gentle, loving care by the nurse inspires confidence in the child patient.

to relax and work with her for her recovery. The intelligent sympathetic care which the patient is given, the guidance and understanding that the relatives and friends receive, will determine her attitude toward this illness as well as toward nurses, doctors and the hospital. Precise, automatic doing of procedures, slavish adherence to routines, impersonal management of patients have dominated the hospital atmosphere in the memories of many persons. Such care has a chilling influence on the morale of patients; the nurse's human warmth and thoughtful performance can help make a hospital experience, even with illness, a pleasant, constructive interlude for the patient.

Children Are People, Too. Children and sick people know their friends. Indifference is recognized, deception is sensed. The nurse who listens attentively to remarks and questions may gain an insight and understanding which will stand her in good stead not only in the care of the present patient but in being effective in the care of future patients. The nurse requires an understanding of the growth and development of children. She must keep in mind the wide range of differences occurring in these little people; she must appreciate that learning takes time and that these are the years when habit patterns are forming. The helpless and growing infant is striving to grow out of the period of dependency; the preschool child by his manipulative explorations and interaction with the people around him is discovering how to adjust to people as well as to the physical environment; the school child who has periods of taking refuge in dependency and rebelling against the restraints which elders impose and enforce is groping for the right response; the adolescent who seeks to guide his own behavior but is not yet schooled in meeting responsibilities is also learning. All of these types the nurse will meet when she assists in the care of children. She has the privilege of guiding their appreciations and practices for their well-being. She has also the knowledge which contributes to health. She must be aware that health for the total person is not confined to feeding, bathing and keeping him warm and dry but concerns the expression of the mental, emotional, social and spiritual aspects as well. She must know the normal child in order to recognize signs and symptoms which are present in the sick child. The child patient tests the nurse's acuity of observation, with sound judgment in interpretation and the wisdom to report what is pertinent, as probably no other patient does, with perhaps the exception of the unconscious patient.

The proper relationship of nurse and child is shown in the picture of the little girl in the wheelchair (Fig. 4). Wonder is expressed in the child's wide open eyes; her position suggests confidence in her nurse. The nurse portrays concern for her little patient; one can well believe that "gentle loving care," the ingredient sometimes ordered by doctors in pediatric divisions, is included in the nursing she does.

The child who is brought to the hospital should be greeted pleasantly; he should be given information and explanations which he can understand and requires for feelings of security. Since the uniform gives a nurse a different appearance from that of women the child usually sees, it is proposed that he have the opportunity to get used to the uniform as well as the person in it. The nurse should not try to force acquaintance. Gentleness is called for in the handling which may be necessary in bathing, feeding or treatment. Diverting the attention of a child is usually not difficult, but maintaining the diversion requires an interest on his level, as many baby-sitters can testify. The nurse who likes children, who can establish a person-to-person relationship without condescension, who has patience to keep trying when there is a difference of opinion as to what the patient should do, who is faithful and conscientious in meeting his needs, is entering an experience rich in satisfaction.

PRINCIPLES IN PRACTICE

Each nurse should recognize that good nursing is possible only in so far as she keeps in mind the *principles* which the nursing instructors constantly emphasize. Because of their great importance, they are reviewed here:

Know the *purpose* of every act, of every procedure which is undertaken.

Safety requires mastery of all related knowledge, adequate equipment in good repair, sufficient assistance, alert attention and skill in performance.

Effectiveness of the *therapy undertaken* is determined by the correct position of the patient and change of position as indicated; by administration of the right amount of therapy; by careful observation of the patient's reactions and immediate action as idiosyncrasy, fatigue or undue symptoms are noted. The action required may be to omit, decrease or increase, and it always includes reporting observations to the head nurse or doctor.

Comfort depends upon deftness in performance of skills, related supportive measures, specific protective measures, correct temperature, best position, assurance of privacy and avoidance of exposure, careful timing, a choice for the patient whenever possible, satisfaction of all needs, good rapport between patient and nurse.

Good use of resources includes having all equipment which is needed, when it is needed, where it is needed and in the amount needed; proper protection and care of equipment with necessary change and repair; sufficient personal assistance for economy of motion, effort and materials.

Fine workmanship is demonstrated by smooth, finished performance, which is thorough but not deliberate, expeditious but not hurried, gentle, yet firm. It is shown in relations with the patients which reflect mutual liking and respect to the end that they are assured of mental contentment and confidence as well as physical comfort.

Cooperative effort is achieved by a careful explanation to the patient of what the nurse's procedure is in which she will be a joint partner, how she can help so that hoped-for effects may result. Patients who are scheduled for operations especially require preoperative guidance for postoperative cooperation.

Teaching measures of positive health in so far as each patient's needs are noted. This includes guidance in habits of self care in relation to the diagnosis as well as to general practices for maintenance of health. It includes simple statements of scientific information as well as cautions of dangers which the forewarned person may avoid.

Supervision for Safety. The responsibilities gradually assumed by student nurses are of exceedingly serious nature. It is for this reason that careful instruction must be faithfully followed by classroom practice. It is only when such practice has resulted in competence that procedures may be done with patients in hospital wards, still under the watchful eye of the instructors. Such supervision, accompanying early practice, serves to protect the patient as well as the student, although occasionally both find it trying. It is the student, however, who should be most aware of the purpose of this supervision and she should seek it whenever uncertainty of principle or practice exists. She should, in her learning, develop the insight and skill which will enable her to do each step of the procedure, making such modifications as are indicated by the needs of each individual. She should be sure that the patient knows what she can do to cooperate and in so far as the patient can understand and her condition permits, she should be advised of the purpose of the procedure. As the patient's recovery continues and her strength permits, she should be encouraged to do things for herself. At this time, the student nurse gives guidance and supervision. It is, then, exceedingly important that the student should recognize her own need for assistance and secure it from instructors, head nurses or doctors as necessary.

THE GUIDANCE OF HEALTH

Nursing Is Also Teaching. The success of the nurse in teaching, as well as in her other functions, depends also upon her total personality. She may do much by positive suggestions but she may not be too arbitrary. The nurse who sees in a teaching situation an opportunity to boss is likely to arouse antagonism and dislike. A patient's need to know something that the nurse can explain to her by no means immunizes her from boredom. Therefore, skill in making information interesting is necessary. The good-natured nurse who recognizes the patient's improvement, and gives praise and encouragement on daily efforts to cooperate, sets the situation for a good learning response. It is just as important to have the right thing to say to each individual patient as it is to avoid garrulousness or stereotyped conversation. Recently, a student nurse who was impressed with the lack of original conversation in the hospital ward asked several patients to keep a record of greetings extended to them by nurses and by other personnel with whom they had contact on a given morning. "Good morning. How are you?" was the favorite greeting, repeated seventeen times! Surely a bit tiresome.

Also important are a friendly tone of voice, distinct articulation, a rate of speech slow enough to be soothing, and tact in recognizing when conversation is desirable as well as when silence is preferred. The nurse worthy of confidences and willing to receive them without a hint of curiosity or prying is a comfort. All these suggestions illustrate good psychology or, to use the layman's term, good common sense, which enters into teaching situations.

When congenial relations have been established, the confidence the patient has in her nurse leads her to the nurse as a logical source of help on maintenance of health. The information to be given may vary with almost every patient. Principles of personal hygiene are not yet universally known or practiced. Here, then, is a good starting point. When such knowledge already does determine the practices of the patient, and when the nurse is conversant with what the patient should know relative to her diagnosis, the care and precautions which she should observe are of immediate interest and provide the nurse with a teaching area. Many patients ask specific questions about their own needs as well as about present problems relating to the needs of their families and friends.

Once there is realization that nurses are informed and interested in helping, they should take their places in preventive programs so that public health statistics may be more consistent with what scientific findings could make them. Patients should also be taught what are the authentic sources of health guidance, where they may be found, and how to choose a qualified doctor and a nurse. They should be helped to recognize the dangers of self-prescription. It is only when nurses and doctors recognize their full responsibility as teachers that maintenance of health and prevention of disease will represent an achievable goal for every individual citizen.

Basic Principles for Effective Teaching. There are certain principles or rules to keep in mind when guiding the learning of patients.

Learners differ widely; no two patients are alike in all respects.

Teaching must begin at the level of the patient's present knowledge and skill.

The patient will be ready to learn to the degree that she can be guided to recognize the need for the knowledge or skill.

The patient may learn by listening, observing and doing.

The hospital environment may condition the patient's responses.

The patient's understanding should be checked, clarified and corrected as necessary.

The patient, who is daily experiencing comforts of good personal hygiene, should show readiness for insight into principles and practices of positive health.

The patient, as a member of a family, should be taught authoritative sources of health information.

Although the response of the learners is, undoubtedly, the important activity in this learning, teaching situations and the teacher's performance can be improved by the latter's recognition that her success or failure depends upon basic essentials.

The nurse should have related accurate information at her immediate command.

She should recognize and take advantage of teachable moments as they occur.

She should have the imagination and ability to use the right approach to each patient.

She should be specific in her teaching and check her patient's interpretations.

She should recognize her patient's limitations, mental and physical, and teach carefully in light of these.

The nurse should be generous with encouragement and commendation of the effort and progress shown by each patient.

She should know reliable sources of reference which are expressed in the language of the lay person.

The nurse should, herself, personify positive health.

Methods of Teaching in Health Guidance and Care of the Sick. The methods of teaching with which we are familiar would seem, on first thought, to be formal. Where have we had our most successful learning? What methods were used? We have all had experience with the *telling* method. In our homes, our parents have told us what to do and what not to do. When this guidance was based on good reasons, we were, presumably, teachable. This method usually works with patients, too. In situations where every teachable opportunity must be seized and where conversation may become question and answer exchange on health needs, it is important to be able to talk easily and to the point while doing what the patient requires to have done. There may also be an opportunity for demonstration. People of all levels of intelligence, and especially those of average or lower levels, learn more readily if they can be shown. Perhaps the mother of a family, who is now ambulatory in the ward, could be given a demonstration on how to change the bottom sheet of a bed with a patient in the bed. Many mothers who could use this skill to good advantage may never have a chance to take a home nursing course. The mother who is taught what constitutes a well balanced diet for her growing family may find pictures illustrating effects of good versus poor feeding of test animals more convincing than merely being told what is included in the proper diet.

There are available many pictures, charts and exhibits which make excellent teaching tools. By writing to State Departments of Health, one may often secure free material for distribution to patients. This material is often, however, made up of written content rather than illustrative; it therefore lends itself less readily to the hospital patient because of the effort required for concentration. The best method of teaching here, as in planned programs, is by doing. The patient who can be cheerful in spite of pain, who can eat when there is no appetite, who develops the time habit in elimination, who does exercises faithfully to regain lost motion of a part, is learning; and the new knowledge, habits and skills become a part of the person. The nurse then teaches by telling, by showing and by example; the patient learns by listening, seeing and doing.

These methods are used in formal programs of health guidance as well as in opportunistic teaching. The degree to which they are successful always depends on the individual learner as well as on the individual teacher. An excellent method of teaching is one which leaves the learner unaware that she is being taught; the teacher, however, is keenly conscious of her purpose—significant and sound health guidance. She should also be conscious of the varying interests of different age groups, and change her teaching approach and subject matter to suit individual needs.

Setting Patterns of Self Care in the Young. The nurse's work with children may be preventive, corrective or curative; it should always be educative. Children are probably the nurse's most teachable patients whether it is her intent to teach or not; it is therefore important that, when assigned to the children's unit, the nurse recheck her own usual behavior pattern for the following characteristics: Is she gentle but firm, clear-cut in her own decisions, friendly, serene and consistent in her reactions? It is important to understand and love children so that their sense of security may be assured. One should dress up ideas, information and skills in the kinds of packages that intrigue children, thus showing consideration of their interests.

1. Children love fun. What health practice can be tied up with this interest?
2. Children are curious.
3. Children seek new sensory experiences
4. Children are born imitators.
5. Children are keen competitors.
6. Children crave attention and approval.
7. Children yearn to grow up.
8. Children are endlessly seeking answers.

Adolescents, the Parents of Tomorrow. Adolescent patients, fifteen to twenty-four years of age, are that portion of our population that loses fewer days due to illness than any other group. This lower illness incidence, however, does not mean that this age group is better informed or more consistent in practicing good self care. The individual is then by nature at the peak of his well-being, and the guidance should be given which will contribute to his positive health. It is also usually found that teaching adolescents before ways of doing are established is more fruitful than the reteaching necessary with adults. With this group it is especially advisable that teaching should be done without being too obvious. In planning content, it is necessary to keep in mind that these individuals, the parents of tomorrow, are now maturing intellectually and socially. They need simple but sound information on such subjects as infectious diseases and how they spread; means of immunization against infectious diseases; the value of periodic health examinations; the need of protection against fatigue by adequate rest, sleep, food and exercise; the importance of daily satisfactions for mental health; the value of wholesome attitudes toward themselves and other people; and, of immediate importance, the information which relates to the diagnosis responsible for the present hospitalization.

Adults of All Ages. Those patients who are about to or have just become mothers are usually the eager learners. It is a delightful experience to teach a mother how to give her baby safe and sensible care. Fathers, too, should be taught these fundamental principles. This content is included in the obstetrical course and service experience. It behooves the student nurse to be sure that she knows the correct answers, because this is universally needed subject matter for nurses as well as for parents. The latter group frequently lack the necessary knowledge, often because some nurse failed to take advantage of an opportunity to teach.

Persons who have passed middle age may find it difficult to be taught by student nurses who are in their grandchildren's age group.

Usually, they are curious about their own diseases, and as the related personal problems are considered they seek information. The nurse should keep in mind the fact that, while change of point of view as well as habits of doing becomes more difficult for many people as the birthday anniversaries increase, the need is no less.

Does the Patient's Hospital Experience Hold Health Value? Almost every individual who is admitted as a hospital patient should, on discharge, know what self care is basic to complete recovery as well as what underlies the maintenance of positive health. Or is this an unreasonable expectation? If it is, on the whole, reasonable, who should give this guidance? The nurse represents one group of medical workers; she must learn what she may teach patients and what she should refer to others who are better qualified; she must know when information will be of value and when it may do harm; and if it needs to be given, how it should be given. In this function of the nurse as in bedside care, the effectiveness with which she coordinates her efforts with the teamwork of the total group determines the health value which the patient receives from her experience in the hospital.

Teaching Is an Art and a Science. Each student nurse recognizes that it is study, practice and experience which have given her a sense of security in her conduct of nursing procedures. In teaching, likewise, study, practice and experience will enable her to select and organize materials in an interesting manner. Upon graduation, she will be expected to teach groups as well as individuals, to do formal as well as informal presentation, to give emergency as well as carefully planned instruction. If she would be effective as a nurse-teacher, some daily preparation and practice in this art will contribute to the achievement of that goal.

THE HOSPITAL SITUATION

Contented, satisfied patients are the hospital's best public relations representatives. Nurses who use sound psychological principles in giving effective nursing care, in establishing good rapport with patients, in maintaining cordial working relationships with all members of the hospital team, contribute to the favorable impressions that the patients express to their friends and acquaintances, the personality which the hospital reflects.

Hospitals vary in size, but their organization patterns, according to departments, are much the same. It is not enough for the nurse to become acquainted with the unit within which she is active at the time, but she should continually investigate and explore the functions of all the departments. The hospital center is a fascinating place to those who would learn. And the nurse's contribution does not stop within hospital walls, as illustrated in Figure 5, which shows the hospital to be merely the beginning whence the nurse may penetrate into every corner of the community and the world. As the student grows in her concept of nursing as a profession, she will come to see that the horizons for service are indeed worldwide. As one of our nursing educators aptly puts it, "The work of the nurse is an integral part of the national and local programs that are planned to help human beings to maintain a high standard of health."*

Fig. 5. Showing how the hospital reaches out into the community.

What Is Meant by "Organization." The semimilitary relations between students and supervisory personnel sometimes create tensions within the student which interfere with her best performance. From her study of the history of nursing, the student will recall that nursing as a profession emerged in part from the military orders whch sprang up during the Crusades. This semimilitary relationship is traditional. Because of the nature of the nurse's responsibility, this relationship is slow to disappear, if it ever wholly can. To quote from the Officers Guide, "Why do we need discipline in the Army? The answer is that *there can be no orderly effort of any kind*, in the Army or out of it, *without teamwork*, which is merely the ultimate expression of *disciplined organization*."† In the hospital ward it is the teamwork of all

* Harmer and Henderson: Textbook of Principles and Practice of Nursing. Fifth edition. Page 18.
† Stewart, Major General M. B.: *United States Army Officers Guide*. Military Service Publishing Company. Chapter XXV, "Discipline and Leadership."

the personnel that will save lives, even as in the army. It is important for the nurse, in her attitude and conduct, to recognize the fact that the supervisory personnel are there to safeguard the patients and to assist in best adjustments to grave responsibilities; therein lies the answer to a mutual strength relationship.

The team approach to patient care in hospitals is becoming increasingly common; the team organization patterns may vary but the important point is that unity of purpose, namely "total patient care," can thus be more effectively achieved.

Other Workers Are Also Important. Equally necessary to making the right approach to patients are cordial relations with the many levels of workers with whom mutual adjustment to the ever-changing situation must be made. One should remember Emerson's well known saying: "Life is not so short but *that there is always time enough for courtesy*." Cordiality and recognition of the common purpose for which all the personnel are striving should serve to set an atmosphere making possible best achievement for all. Avoidance of personal familiarities and conversation is requisite. Recognition that co-workers are subject to the same drives and frustrations as oneself should serve to unify effort. Respect for every worker and for the product of her effort is a just demand in a democratic institution. Second in importance, in going into any situation, is for the nurse to know what her own duties are and to make every effort to do them well. Thought in planning her own work and readiness to seek help when it is indicated contribute to the effectiveness of all the workers in any situation. In most hospitals there are found on wards or units lists of duties of the various groups of workers active there. It is the mark of the promising student nurse to familiarize herself with this information at the earliest possible moment and to make use of it to facilitate her own smooth adjustment to the entire situation.

Good working relationships help to establish an atmosphere of mutual confidence and liking. They are important in the maintenance of good morale in any group. One's behavior is the product of many causes; it illustrates interaction between the individual and all the factors present in the situation which, with its elements of human nature, changes from moment to moment. Certain fundamental truths have already been presented as guides to the student's responses. This would seem a logical time to summarize several principles which will contribute to cordial relations with hospital personnel. The student is advised to examine these and identify them as she recognizes how they function in the institutional situation where her interaction adjustment is being made.

Each individual should assume responsibility for her performance as she grows in the required knowledge and skill.

Supervision has as its aim the safeguarding of the patient as well as the student.

Reasoned behavior is based on recognition of the possible consequences that may result from the many possible responses.

Organization determines regulations as well as sets limits for the unified efforts of a group.

Individual likenesses as well as individual differences should be included in consideration of the nurse's approach to the total hospital personnel.

Respect for the dignity of each person, as well as for her ambition, her beliefs, her abilities and her work, is requisite in achieving the ideals of democracy in a working situation.

It is hoped that as all persons grow in the appreciation of what democratic working relationships include and learn to practice them daily, the autocratic regime which has characterized hospitals may give way to democratic relationships. Student nurses who read these pages may be the nursing leaders of tomorrow; theirs will be the opportunity and the privilege to work for this goal.

Policies. What is meant by a policy? How does it differ from rules and regulations? A dictionary defines policy as "a settled or definite course or principle of procedure or conduct."

In giving thought to this definition, the student nurse becomes more fully aware that the nursing procedures which she has been taught represent policies determined by the administrators and teachers of the institution. Policies are to institutions much what laws are to nations. They are rules and regulations which have been sanctioned by the administrative body of the hospital. It is not, then, within the province of any nurse to change essential procedures. When modifications seem desirable so that the needs of individual patients may be met, the young nurse should check such changes with her head nurse. It is each student nurse's responsibility to acquaint herself with the established ways of the hospital with which she is affiliated. She should recognize that some policies have general application, while others are specific to certain services. A few familiar ones are mentioned here. These may or may not be in agreement with policies existent in the student's hospital, since variations in policies do exist among hospitals.

Solutions for intravenous infusions must be checked with a doctor or another nurse before administration.

A doctor, not a nurse, starts all intravenous infusions.

Visitors are not allowed on the obstetrical divisions during the infant nursing periods.

A doctor's order must be written by him or at least signed by him before the nurse may act upon it, except in case of emergency.

These are policies to *safeguard the nurse as well as the patient*. The purposes of established policies need to be examined because, as social change goes on outside the hospital, policy changes within hospitals need to keep in step. The questions of student nurses should assist the administration in detecting needed changes.

Students will find various written aids, such as the Routine Manual, the Charting Manual, the Head Nurse's Manual, the Non-Professional Worker's Handbook, as sources of reference on policies, procedures, routines and duties in the patient division. Much effort is being made in hospitals to increase the smooth functioning of performance in the business of the hospital—the care of patients. It is believed that this is more readily achieved when definite and accurate statements of procedure are available in writing, and when clearly defined objectives of each member of the hospital team and their lists of duties are used as a source of reference, than when reliance is placed on word-of-mouth passing of information. These sources of reference will have value only to the degree that workers consult them and translate them into practice, also to the extent that the administration keeps them up-to-date.

Equipment, Too, Must Be Understood. Our discussion in this chapter thus far illustrates in how many ways the student nurse must consider getting along with people. There are, however, also physical facilities which require a fair degree of familiarity as well as mechanical insight and coordination. As the nurse proceeds from the classroom to the ward, and from ward to ward, she will find that equipment varies, that it is sometimes insufficient or inadequate. It may be in need of repair, or it may be wholly unfamiliar to her. She should be informed of the equipment needs for simple nursing procedures. She should be alert during excursions to the wards when demonstrations of the use of special equipment are given. She should seek opportunity to adjust and use mechanical contrivances which are peculiar to certain nursing procedures. She should discuss with her instructors the principles underlying the performance of these devices. She should familiarize herself with the purpose underlying the use of the many types of equipment.

The student nurse who has learned to carry out mentally each procedure with all the adjustments of equipment, before actually embarking on the procedure in practice, will foresee difficulties which she may encounter. Again, her source of decision, when uncertainty exists, is her head nurse or supervisor. There should be a growing ability, however, to choose desirable rather than undesirable substitutions and an alertness in seeking opportunities for observing more experienced students carrying out procedures. Probably most important is a concentrated and searching attention when her own demonstration classes with equipment are presented.

The nurse should have some idea of the cost of various items of equipment. Hospital administrators require cooperation in conserving equipment by proper care from all the personnel who participate in its use and care. We know that the cost of food and clothing has risen; few hospital workers are informed on the high cost of surgical instruments, oxygen therapy devices, drugs and many other materials used in hospitals. To have an understanding of the problems confronting the accounting and administrative personnel in their hospital, it is proposed that nurses seek information on cost expended annually on specific items by contacting the purchasing agent and the pharmacist. Awareness of their problems paralleled by a high degree of cooperation in conservation of materials represent one more unified effort which it is believed would not only enable them to help in the hospital's economy but would serve to improve working relationships with the personnel in those departments.

Other Psychological Factors in the Hospital Surroundings. There are attendant factors which serve to make hospital surroundings pleasant and restful; lack of the worker's attention to them is likely to result in unfavorable comments. Cleanliness and order in themselves contribute much to the average person's impression that capable people are in command, that they have the situation well in hand, that there is no need for the patient to worry or fret. One has only to compare one's experience in two stores—one, where prompt service is available, desired articles are on the shelves and courteously displayed on request, a friendly relationship exists in the process of making one's purchase; another, where confusion is reflected in disorder on shelves and counters, and harassed clerks are unable to find what is desired. It is apparent that little satisfaction can result either for the clerk or the purchaser in the latter store. It is important, then, for the nurse to give constant attention to the tidiness which she can encourage and maintain, avoiding at the same time the appearance of regimentation which is probably even more tension-producing for the patient.

Proper ventilation, but avoidance of draughts, is refreshing and conducive to improved morale as well as circulation, appetite and a feeling of well-being. Nursing arts instructors teach proper methods for ventilating a room or ward, but since student nurses are not required to check this item on an order sheet it can easily be forgotten.

The maintenance of quiet is considered sufficiently important so that notices appear on the streets close to hospitals, requesting quiet on the part of persons using those streets. It has been the authors' experience that patients are troubled more by the noises in the hospital than those on the outside. It is probably one of the most frequent complaints that the administrative personnel encounter. It will only be when each worker recognizes what she can do to lessen unnecessary noise that some degree of quiet can be achieved. Hospital architects will also need to give more thought to this problem. However, the nurses should be prepared to give constructive suggestions. The drip of a faucet may be the sound which keeps a patient awake; dropping a basin may awaken several patients. The nurse should be alert for the sounds which she can control. Management of lights can contribute to a cheerful appearing unit. The nurse should avoid turning on bright lights without first advising the patient, adjusting lights and window shades so that glare does not result, utilizing natural light and sunshine which can contribute to a more pleasing hospital environment. These may seem to be minor concomitants in the total care of persons in hospitals but their importance should not be minimized; they influence the state of mind of the patient, the visitor and the worker.

Patients Have Families. As nurses, it is important for us to remember that each person who occupies a hospital bed is also a member of a family and a community; his presence in the hospital is temporary. He is being prepared to return to his home and community to resume his responsibilities there if the nurse and doctor are doing their jobs well. He will know how to use intelligently the health agencies of the community, including the hospital, when nurses and doctors themselves know and teach the concepts of the organized community health programs.

THOUGHT PROBLEMS FOR THE STUDENT

1. Select a patient to whom you have given nursing care and develop a study including the points emphasized in the "approach to the patient" in this chapter.
    (a) List the informations and skills relating to maintenance of health as well as to recovery from illness which you believe this patient requires.
    (b) Develop a plan including the content you will teach, the methods which you believe can be used and propose when teaching may be done.
2. Select five principles of health teaching and illustrate how they have functioned in your learning experience. Illustrate how you would proceed so that they would underlie your teaching.

3. State one idea related to personal hygiene which you believe should be universally taught.
4. Outline content which you believe every diabetic patient should be taught. Now consider what methods you would use to teach an ambulatory patient who is a cook by occupation. She is fifty-two years of age and had a seventh grade education.
5. Plan a list of authentic sources of reference on health information for a young woman who is expecting her first baby.
6. Suppose your uncle, having just moved from Boston, Massachusetts, to Atlanta, Georgia, asked you how he should proceed to choose a doctor. What would your advice be?
7. Discuss the learnings which you believe might be included to advantage during a hospital experience for patients of twelve years or older.
8. What guidance does this chapter offer on the writing of meaningful nurses' notes?
9. How does a policy differ from a law? Be able to cite one of each with which you have had personal experience.
10. What are some hospital hazards which give you a feeling of insecurity? Write clearly and concisely precautions which you believe should be instituted.

SUGGESTED READINGS

Books

Crow, L. D., Crow, A., and Skinner, C. E.: *Psychology in Nursing Practice.* New York, The Macmillan Co., 1954.

Emphasis is placed upon the applications of the principles of psychology and mental hygiene as they function in the many varied activities associated with nursing.

Cruze, W. W.: *Psychology in Nursing.* New York, Blakiston Division, McGraw-Hill Book Co., 1955.

Presents a scientific approach to each important area of psychology. Deals with problems the student and professional nurse will face.

Gill, H. Z.: *Basic Nursing.* 4th ed. New York, The Macmillan Co., 1955.

Contains especially good material on practical nursing and the care and comfort required by patients in hospitals and at home.

Harmer, B., and Henderson, V.: *The Principles and Practice of Nursing.* 5th ed. New York, The Macmillan Co., 1955.

Deep and sympathetic understanding of the patient's needs, which makes nursing an art as well as a science.

Periodicals

Beland, Irene: A Project in Evaluation. *Nursing Outlook,* January 1955, pp. 35–37.

Students who are aware of educational objectives can evaluate their progress in achieving desired outcomes.

Carl, Opal: The Professional Nurse's Responsibility in Health Education. *Nursing Outlook,* August 1954, pp. 431–433.

All nurses wherever they function have opportunities to teach basic essentials of sound health care.

Gregg, Dorothy: Reassurance. *American Journal of Nursing.* February 1955, pp. 171–174.

Meaningful reassurance should be an ingredient of all nursing.

Hollister, William G.: Bettering Human Relations in the Job Setting. *American Journal of Nursing*, May 1954, pp. 566–569.
    Helpful suggestions for achieving this very important essential "togetherness" in our patient care situations.

Kempf, Florence C.: The Person Centered Approach. *American Journal of Nursing*, October 1954, pp. 1246–1247.
    Ingredients for good interpersonal relations can be the stock in trade of every member of the medical care team.

Norris, L. W.: A Philosophy of Health. *Nursing Outlook*, June 1954, pp. 293–295.
    Philosophical concepts that are fundamental to successful health teaching.

Oliva, A. T.: Personality Factors in Human Relations. *Nursing Outlook*, November 1954, pp. 578–579.
    Self understanding can clear the way for devotion of efforts to unity of purpose.

Owens, Charlotte: Concepts of Interviewing. *Nursing Outlook*, October 1953, pp. 577–580.
    The suggestions on the nurse's approach and conversation with patients should be helpful.

Pendall, Rudolf: Speaking with People. *Nursing Outlook*, February 1954, pp. 96–97.
    Communication is that dimension which reflects the nurse's understanding of people.

Robinson, Alice M., and Mann, James: Praise, Blame and Gossip. *Nursing Outlook*, December 1954, pp. 644–646.
    These are forces which exert effects on the hospital's personnel and patients.

Safford, Beverly J.: My Experience with Self-Evaluation. *Nursing Outlook*, January 1955, pp. 30–31.
    Student self-evaluations on progress contribute to learning.

Smith, Dorothy M.: Patient Centered Teaching in Medical and Surgical Nursing. *American Journal of Nursing*, May 1950, pp. 314–315.
    Guidance of student teaching as part of the nursing performance in first experiences of patient care increases likelihood of this as part of the nurse's total patient care.

Unit 2

How to Study Effectively

Chapter 4

> The man who has acquired the habit of study, though for only one hour every day in the year ... will be startled to see the way he has made at the end of a twelvemonth.
>
> BULWER-LYTTON

SELF GUIDANCE IN STUDY

A LARGE PART of a nurse's time in preparing for her profession will be spent in study—study of books, of reference materials, of notes, of lectures, and of other sources of information. Economy demands, therefore, that she shall discipline herself in the fine art of study so that her time may be spent effectively and may yield good returns for the effort invested.

This chapter is placed early in the book in order to help the student to use her time wisely and economically in study and learning. Relatively few students receive sufficient training during high school on how to study effectively. Even to those who have had such training, a careful study and analysis of this chapter should be helpful.

Good learning, and *poor* learning: what do these phrases mean? To what extent is one's method of learning—i.e., her method of *studying*—improvable? And what ought one to do in order to make herself more effective in it? These are serious questions, and they merit serious and thoughtful consideration. One of the discouraging aspects of our educational setup is the circumstance that *so many of those who have passed through the schools have failed to learn how to use their minds economically and efficiently in learning.*

What would one say, for example, of the quality of learning represented by a pupil who tried to *memorize* verbatim her American history lesson? By one who read mechanically three times, half aloud, her geography assignment, and then closed her book with the comforting thought that she had "learned" her geography? By a student who with her eyes "read" her physiology assignment and listened with her ears at the same time to a radio skit? By one who read *words* without any serious attempt to translate them into *meanings* or to think through relationships?

There is, of course, but one kind of opinion to be expressed regarding such learners as these: all of them are poor. Good learners do not attempt to learn anything *verbatim*, at least beyond an occasional bit of well expressed or striking material; they do not content themselves with "putting in their time" reading assigned materials over and over, without analytical attention to their meaning; they do not let competing stimuli distract them from their work; they do not take the edge off their mental keenness by everlasting grumbling and fuming about what they have to do; they do not trust to luck that they will not personally be called upon in the discussions in the classroom to display familiarity with the block of material under investigation; and finally, good learners do not get lost in a maze of words and miss the meaning and substance of their content.

SOME RULES FOR SELF GUIDANCE IN STUDY

1. Getting Off to a Prompt Start. One of the principal difficulties that most learners appear to experience when they approach their study materials is the obvious circumstance that they find it so desperately hard *to get ready to commence to start to begin.*

A student sits down at her table and lays her books out before her; she finds the place in one of them and turns over a few pages mechanically in a languid effort to size up the difficulty of the lesson; she reads the captions of any pictures or illustrations that may be included; she glances at the clock or her wrist watch; she adjusts herself in her chair and is just about to start work when she discovers that her pen is empty or that her pencil is blunt, and she stops to rectify the condition. All might yet be well if she did not happen to recall that she ought to make a telephone call to a fellow student in another dormitory, following which happy thought she goes to the telephone. During the ensuing five minutes she exchanges with her friend comments about a number of unrelated matters. Coming back shortly to her table, she reflects gloomily that she has "an awful lot to do," and finally settles down to her books.

Settles down, did we say? Yes, for the time being; how long she will resist other distractions, however, is problematic. The chances are good that within fifteen minutes it will be time for her favorite TV program, and that she will feel constrained to "tune in." By bedtime, though little real studying has been accomplished, our so-called student can look forward to "studying some before classes" in the morning.

If the above picture has been overdrawn, it suggests that the only way to apply one's mind in studying is to start out promptly at the customary time and place. One ought to form the habit of getting books, reference materials, paper, pen and other paraphernalia in readiness, and then of sitting down and plunging directly into her work. It is amazing how much studying can be done in an hour if the entire sixty minutes are included in it. If thirty minutes are thrown away in idleness or distraction, however, not only will surprisingly little be accomplished in the other thirty, but also the dominant mental attitude will not be conducive to economical and effective study.

2. **Maintaining an Optimistic Mental Attitude.** Our mental attitudes determine in considerable measure our conduct and our general reactions to stimuli. From the standpoint of the effective use of the mind in studying, we may suppose that the attitudes with which the learner approaches her tasks will prove of significance in the performance of them. Suppose, for example, the learner has been in the habit of failing in her work, or of being just on the "borderline" of it: can it be otherwise than that she will approach her study assignments with a feeling of defeat and helplessness? Suppose, on the other hand, that she has enjoyed frequently, if not usually, the experience of success in the classroom: will she not approach the study of new materials with an attitude at least of confidence, not to say of eagerness and anticipation? Numerous investigations have indicated that whatever operates to promote in the learner a realization that she is progressing will act as an aid to her continued learning. On the other hand, whatever experiences she may have had which tend to make her skeptical about her progress or about her capacity act as obstacles to her continued learning.

Elbert Hubbard once wrote that "success is 10 per cent opportunity and 90 per cent intelligent hustle." Most people, granted that they have ordinary intelligence, fail, if they do fail, because they have not formed the habit of intelligent hustle. The thrill that comes from vigorous and purposeful activity in the classroom is likely to supply sufficient motivation to urge the learner forward. Working at capacity is a great emotional tonic to the pupil in the primary grade, to the student in high school, nursing school or college, and to the adult manual or professional worker, alike. The student should be sure that she personally throws herself into her study of the materials of nursing education so actively and energetically that she experiences often in the classroom and in her ward practice this agreeable emotional lift. It will help in stimulating her to maintain a favorable mental attitude toward study and work.

There is found among a certain class of students in our secondary and higher schools a type of "smart aleck" attitude toward studying and the performance of careful mental work which satirizes the faithful and conscientious student, holding her up to ridicule and making her the uncomfortable recipient of such epithets as "bookworm," "shark," "teacher's pet," and the like.

It is a fact that the world does not usually hear from this group in later years after they engage upon their life tasks, but that it commonly does hear from those who were dubbed bookworms by their jealous or lazy schoolmates. All worthwhile things of life come to most people, if they come at all, because they have set themselves with determination and earnestness to achieve them. The attainment of success in a great profession like that of nursing is no exception, and the student who fancies that she can adopt the attitude of indifference toward the study or the performance of nursing tasks makes a serious mistake. Besides, there is an agreeableness in using the mind thoughtfully which contributes no small amount to the satisfaction that all professional people experience in their work.

3. Searching for Essentials in an Assignment. Every writer of a textbook in any field prepares first an outline of the chapters which he proposes to include in his book. The major portion of each chapter, when he comes to write it, is devoted to a discussion or clarification of a few fundamental truths or principles which he is developing. Much space is devoted to illustrations and examples to suggest more clearly the meaning of the principles or the viewpoints presented.

In studying a chapter in a textbook, the student is faced with the problem of discovering just what are the essential ideas that the author has enunciated. She must clear away the surface growth of phrases in which the facts are couched and find the central facts themselves. The author's style may be simple or it may be involved; the examples which he introduces may be interesting or they may be matter of course; the meaning of the underlying point may be easy or hard to glean: these things are all unimportant details. The important thing is that the learner shall search for the *essentials* until she has found and understood them. It will not do to guess at them; it will not do to overlook important aspects of them; one must not mistake the educational trees for the educational woods, and run away with a few of the inconsequential or incidental particulars; she must not attempt to absorb everything on a printed page, as a sponge will absorb water. Her task is to grasp the meanings and, through the help provided by the illustrations and the "filling" of a paragraph, to assimilate them intelligently. When she has completed her study of a chapter in the textbook, the student should have comprehension of the author's fundamental ideas and viewpoint. Of the "filling" and incidental or illustrative materials which the author includes merely as pegs on which to hang his facts, she will have no need.

4. Taking Meaningful Notes. In the process of searching out the essential meanings of a chapter or an assignment or problem, the good learner will soon discover that she needs to make some sort of logical outline of what she reads. One of the mistakes that the poor learner makes is supposing that she is actually studying if, as she reads, she gets an occasional faint glimmer of the author's meaning sufficient to answer a possible question or two that she might conceivably be asked regarding it later on by the instructor. The classrooms and libraries of our schools contain too many "students" who have no rightful claim to the distinction. They are not really *students;* they have never learned the importance of thorough intellectual mastery of the materials assigned them.

The making of an outline of the content of a chapter in a textbook is indispensable if the material is to be properly apprehended. The very fact that one is mentally set to use a notebook and pen as she studies, and to take notes on the content of her reference sources, compels her to use pains in digging out meanings so that she may put them down intelligently. If she is intellectually honest with herself, she will not be satisfied merely to record *verbatim* a hodge-podge of words and sentences; she will realize that such passive recording indicates careless and slipshod reading, with a minimum of thoughtful and analytical *study*. In order to make a meaningful and honest entry in her outline, she will find it imperative to use her mind actively and analytically in discovering meanings.

Students should take notes on what they read and on the lectures they hear. Note-taking is essential in both situations, for only through this means can one preserve for her own use digests of the materials to which she is exposed in the course of her educational career. Within the relatively brief compass of an ordinary notebook, the gist of scores of lectures and many books can be recorded for future review and reference.

There are, however, notebooks and notebooks. Some of them are good; some are bad; some are indifferent. Only *good* notes are worth having. If the student will thumb through some of her notebooks, she can estimate whether they are valuable or valueless.

Probably the greatest single defect of most notebooks is the slavishness with which they copy the exact words of the author. Many a notebook is little more than a collection of the paragraph headings and the boldface captions transferred from the source books. The student judges that they are important, if for no other reason than that they are set in special type; hence she lifts them bodily from the one setting and deposits them as bodily in the other. She does not trouble to translate them into her own language. Consequently, when she comes later on to review them, she finds them to be almost devoid of meaning. Had she taken care to strain through the discriminating sieve of her own mind the lessons she studied, she might have derived much meaningful material which she could have recorded in her own words. Then, when she turned back to review them she would have been able to revive much of what she had studied.

Other common defects of students' notebooks include: (1) emphasis upon subordinate ideas or topics in place of major ones; (2) careless use of English mechanics, including spelling, phraseology, and the like; (3) illogical arrangement of ideas; and (4) "artistic" decorations of margins. The first of these defects is unfortunate because the student establishes a false perspective and an erroneous sense of values. The second is bad because it confirms her in careless habits connected with the language when she ought to be practicing desirable ones. The third is bad because it trains her in methods of mental work that are the reverse of proper ones. The fourth is reprehensible because it makes a notebook unsightly and gives one the impression that while the instructor was lecturing, the student was permitting her thoughts to go "wool gathering."

A notebook ought, in brief, to be the embodiment of the best that is in a student. It should be (and is) an eloquent witness to her studiousness, her capacity for logical thinking, her mental alertness, and the orderliness and singleness of her mind. A student should ask herself: "What sort of impression of me would one get if he were to turn over appraisingly the pages of some of my notebooks?"

It might even be a good idea for the student to go through two or three of the notebooks she has been keeping in her program at the school of nursing, in order to see how worthwhile her outlines are in the light of what she now knows to be important in making résumés and synopses either of materials read or of materials garnered from lectures.

Characteristics of good notes may be summarized as follows:

1. They transfer the thought of the book or lecture into the language and vocabulary of the student.
2. They are confined to a digest of the basal ideas or facts contained in the material read or listened to, with a minimum of reference to supporting or secondary ideas.
3. They record succinctly. Voluminous notes tend to be redundant and confusing.
4. They follow the same logical scheme of development employed by the book or speaker in the original presentation.
5. They are kept strictly meaningful and intelligible so that their long-time validity may be assured.
6. They are neat, well phrased, and exemplify all the mechanics of good English expression. This does not preclude free use of abbreviations and of the personal "shorthand" system developed by the student.

5. Making Continuous Use of Previously Learned Materials. The learning process would be a simpler activity than it is if everything new one ever learned could be filed away in some mental pigeonhole, there to remain inert but intact until one needed it again. The human mind is not, however, like a filing cabinet with its neat array of folders, all alphabetically arranged and readily accessible to an office clerk. While the comparison is, in other respects, absurd, one might better liken the mind to a bowl of colored liquid into which—when one learns—a bit of liquid of a different color finds its way. The new element relates itself to the old content, both influencing and being influenced by its nature. In all learning, the new fact or principle or truth which is added must be interpreted and assimilated in the light of the earlier relevant facts and principles previously learned and assimilated. Mere facts learned in isolation cannot be long retained in the mind.

The good learner is always searching for connecting links through which to join and interrelate the materials of education. She strives to keep her knowledge in such an orderly and active state that it is readily accessible to the interpenetration of the new data which she acquires from day to day. Her total fund of relevant knowledge and information should represent an apperceptive basis for the potential integration of any given bit of new knowledge. What one has learned she must continue to *use* in ever lengthening radii, as the circumference of her knowledge increases, in order to add richer meaning to the totality of her mental acquisition. This relating of a new bit of information or experience to old information or experience of the same general classification is quite as important an element in good learning as is the actual acquisition of the new material in the first place.

6. Using the Active Method in Studying. We have referred previously to the folly of mere passive reading and rereading of textbook materials. In order really to *learn* anything the mind must be kept in an active, inquiring state. The moment it becomes passive and mechanical, from that moment, vigorous and economical learning ceases. The student who permits her thoughts to go "wool gathering," or who allows her attention to scatter, will be greatly disappointed in the outcome of her studying. Only those things to which one pays active attention register in the mind.

The reader has no doubt had the humiliating experience of finding her thoughts straying away from the page of the book she was studying—although her eyes kept moving across the lines and down the page mechanically—and of suddenly coming back to earth with a mental thud to find that she had read down an entire page without comprehending a single idea.

When studying, the student should keep her mind continuously and aggressively active. Instead of *reading,* she should be *analyzing.* Some such challenging ideas as these should dominate her thinking as she reads: What is the author's meaning here? How can I restate this idea in my own words? What is the important content of this paragraph, or section? Do I comprehend it clearly? Is my experience in agreement with the viewpoint of the text? What illustrations from personal experience or observation can I think of as examples of the principles or contentions here set forth by the author? Can I recite to myself honestly the essential content of this section? So long as her mind is kept thus active during study, she will be carrying on a running comment upon what she reads. She will be likely, too, after the learning task is over, to have the satisfaction of realizing that she has worked over the new material analytically and has made it a part of herself. Some psychologists have called this method of active studying the *recitation method,* as opposed to the merely passive *reading* or *repetition method.*

7. **Studying Materials Well in Advance.** Some students wait until half an hour before class to study the day's assignment. The process of studying is not a mental activity that can be rustled up at the last minute, like putting on wraps just before going out, or like inserting a key in a lock before swinging a door open. Studying is, at its best, a somewhat leisurely process of thinking, turning over in the mind, "sleeping on," reflecting, weighing, cogitating, *after* the mechanical act of taking in the new data has been completed. Materials studied need time to "set," as it were, in the nervous system; only time and reflection can congeal them out of their initial fluidity into a stable and sturdy fund of knowledge that will be reasonably likely to be permanent.

An assignment of work should be attacked as promptly as possible after it has been made. A clever student can always find an excuse for postponing study; a *wise* one will clear the decks for early and sustained attack. In the interim between study time and class time there will be opportunity for her to mull over the material and work it into her mental background. She should try actively to relate parts of it to the recurring situations and events that comprise her day.

The study of psychology, especially, lends itself admirably to this practice. Indeed, there are few sections in this book, and in the reference sources cited, that one cannot weave smoothly into her whole life pattern as a student nurse. All that is necessary is to form **the persistent habit of applying the theory of the textbook and the** source book to the conduct and practice of extra-class and extra-library experience.

Only as psychological information can be applied to living and doing does it pay dividends. In the interim between study and class the nurse will find opportunity to make the application, and in making it she will be fixing more permanently in her mind the principles she is studying.

There are other valid reasons, too, for the prompt study of materials assigned. In much of her study of the curriculum in nursing education the student will be finding new words, new expressions and unfamiliar allusions. She will frequently need to consult the dictionary, the encyclopedia and other works of reference in order to understand the pages of her assignments. The procrastinating student who puts off studying will have no time for consulting helps such as these.

Studying well in advance of class time, moreover, provides a good basis for a hasty review later when class time approaches. Having become familiar with the materials of an assignment beforehand, the nurse can review them later on, near the time when her mastery of them will be investigated. Having achieved an initial view of the terrain, she is able to see it in more accurate perspective afterwards, and so can discuss it more intelligently and understandingly.

8. Remarshalling the Main Points of the Immediately Preceding Learning. The field of knowledge in any specific subdivision is a totality, a logical unit of events, ideas or principles. In studying it, we have to break it down into piecemeal sections. In so doing, we are apt to overlook the continuity and the unity of the entire field.

In order to build so far as possible a unitary background of information and mastery of a field of knowledge, one needs to keep marshalling the facts constantly. If we expect to develop an ordered mental process, it is impossible to learn one small section of material today, another tomorrow, and another next day or next week, without taking pains to fuse them all together into a dynamic whole.

Questions like the following ought to be continually obtruding themselves into consciousness as one approaches the study of a new unit, and as one proceeds to investigate its content:

> What related facts, events, principles, and the like, have preceded this unit?
>
> What is the stage setting, the background, against which the drama of today's assignment is played?
>
> What sequel might one expect?

This marshalling and remarshalling of the materials of learning in a specific field cannot be ignored or neglected by the student who has the will and the zeal to systematize her knowledge and make of it a working ally. Isolated facts may be learned, it is true; but, unintegrated with previously mastered materials, they have little value or purpose.

9. Making Frequent Summaries. Much of our intellectual life will be concerned with summarizing what we have read, heard or experienced. We will be making digests of what others have said; we will be abstracting, simplifying, generalizing, applying. This is an art that has to be cultivated actively, and one should be practicing it in her day by day study of nursing materials.

When the student has gleaned the essential meaning of a block of material, she should make it a habit to pause long enough and frequently enough to summarize it as she proceeds. What the author has written, he has organized in advance for his readers; but the student must do for herself the personal summarizing; she will have to reorganize his materials in her own mind and incorporate them into her own interpretative background. Nobody, neither author nor teacher, can do it for her.

The student must beware, too, of being dependent upon the author's phraseology and of trying to retain what he has said in his own language. She must declare her independence from the language of the printed page; she must be a *thinker*, not a parrot. She must compel herself to summarize in independent phraseology, and preferably in writing, the new materials she studies. Good studying is good summarizing. If it is true, as McMurry insists, that a textbook is merely a book of texts, it is equally true that a student's notebook ought, in all conscience, to be a book of summaries. The student cannot school herself too emphatically in this discipline.

10. Learning to Read with Discrimination. Every student has learned to read. But not very student has learned to read critically and with discrimination. It should be obvious to us all that certain passages in books and sources to which students constantly refer in preparing their work are of greater significance than others. Only through practice does one learn to weigh what she reads critically, with an eye to selecting the important and the relevant, and to ignoring the irrelevant and the unimportant. Even textbooks in psychology, in nursing, in science, in bacteriology, and the like, carry materials of varying importance.

Some passages or sections in books are rich with meaning and significance for the reader; others are of minor importance, and are included principally for purposes of illustration or elaboration. One has to learn to read, therefore, with an eye for passages included for literary variety, for paragraphs inserted principally for filler material, and for repetitions made for purposes of emphasis, example and illustration. The student should be increasingly able, as she proceeds through her course, to evaluate printed materials in terms of relative values, and in consequence to skim lightly what is extraneous and to read analytically what is of prime importance.

An important aspect of good reading skill is the vocabulary of the student. In such a scientific subject as psychology the student will find as she goes along that she is developing a surprisingly large vocabulary of new and unfamiliar words. It is of importance as she proceeds from unit to unit in the study of this subject—as indeed it is in every subject in the curriculum—that she shall master the new words as they are introduced by authors and instructors. Reading large amounts of material, which any individual enrolled in a professional school is obliged to do in connection with her courses, will be an increasingly bewildering and painful process if one allows her vocabulary to remain unenriched and unexpanded. Reading skill develops in a college student through her increasing ability to understand and use the language of mature minds which she encounters in her books. An English dictionary and a psychological dictionary are excellent aids to have at hand as she proceeds with the preparation of her assignments.

11. Maintaining the Problem Attitude. One difficulty with much of our study is that we do not have a definite purpose in mind when we start studying a unit of material. We have become so accustomed, as assignments succeed assignments, to accept each one as a new imposition of reading in source books that we enter upon each day's schedule without interest and without illuminating purpose. Our goal for the assignment is to "get it read and get it over with," trusting that the little we may be able to recall subsequently in the classroom will happen to hit what the instructor wants.

When the student gathers her source materials around her for an hour's study—or an evening's—she ought to have definitely in mind an actual problem or series of problems which she wishes to resolve; she ought to know what it is that she is looking for, exactly what new information she needs, exactly what goals she is seeking to achieve. She should not make the mistake of going at her work as if it were a repetition of blind searching after indistinct or actually invisible goals. No searcher after anything should ever allow herself to proceed without any goals.

The student should learn, then, to ask herself these very pertinent questions as she settles down to her studying:

What specific problem am I actually investigating?
Of what larger problem or unit is it a part?
What angles of it need clarification in my mind?

What light will this throw upon the larger problem of the whole unit?

She will soon find, if she motivates all her study with some such purposeful orientation as is embodied in questions like these, that studying will shortly become for her something more interesting and exciting than the slavish poring over dry assignments that conventional "studying" often is in our schools.

Using one's mind actively, investigatively, analytically, ought to be a pleasurable experience, not an annoying or disconcerting one. During his life upon the earth, man has amassed such a fund of experience, which has been embodied in principles, facts, sequences, philosophies, and the like, that studying about them ought to be a fascinating adventure for us. Let every student who aspires to be worthy of the name *student* separate herself completely and permanently from the popular conception of mental activity as boresome, and recognize it instead to be the highroad to challenging and romantic intellectual experience.

12. Maintaining the Proper Physical Surroundings for Study. After one has provided for the psychological factors that condition efficient and economical study, there still remains the question of the physical environment in which the student works. A few simple rules should suffice here. First of all, beyond a certain obvious minimum of noise and confusion in the immediate study environment, distracting influences are to be avoided. The study hall or room should be reasonably quiet and free from distracting agents. Experiments have shown that, even though with grim determination one can compel herself to work at mental tasks in confusing surroundings, this persistence uses up more energy, and so leads to fatigue more quickly, than when disturbances are kept at a minimum.

However, it should be borne in mind that a mild degree of moving about, rustling of papers, clicking of typewriters, occasional bits of conversation, and the like, do not reduce the efficiency of mental work. One should not seek, in other words, to create the profound quiet of a vacuum in her study room. Our nervous systems appear to require a moderate amount of bombardment by nonfocal stimuli in order to perform at capacity.

Second, one should avoid an indolent, languid kind of comfort while she is engaged upon mental work. There is no virtue in being actually *uncomfortable*, of course; on the other hand, the student who customarily sinks into an upholstered chair, or drops on to a couch or divan or bed, should not be surprised to find that her position and her mental attitude are conducive to sleep rather than to vigorous study. A student is advised to sit erect in a comfortable, straight-backed chair when she is studying, with a degree of muscular tension in her back and shoulders. Doing mental tasks is actually doing *work;* relaxation is unthinkable in any vigorous work situation. By "putting some tension into attention," she galvanizes her mind into sustained application to the intellectual task in hand. The brain appears to take its cue, as it were, from the tone of the postural muscles; if they are relaxed, the brain tends to be groggy; if they are taut, it tends to be alert and resourceful.

Some additional rules governing the physical environment of the mental worker should also be observed by the student.

(a) Work, so far as feasible, in the accustomed place. The familiar room, the familiar table, the same chair and place—these will all help. We tend to become conditioned to such externals as these and to work more smoothly and economically when they obtain. One ought not, on the other hand, to become so enslaved to routine surroundings as to be unable to study under unusual conditions when they cannot be avoided.

(b) Avoid studying immediately after a full meal. If the student will cultivate the habit of relaxing for a half hour or so following dinner, she will give her stomach a better chance to initiate the digestion of her meal. After gastric activity has gotten well under way, more blood will be available for the brain, and the mental processes will flow more smoothly and purposefully.

(c) Keep an eye on the thermometer. A room temperature much in excess of 68° to 70° F. is not conducive to alertness.

(d) Conserve your vision. Our eyes are about the most precious servants we have. That being the case, it follows that we ought to take proper care of them, so that they may continue to serve us all our days. Unfortunately, too many students take their eyes for granted and not only fail to take reasonable care of them but actually abuse them. Whenever one reads in a light that is too dim for sharp retinal images, or too bright for retinal comfort; whenever the source of light glares directly into the eyes; whenever the student continues to read as dusk falls around her, bending closer and closer to her page or otherwise neglecting to do the sensible thing—namely, to switch on the light—and whenever she reads in a half-reclining position, with her book elevated at a changing angle she is playing fast and loose with the only pair of eyes she can ever have.

If conditions of illumination in the room are poor, they must be corrected; if one commonly reads on a jerking bus or in a recumbent position, such habits must be broken; if the student's eyes appear to be weak, or to give her discomfort or pain, she should report to her Health Service and have the condition remedied. It is poor policy that allows eyestrain to develop, with its attendant headache and nervous irritability, whether the cause be habitually careless habits or whether it be neglect. Nurses, even more than most people, need clear, sharp vision and clear heads, which result in part from keen eyesight and vivid ocular impressions.

THE WIDER MEANING OF STUDY

Students are apt to make the mistake of interpreting *study* in a too narrow sense. To many people, studying means reading a book, or books, in order to absorb meanings. This is, of course, all right as far as it goes. But it falls annoyingly short of the rich purpose of true study and true learning.

In the better schools today, at least on the elementary and secondary levels, a greatly enriched concept of the study process is in operation. Much attention is devoted to guidance of pupil study. Not only are the teachers at constant pains to encourage the application of the twelve principles of studying that we have been discussing in this chapter, but in addition they give a great deal of time to individual and group guidance. The student learns not alone or principally from reading and "reciting" from books, but also from such activities as the following, which ought to be an integral part of studying:

Making a study schedule, allocating available time to specific preparation.

Planning together with other students ways of attack upon a problem.

Cooperative and comparative studying of several authors in resolving the problem.

Preparing oral and/or written reports on findings.

Carrying out panel and group discussions.

Following up relevant interesting problems that are encountered as work progresses.

Handling dictionaries, encyclopedias, indexes, readers' guides and reference books in order to find needed helps.

Carrying out field trips, visits and conferences in search of helpful materials and experiences.

Constantly practicing the weighing of evidence, judging points of view, and arriving at valid conclusions from the data.

Participating actively in classroom, club, school and community projects.

Carrying out constructional, manual, artistic or other creative activities related to the aims and purposes of the unit.

Learning as far as possible through doing.

In brief, the teacher of today regards the learning-study process as an integrated activity in which the learning situation is skillfully directed so that the learner invests in it all her powers, develops from it a rich and satisfying understanding of its human implications, and achieves through it demonstrable outcomes in terms of new skills, new information, widened viewpoints and broadened interests and enthusiasm.

In endeavoring to apply all this specifically to her own study-learning in nursing, the student should realize the importance of cooperative planning and discussing, both with other students and with her instructors, in order that real life and substance may be given to theory and book-learned facts. She should identify learning with searching, comparing, observing, conferring; with reasoning, weighing, judging, reaching conclusions; with originating and carrying through. She should see to it that her growing acquaintance with every course and her increasing mastery of selected units in every course shall be infused into every other course and every other unit, to the end that her whole mass of acquired knowledge and experience may be incorporated into a flexible and usable whole. She should not only welcome but actually seek opportunity to utilize her background of skill, of information and of experience in shedding new light upon new learning situations as they are encountered.

THOUGHT PROBLEMS FOR THE STUDENT

1. Contrast with some piece of good learning that you recall having done some piece of poor learning. Show in what respects the former was superior to the latter in results derived.
2. Think over carefully your habitual procedure in mastering an assignment from source books. Do you feel that on the whole you know how to study effectively and economically? Explain.
3. List as many as possible of the principal distractions to study that you have noted in your own experience or that you have perceived in the study of your friends.
4. Try especially hard during the next few study hours to get down to work immediately, without loss of time, in an effort to establish it as a habit. Talk over with others in class the results of your experiment.
5. On the assumption that, as McMurry opines, a textbook is "a book of texts," go through the present chapter of this book and list the "texts" which the authors appear to be developing.
6. Make special effort during the coming weeks to make your note-taking more meaningful and worth while. Thumb through several of your notebooks and try to discover their points of weakness and of strength. In your subsequent note-making, try hard to eliminate the former and to multiply or intensify the latter.
7. Suggest practical values you derived from your study and discussion of the content of Chapter 1 of this book, dealing with problems of personal adjust-

ment in the nurse. In other words, how are you making continuous use of some of the important principles there considered, either in your relationships with others, or in your professional ward duties, or in any other connection?
8. Do you ordinarily maintain an active, analyzing mental attitude of alertness while you are studying, or reading, or listening to a lecture? (Don't be discouraged if some of the time you find your mind wandering on such occasions: that happens to all of us. The important thing is to learn to curb promptly such "excursions" and bring the mind back to the focal event.) Why does it require real self-discipline to preserve the alert attitude?
9. During a five-minute period of careful thinking, summarize orally in your own words the principal points made by some lecturer or speaker whom you have heard within the past week. If you will form the habit of doing this sort of thing frequently after listening to a speaker, you will find that it will help you greatly.
10. "The art of reading," says Hamerton, "is to skip judiciously." Suggest various types of reading materials, e.g., in newspapers, magazines, brochures, and the like, which are to be read (a) carefully, (b) by skimming.
11. Check over your own personal study room and endeavor to evaluate it in terms of the suggestions incorporated in the latter part of this chapter. Note especially whether it is reasonably quiet and free from needless distractions; whether the chair in which you sit is a comfortable, straight-backed one; whether the temperature meets the requirements for brain work; and whether the standard of illumination is satisfactory. What aspects of your physical surroundings will you need to change?
12. List all the principal learning activities (e.g., searching, weighing, judging, planning, discussing, etc.) in which you have engaged during the past week in connection with the study of some one of your courses. Try to estimate how much richer is your resulting familiarity with the particular unit than it would have been if your study of it had been limited to mere reading and reciting.

SUGGESTED READINGS

1. Crow, L. D., Crow, A., and Skinner, C. E.: *Psychology in Nursing Practice.* New York, The Macmillan Co., 1954.
    Includes a very readable chapter on "Suggestions for Study."
2. Cruze, W. W.: *Psychology in Nursing.* New York, Blakiston Division, McGraw-Hill Book Co., 1955.
    The first two chapters contain helpful material on studying and learning effectively.
3. Karn, H. W., and Weitz, J.: *An Introduction to Psychology.* New York, John Wiley and Sons, Inc., 1955.
    Contains a brief but excellent section on "Study Efficiency."
4. Ruch, F. L.: *Psychology and Life.* 4th ed. Chicago, Scott, Foresman and Co., 1953.
    Chapter 12, "Learning and Remembering," will be particularly helpful to the young student desiring to know how to improve her own studying and learning.

Unit 3

Why People Behave as They Do

Chapter 5

> God made man to go by motives, and he will not go without them, any more than a boat without steam, or a balloon without gas.
>
> HENRY WARD BEECHER

THE ORIGINAL FOUNDATIONS OF BEHAVIOR

THE TERM BEHAVIOR in its psychological setting is used to include all the varied responses which the organism makes, or which it is capable of making, to any and all situations with which it may be confronted. Thus, *human* behavior, which comprises the scope of human psychology, consists of all our physical responses, habits, skills, and the like; all our organic responses, feelings, emotions and tensions; all our intellectual responses, perceiving, thinking, recalling, reasoning and willing. The term behavior is, in other words, employed by the psychologist to include the entire gamut of human experience and reaction. Whatever is comprised under the general behavior of human beings anywhere and under any conditions of time or circumstance has to do with psychology. Psychologists are interested in every aspect of human behavior, wherever it is found and whatever its manifestation.

Animal behavior, we may note in passing, represents another field of psychological study, but one with which in the present volume we are not directly concerned. The student should understand, however, that animal psychology—or *comparative* psychology, as it is more appropriately termed—is concerned with the investigation of animal behavior and motives, and that through research in this area psychologists often achieve striking insight into human problems and human conduct. It is obvious, of course, that the mainsprings of animal behavior are limited rather sharply to organic drives, whereas our human behavior is, at its best, activated by purposes and aspirations that are often foreign to animals.

The Importance of Our Motives. One of the most interesting and sometimes perplexing questions which confront the psychologist has to do with the motives that lie back of our human behavior. We observe, for example, that a child pouts, or cries, or smiles; we observe that a man fondles his dog, reads his newspaper, argues with his neighbor; we observe that a woman dresses neatly, darns the family socks, gives a bridge party. Most of the things people do are obvious and readily noted; but the reasons why they do as they do, or why they refrain from doing what they do not do, are not always so obvious and understandable. For this reason, the question of motivation becomes one of the most important as well as intriguing subjects of inquiry to the psychologist.

Why is it, for example, that the child at the seashore finds enthrallment in filling his gaily painted pail with sand, forthwith emptying it, and then refilling it? What motivating forces are at work in shaping the behavior of the young adolescent who is experiencing the first delightful thrill of "romantic love"? What drives a man to steal, to lie, or defame? What impels him, on the other hand, to be honest, to tell the truth, to extol or magnify his friend or his God? What are the forces operating in the heart of a Hamlet? Of a Florence Nightingale? Of an Albert Schweitzer?

These are baffling questions but they are questions with which psychology must concern itself, for we can never understand a person or interpret his conduct until we have delved deeply enough into his organism or into his personality to find the underlying motivation which activates him. It is of little value for society to catalog a child's maladjustments or misdemeanors, or to establish the guilt of an adult culprit, without attempting to discover the *why* of the antisocial behavior. Society cannot straighten out the twisted lives of its members who have fallen into evil or disfavor unless and until it can put its finger upon the reasons for the untoward conduct of the individual. Neither can society intelligently establish and postulate the standards of right behavior unless and until it knows the motives by which men are activated. Just as the physician cannot intelligently treat a malfunctioning organ until he has diagnosed the cause for its misbehaving, so the social worker and the psychiatrist cannot intelligently handle the maladjusted personality until the hereditary and environmental factors whence the poor behavior proceeds have been explored and their various contributions discovered.

Organic Tensions and Drives. Lying causally behind much of our human behavior are certain organic tensions which make us restless and keep us seeking for satisfaction of our wants. These urges to action comprise a part of man's original nature. They have come down in the nervous system through a vast human history. They have been stamped into our deepest organism by repetitive racial experience through thousands of generations. They were so essential for our racial survival that nature and time, working conjointly, have built them into the very fabric and fiber of nerves and muscles and glands. Many of these organic wants are found to be powerful in all the higher animals as well as in man, although some of them, owing to the profound organic modification which has come about through the acquisition of human consciousness, find much more varied expression in the human than in the subhuman species.

We shall find two principal kinds of wants that men have, *viz.*: (1) *to find relief from organic discomfort*, and (2) *to gain emotional satisfaction from the environment*. All of our wants and urges come under these two general drives of the organism.

MAN'S FIRST BASAL WANT: BODILY COMFORT

Release from organic discomfort—a prepotent drive in all organisms, animal as well as human—is a highly powerful urge to escape from annoyance or unpleasantness and to achieve physical comfort and freedom from pain. This drive emerges from deeply innate biological neural patterns which require no learning or coaching on the part of the individual. Given a bodily condition in which pain or discomfort is present, or an environmental setting in which potential pain or discomfort is imminent, there forthwith develops a state of restlessness and tension that cannot be reduced until some sort of satisfactory adjustment has been achieved by the individual.

Until one has learned from experience the most economical and satisfying ways in which his principal forms of discomfort may be relieved, he tends, when under the dominating power of pain or distress, to display a varied and uncoordinated behavior pattern in which there is apparent a large amount of diffuse response and random trial and error efforts at appeasement. His organism is obviously restless and tense, and his general behavior indicates that he is uncomfortable and that he is striving, perhaps aimlessly and uneconomically, to rid himself of an unpleasant, annoying feeling tone and to achieve in its stead a more agreeable condition of satisfaction or relief.

Means of Securing Relief from Organic Discomfort

This basal want of our bodies expresses itself in a considerable number of types of activity, which may be summarized as follows:
  1. Hunger and food-seeking activity.
  2. Escaping activity.
  3. Sleep and rest.
  4. Avoidance of overintense sensory stimuli.
  5. Avoidance of low or high temperatures.

6. Relief of distended eliminative organs.
7. Sex satisfaction or adjustment.

These are the oldest motivating forces in the race. They stimulate and condition the basal behavior of human beings and animals alike. They secure the preservation of the individual, the perpetuation of the race and the maintenance of that comfort and freedom from tension which every organic creature craves as his portion in life. At this primitive level of his behavior, man is not differentiated from the animal; only in the resourcefulness with which he achieves the satisfaction of these innate drives does the former differ strikingly from the latter. The stimuli which impel living creatures to seek satisfaction of these wants are as old as life itself. From the simplest ameboid form of protoplasmic energy to the most complex mammalian organism, these drives are paramount and universal. They impel alike the spider to spin his web, the kitten to seek cover and repose in some warm corner, the queen bee to make her nuptial flight.

At the higher human level, these drives likewise impel men to seek and prepare their food, to avoid danger, to sleep away approximately one third of their life span, to seek the physician when pain grips them, to warm themselves by clothing or by fire, and to seek self perpetuation through the siring of children to come after them.

Let us examine more closely the means by which freedom from physical pain or irritation is sought:

1. *Food-Seeking Activity.* The hunger motive has profoundly influenced all species and all races throughout the period of life on the planet. The monotonous trek and migration of animals to and fro across the earth have been fundamentally due to the grim inner necessity of finding new and unfailing sources of food. The nomadic wandering of human tribesmen over the continents before and since the dawn of history has been primarily necessitated by the same dominant inner urge to find a never-failing source of sustenance. In civilized society, the domestication of animals, cultivation of the land, irrigation projects, scientific soil analysis and seed selection, and the development of vast systems of distribution indicate some of the complex ways in which our human kind give rational expression to the fundamental organic urge to insure present satisfaction and future appeasement of the hunger drive.

Organically, the urge for food manifests itself in certain periodic and pronounced biochemical changes in tissues whose food supply is being fast depleted or has been already exhausted. Specifically, in hunger the walls of the stomach are found to contract and it is believed to be this visceral innervation which is the stimulus of hunger. In several brilliant experiments, carried on by **Dr. Walter B.**

Cannon and by Miss Tomi Wada, subjects swallowed soft rubber balloons which were afterward inflated through a rubber tube in the throat. The experimenters were able to demonstrate in every case that the periods of visceral contraction of the stomach corresponded closely with the subjective experience of hunger. Even when one is sleeping, Miss Wada found that the periods of restlessness and turning were approximately identical with those of stomach contractions, indicating that there may be tissue hunger during sleep as well as during wakefulness. Here is, then, a powerful organic drive that expresses itself in general bodily tension and restlessness which persist until relief has been achieved. The satisfaction of thirst and the satisfaction of tissue hunger for oxygen are allied forms of this drive. To satisfy these imperative wants the animal will exhibit the most extraordinary behavior.

2. *Escaping Activity When Attacked, Injured or in Danger.* When a man's life is in danger, he will struggle with all his strength to save himself. Any stimulus which is of such a nature as to threaten the comfort or safety of an individual will call forth characteristic escaping or avoiding reactions which do not have to be learned in order to be effective. Thus, an infant will, when his skin is pricked, or cut, or burned, or bruised, react with diffuse writhing or wriggling and screaming. Or, if his movements are hampered by the restraining hands of the experimenter, or by clothing drawn closely about him, or by confinement in a close space, he will set up at once random movements of struggle and will give every evidence of a determination to resume full and unhampered control of his movements. There is no question that this urge to escape from organic or bodily discomfort is a dominant one in every living organism.

3. *Sleep and Rest Activity.* Another powerful drive by which the body seeks to rid itself of discomfort is the strong urge for sleep or rest. The organic condition which sets off this impulse is not yet definitely understood, but it appears to be due in part at least to a residual accumulation of catabolic products and a drawing off of blood from the cerebral areas. Sleep is rhythmical and periodic in nature, and it represents one of the most powerful of all the wants of the organism, whether animal or human. Approximately one third of the human life span is passed in sleep, and a sizable part of it in addition is spent in siestas, in resting, dozing, loafing, and in various other forms of relaxing. For any individual to be long deprived of sleep is to generate in his body such annoyance and discomfort that he is almost beside himself. Whatever long interferes with this rhythmic drive becomes a source of intense annoyance. Conversely, whatever

THE ORIGINAL FOUNDATIONS OF BEHAVIOR

operates to encourage it when the organism is ready for it becomes equally satisfying.

The same mechanism is responsible for the sleep behavior of the savage who, having gorged himself with food, falls into a long, deep slumber; of the animal which, after a period of foraging activity followed by a full meal, makes whatever bed it is accustomed to and crawls into it; of the infant who, tired of the endless in-pouring of sensations or quieted by his bottle, trails off into slumber; of the housewife who indulges her afternoon nap after the children have gone back to school and the dishes are cleared away; of the business man who, returning weary from his counting-house, stretches out on the sofa before dinner and is soon fast asleep; and of all others who, when the bedtime hour comes, hie themselves away to the land of recreation and rejuvenation.

As Shakespeare has it:

> The innocent sleep:
> Sleep that knits up the ravell'd sleave of care,
> The death of each day's life, sore labour's bath,
> Balm of hurt minds, great Nature's second course,
> Chief nourisher in life's feast.
> *Macbeth, ii, 2.*

While it is no doubt true that many people sleep more than they need to or should, the fact remains that the sleep drive is powerful in everybody, and, regardless of what habits one may have formed with reference to its satisfaction, he finds periodically in sleep the release of accumulating discomfort which becomes unbearable if too long continued.

4. *Avoiding Overintense Sensory Stimuli.* Another native source of organic discomfort is to be noted in overintense sensory stimuli. We tend to recoil at a loud noise; or at an intense, blinding light; or a bitter taste; or a painfully pungent odor; or a frigid blast; or a scalding burn; or a sudden loss or reversal of balance; or a plunge downward; or distressing pain from any of the internal organs.

These experiences are always disagreeable; often they are highly so. One is restless, uneasy, or actually terrified by such stimuli. They commonly arouse strong emotion, as we shall later learn (see Chapter 14), and because of their association with other neutral stimuli which chance to be occurring simultaneously, they lead frequently to conditioned responses which may profoundly disturb the entire personality.

5. *Certain Other Adjusting Activities.* There are several other forms of organic discomfort, escape from each of which constitutes a powerful urge on the part of the individual. We may refer briefly to

three of them: a surrounding temperature greatly above or below the optimum, a distended bladder or bowel, and an unsatisfied or undisciplined sex appetite. Under stress of one or another of these stimuli, the individual becomes restless or irritable and seeks actively for relief. In the case of a surrounding temperature several degrees below 65° F., the human being tends either to find cover and shelter or else to stir his blood into more vigorous circulation; on the other hand, when the surrounding temperature rises several degrees above the optimum, he tends to remain sluggish, or to throw off his clothing, or else to seek some other means of cooling his body. In the case of distention of the bladder and intestine by the accumulation of wastes, a similar discomfort is experienced, and there is a restlessness and anxiety until the tension can be relieved. In the case of sex readiness, the visceral tension is considerable, motivating the individual to use up the accumulating energy within his organism in some appropriate way.

In all of these types of organic discomfort, of course, the relief achieved may be somewhat different in nature from that biologically indicated by the drive. Especially does this become true in the human animal as distinct from the subhuman species. Man is taught by experience, by precept and by convention to delay or to modify the expression of his bodily wants, whereas wants in animals undergo little if any modification. Thus, human beings adjust to changing temperatures by varying the thickness of their clothing; by turning on or shutting off the heat; by fanning, or building fires. To distended excretory or eliminative organs, they respond by inhibiting the sphincters and deferring evacuation until the time or the conditions are such as to be socially approved; to the tension in the sex glands or parts, they may respond by the expenditure of additional energy in work or in play, or in other activities quite unrelated to the biological release of the impulse, and may delay the latter indefinitely, or even for a lifetime. The fact that these and all other fundamental drives, however, become modified by habit and convention does not in any sense deny the fact that they are found among all people. The only condition that affects them is the degree of culture: in general, the more cultured an individual or a race, the more sharply wants come to be modified to meet the demands of custom, convention and polite society.

Relevancy of This Want to the Work of the Nurse. It is important for the nurse to realize that illness of the body profoundly modifies the status of all the usual forms of expression of this urge to escape organic discomfort. The sick person may be much more sensitive to the stimuli that press upon his nervous system, both from the interior and from the exterior, than is the well person; or again, his sensitivity may be dulled by illness, and hence he cannot react normally. In the large sense, a well person *is* well because his general biological and physiological condition is one of either present or immediately potential comfort. Conversely, the sick person is sick because his organic condition is uncomfortable or painful, and because he cannot immediately escape from his discomfort. In such circumstances, he is quite a different individual from what he is when bodily discomfort is either nonexistent or responds characteristically to simple and appropriate measures taken to relieve it.

In the matter of hunger and food-taking, for example, the sick person sometimes finds himself in an extremely trying situation. His appetite may be poor, and he must force himself to eat his food. His sense of taste may be temporarily blocked and he complains that "nothing tastes good any more." In certain diseases he may have a strong craving for types of food which are prohibited by his physician. Few deprivations or interferences with normal conditions of existence arouse such gloom and iritability as do those concerned with an individual's diet. The nurse must then expect many of her patients to manifest psychological symptoms in connection with their meals, and she must refrain from making matters worse by reproving them. It is important for her to preserve a matter-of-fact attitude in the ward or sick-room at mealtime and to encourage the patient, by her manner and by her power of suggestion, to relish his food. She should realize that for the ill person confined to his room or to his bed the recurring mealtime often represents about the only interesting adventure of his long days, and she ought to do everything possible to make the mealtime pleasant and a thing to be anticipated. Food daintily arranged, placed within comfortable reach and served with good cheer, is likely to be accepted by the sick person. Cool water is commonly craved by the patient, and under ordinary circumstances he ought to be supplied with it often during his waking hours. Water which has grown warm and "dead" in the glass is not satisfying to anybody, least of all to a sick person.

Escape from attack is another of the manifestations of the general urge for organic comfort which illness accentuates. A sick person may be experiencing the full strength of this drive. His body is attacked by microbic invasion or by defect or degeneration and is struggling to restore itself to its former condition of health and vigor. His malady may be a sudden, acute attack, and his organic reaction may be an emergency one that reaches to the deepest resources of his body defenses; or his malady may be a slow, chronic disorder which drags itself on painfully and uncertainly over a period of weeks and months, and his organism may have settled down into a grim and disconcerting struggle against the invading hosts or the disintegrating forces unleashed within it.

It makes little difference whether her patient's siege be brief or prolonged: the significant thing for the nurse to understand is that his fundamental urge to organic comfort and health is for the time undergoing pronounced thwarting, and that in consequence his serenity and peace of mind are disturbed. He may be resentful of his condition and apprehensive of the outcome; he may be optimistic or pessimistic, hopeful or despondent. His emotionally disturbed condition may check the normal flow of digestive juices, and so impair his appetite. Over and through it all is his unvarying desire to escape from pain, from uncertainty, from the restraints of the sickroom, from the inactivity and helplessness of his body. It is important for the nurse to perform her functions conscientiously in order that the unpleasantness and suffering attendant upon the patient's struggle to overcome his handicaps may be reduced to the lowest terms possible. In this connection, promptness and systematic procedure in giving medicine, taking temperature, changing linen; gentleness in performing all procedures; readiness to bathe or to massage tired muscles and aching back; prompt and willing assistance into the wheel chair or down the corridors to the sun porch as convalescence comes on: these are among the expected services which the nurse is in duty bound to render in order to make the struggle between patient and infirmity as bearable as may be.

The sleep and rest rhythm has likewise been disturbed by the coming of disease into the body. Sick people often sleep very lightly and are easily awakened. The quality of their sleep is likely to be somewhat poor, and they incline to fret and complain about their disturbed rest. Proximity to others who may be sleepless or in pain interferes with sleep. Occasionally a patient may be obsessed with the notion that if he does not have a minimum fixed number of hours of sleep, he will never get well. There are many things in the hospital and at home which, while not affecting adversely the sleep of well people, affect adversely the sleep of a sick person. The nurse must be alert to these sleep-disturbing noises or conditions and try to eliminate as many as possible of them. The psychological effect of a drawn shade or curtain, of a muffled footfall, of a cool, gentle hand, of a manner suggestive of drowsiness—is apt to be good, and the nurse may well study the subtle influence of these stimuli. Sleep is one of the best reparative agents in human experience; the sick person craves it far more than the well person, and he may need it far more.

Overintense sensory stimuli are more trying to the sick than they are to the well. An almost universal feature of ill health is a general intensification of the acuity of the sensory nervous system. The nerves are frequently described as being "on edge," as indeed they appear to be. Stimuli that would arouse no discomfort, or perhaps would fail even to draw the attention of the well person, become intolerable in the sick one. Light, for example, falling through a poorly shaded window at the bedside or gleaming from a poorly screened bulb, may be actually painful to the oversensitive receptors of an ill person. Noises and sounds that would pass unnoticed in the one instance may in the other excite discomfort and fretting and often lead to headache. For this reason, the squeaking of unoiled trucks or casters, flapping curtains, creaking springs, jarring voices, heavy heels, and the like, should be eliminated as completely as possible from the sick room and its vicinity.

So, too, with temperatures much above or below the optimum. The skin is more delicately responsive to these extremes than ordinarily. A sponge or washcloth wrung from too warm water or from too cold water may be uncomfortable. A cold draft may be painful and cause uncomfortable skin reflexes. Insufficient or excessive covers may be similarly unbearable. The sense of skin pressure, or the awareness of weight of clothing, bandages, dressings, and the like, is strong in the sick. In some diseases or conditions even the weight of the covers over the feet seems almost intolerable. The thoughtful and effective nurse will understand the oversensitiveness of her patient and will be careful so to order the details and appointments of the sick room as to soothe and quiet his receptors.

A frequent source of discomfort in the patient is the distention of the bladder and the bowel. The sick person may be compelled to empty the bladder, at least, more frequently than is the well person. The kidneys are eliminative organs, and in times of bacterial invasion of the body tissues, or in times of organic poisoning, they may secrete more urine than customarily. Moreover, because of the presence of toxins in the urine, though its volume may be no greater, it is often more irritating to the bladder to retain it. Frequent micturition may become therefore necessary. The uneasiness and distress of the patient who cannot secure prompt relief are considerable. The nurse should understand these matters and be prompt and thoughtful in her attention to them. Evacuation of the intestine, too, belongs in the same category and facilities should be provided promptly for the patient when the need occurs.

Ordinarily the sex urge is suspended during illness, the body needing all of its resources in repairing and rebuilding damaged or diseased tissues. There is no question, however, that at least subconsciously a part of the restlessness and uneasiness of an unwell individual may be attributed to tensions because of his inability to adjust as he habitually does to this drive when he is well. Of course, at certain stages of life, notably at the climacteric, there may be deep psychological reverberations from the biological turmoil going on in the reproductive and the glandular systems. The nurse should understand the fundamentals of such profound adjustments as the body and mind both are endeavoring to accomplish in these critical life periods.

It sometimes happens that a patient is tempted by the novelty of having his body cared for by a young student nurse to direct her attention needlessly to intimate parts. While his motive may be no more than a vague, unconventional pleasurableness, it may be the expression of the sex impulse in an individual of somewhat loose morals who is venturing a thinly-veiled exhibitionism for the edification of his nurse.

The effectiveness with which the nurse meets a situation wherein unseemly remarks or exhibitionism occurs will depend largely upon the manner and upon the adjustment and control of the nurse herself. It is to be assumed that she understands the nature of the sex drive in the male, that she realizes that enormous numbers of adults are unadjusted sexually, and that in the intimate relationships of the hospital ward some of them will show their unadjustment plainly. Toward those of her patients who are thus unadjusted, as also toward those at the other extreme who are greatly embarrassed by the exposure of their bodies, the student nurse will strive at all times to maintain a professional detachment and unconcern that will promptly discourage the prurient attitudes of the former and as promptly set at ease the inhibitions of the latter.

THE DRIVE FOR EMOTIONAL SATISFACTION

This Want Is Conspicuous in Humans. Thus far, we have limited discussion of our human wants to those by which the organism seeks escape from physical discomfort and the achievement of physical complacency and satisfaction. There is, however, another group of activities common to human beings which arise from that peculiarly human passion to derive satisfaction from the environment. Almost completely lacking in animals, although not entirely so, this drive has developed greatest strength in the human species and has ramified into a large number of forms of expression. So long as the organism remains definitely animal, regardless of its place in the series, its capacities for expression are sharply limited and its wants are principally those which enable it to survive in a primitive habitat.

True, there is some expenditure of energy which is not immediately or directly related to safeguarding the life of the animal. Thus, there arise struggles between the males of a species to determine dominion and leadership; there is a considerable amount of prowling and aimless mass movement; and there is, particularly among the young, even a type of play; it is extremely likely, however, that all such vague and restless behavior as this is subtly related to the strong organic drive for the relief of bodily tension and discomfort, and is not to be interpreted as an evidence of protection of the animal ego.

Be that as it may, it is in the human being that we observe the urge for emotional satisfaction most strikingly. There are many good reasons why man, placed as he is at the top of the series, should have this drive so powerfully developed. First, the environment of man has been cleared of most of its dangers and much of its harshness; as compared with the animal habitat of the jungle, the human habitat is tolerably secure. This circumstance gives man a far wider range of potential exploration and manipulation of his surroundings than the animal enjoys. Secondly, man has an infinitely more elaborate brain than the animal; he has vast associative areas in his cerebrum; he has delicately discriminative sense organs and nerves; he has intellect, mental power and imagination; he possesses the crowning boon of reason. These attributes compel him to project himself and his personality upon and into his environment and to a degree shape it to his wishes. Third, man is endowed with a flexible skeleton, with hands, with numerous fine muscles, with highly discriminative receptors and with an upright stature. Attributes of this order render it possible for him to develop skills and motor powers of high precision. Fourth, man is born into a social heritage wherein he develops language, culture, customs, mores and ambitions. This circumstance places him peculiarly in a position to communicate with his kind and to seek actively for some sort of satisfactory recognition or achievement in the social group.

The lower animals, denied as they are these four strongly stimulating agents, lack almost completely the corresponding forms of self expression. For the most part the animal craves organic satisfaction of its biological wants and is content if and when they have been satisfied.

This Want Is Younger in the Race. Man is, then, driven by a second type of want: the urge to set his brain at work upon his surroundings, to control or bend them to his wishes. This drive is not so old or so powerful in the race as is the purely biological one of escape from discomfort and pain. In consequence, it is less fixed, less invariable and less blind than the former. It is, none the less, an essential part of the equipment of every human being and as such plays a major role in motivating our behavior. Among primitive peoples, this urge is obviously less strong than it is among highly cultured peoples;

the former are closer to the animal environment and have fewer needs and opportunities for projecting themselves constructively upon their surroundings. As one goes up the scale of civilization, however, he notes that this drive becomes more strong, that its forms of expression become more varied, and that it tends to be overlaid more with habit and the results of learning.

Avenues through Which Emotional Satisfaction Is Commonly Achieved. The following list represents some of the most universal types of human activity in which people engage in order to experience emotional satisfactions from their surroundings:

1. Manipulative behavior.
2. Vocalization.
3. Curiosity.
4. Creativeness.
5. Play.
6. Possession.
7. Gregarious behavior
8. Mastery.
9. Fighting.
10. Rivalry.
11. Display.
12. Wanderlust.

1. *Manipulative Behavior.* This medium is exemplified in infancy by the incessant exploratory use of the hand as it seeks to find out new sensory information about the tangible objects in the environment. In a real sense, the baby becomes a master of his objective surroundings in proportion as he learns to manipulate them. Thus, in his zeal to find out, the younger child clutches, pulls apart, throws, feels over, squeezes, traces with his fingers, strokes, pushes and weighs more or less continuously during his waking hours.

The older child continues the same form of behavior, though in a somewhat more controlled and sophisticated manner. He enjoys performing feats of manual skill, handling tools, constructing simple toys, cutting-out work, drawing, building, and the like. The adult individual finds pleasure likewise in using the hands, for example, in amateur constructional activity, carpentry, puttering about the family car, performing manual activity in connection with hobbies and avocations, knitting, constructing puzzles and dabbling in art. In these and innumerable other ways the individual, regardless of age, derives a gratifying amount of pleasure and prestige from contact with his surroundings.

2. *Vocalization.* From his earliest weeks, the young infant babbles and gurgles. His earliest efforts bear only the remotest resemblance to actual speech, but they represent such efforts toward making known his emotional and mental and physical condition as his immature language mechanism is capable of producing. Later, he finds in his speech apparatus not alone a medium for conventional communication, but also one for a vast amount of informal linguistic self expression. He delights, for example, in yelling, shouting, singing,

whistling; still later he develops a strong penchant for alliterative repetitions and for a vast range of vocal expression by which to present himself and his ingenuity to other personalities that are evaluating and labeling him. The incessant chattering, gossiping and conversing that distinguish humans generally from animals are a form of the same satisfaction-seeking behavior.

3. *Curiosity.* This is one of the most socially valuable of all the avenues through which man pursues his quest for satisfaction. Without it, few discoveries and no inventions would ever have been made in the past history of the race. Without it, man would have remained in the Stone Age, indifferent to the opportunities which his environment offered, uninspired to push out the bounds of his knowledge and experience, and uninterested to "think the thoughts of the Creator after Him." Curiosity is strong in the little child, stronger still in the older one, and, though often jaded and its edge turned by the humdrum pedagogy of the home and the school, it continues to spur on the best of us for the greater part of our lives, or at least for as long as our minds remain young and our outlooks bright. The inquiring eyes of the infant following a flickering beam of sunlight upon the wall of the nursery; the recurring "why" questions of the preschool child; the intense will of the older child to get at the causes of events; the interest of grownups in street advertisers and salesmen, in seeing notable personages or places, and in traveling in foreign lands; and the eagerness of the scientist to investigate obscure phenomena—these are all forms which curiosity takes in various individuals according to their age, their opportunities or their capacities. The universe is filled for most of us and at every age of life with challenging and intriguing situations in the investigation of which our urge for emotional gratification commonly finds engrossment.

4. *Creativeness.* It is perhaps a far cry from the first clumsy attempts of the little child to build up his blocks into a tower to the writing of a great book, the painting of a great picture, or the conception of a great opera. These two extremes of achievement, however, represent the satisfaction impulses of a child, in the one case, and in the other, of an adult genius. The restless and timeless urge for self expression impels every normal person, young or old, to play the role of creator; in the child, it may eventuate in a whittled boat, a dammed-up gutter, or a crudely sewed doll's dress; in the adult, it may eventuate in a braided rug or a painted canvas: the form which the created product assumes is immaterial; the significant thing is that the personality seeks to express itself satisfyingly upon the environment which surrounds it.

5. *Play.* Human beings share with certain of the higher animals a

strong propensity for play. Play activity represents a particularly promising field for the achievement of satisfaction, since it is ordinarily social and hence affords plenty of opportunity for the player to match his wits or measure his capacities with those of other individuals. The solitary play of earlier childhood is probably not true play, since it lacks this social setting; rather, the solitary play of the toddler is a manifestation of manipulative behavior, of curiosity, or of some other more individual type of self expression. The play of children in groups, however, whether they be large or small, free or supervised, is true play in the sense that the personality is thrown into competitive juxtaposition with other competing egos and hence has the satisfaction of impressing itself upon others. Similarly, the play of grown up people is rarely solitary; there must be the social stimulus of other people in the group to make worth while the expenditure of play energy, and there must be also the challenge of the competitors to draw out the resources of the individual player and inspire him to do his best.

6. *Possession.* The pleasurableness and comfort derived from possession spring from the circumstance that one who possesses has given flattering objectivity to his cleverness, his talents, or his industry. The things possessed represent, in other words, powerful evidence of the reality and achievements of his selfness. The satisfaction which the possessor derives from his possessions is exemplified in the joys which the little girl experiences with her doll, the little boy with his knife, the youth with his bicycle or his stamp collection, the girl with her bracelets or her new dress, the man with his automobile or his house, his wife with her silver service or her antique bedroom suite. Our possessions mean a great deal to us in terms of what they have cost us in effort; they represent often the culmination of long-delayed ambition or desire; they stand for much expenditure of ourselves, our talents, our self denial and perhaps even our very life-blood; they embody the objectification of our wants upon our material surroundings. We should be far less worth while and the world would be a far less interesting place in which to live if it were not for the achievability of things which we may call our own. From a sociological standpoint, also, man's possessions have positive value in that they tend to steady him and make him a more responsible and aggressive creature than he would otherwise be.

7. *Gregarious Behavior.* Human beings can express themselves best in relationship with other human beings, as we have noted. Gregarious behavior in the animal series is undoubtedly called forth by the necessity for mutual self defense and protection against enemies, and is therefore a phase of the drive to escape from annoyance and to

achieve comfort. In human beings at the culture level, association with other personalities may be thought of as providing us with superb opportunities to extend and expand our own, and so to achieve profound emotional satisfaction.

Gregarious behavior is typical of human beings at all ages and at all stages of their development. Children develop socially and emotionally as well as physically and intellectually by their chumming, their moving in "sets" or gangs, and their playing, hiking, camping, and the like. In the bosom of his fellows, a boy can express himself and display himself as he can in no other setting. Adults, too, find themselves challenged by their social contacts to match their skills or their personalities with those of their fellows. Women's clubs, men's clubs, service clubs, lodges, fraternities and church societies, while often committed to some form of altruistic or philanthropic work, all provide the media in which the members may demonstrate each and severally their capacities and interests and afford their personalities opportunity for agreeable expansion and display. It would certainly be a dull world if people did not thus find satisfaction in social intercourse.

8. *Mastery*. A striking aspect of this drive is to be noted in the common human desire to master or dominate. It is flattering to most people if and when they can acquire control or power over other personalities or over certain objective phenomena. The boy who succeeds after many failures in balancing and riding his bicycle knows something of the thrill of mastery. The mechanic who can locate trouble in a motor, the high school student who succeeds in solving a baffling problem, the scholar who achieves a position of authority or eminence in his chosen field—these are all examples of the triumphing of somebody over something and furnish striking illustrations of the longing of the individual to work his will triumphantly upon his surroundings. To dominate, to be listened to with respect, to make one's influence felt, to be influential—these things have always been sweet morsels under the tongue for human beings.

9. *Fighting*. It frequently happens that the individual encounters opposition in his search after self expression. Other individuals may, instead of welcoming his aggressiveness, actually rebuff or thwart him, in which event there ensues a clash of wills and purposes. For after all, everybody else is seeking similarly for emotional satisfactions, and it is inevitable that there should arise conflict when areas of individual projection chance to overlap. In its grosser form, the crisis which occurs when striving personalities run into conflict with one another manifests itself in physical fighting. Witness, for example, the boy pummeling his comrade because he has belittled or provoked him, the poli-

tician clinching with his adversary who dares to malign him or to obstruct his proposals, the nation that sends its soldiers into battle against another nation because there is some clash of interests between them.

In its higher, sublimated form the expression which the struggling personality gives to its aims and purposes is moral or intellectual or spiritual rather than physical. To champion a cause, to fight for the right, to support worthy enterprises, to conquer the evil in one's nature, to sacrifice and struggle for a principle—these represent the higher and nobler forms of satisfaction seeking.

10. *Rivalry.* In our determination to impress ourselves upon objects and personalities with which we are surrounded, we find ourselves frequently in competition with others who are seeking likewise for self expression. Emulation and rivalry result as we strive to maintain our prowess or to defend our prestige. Children show a considerable amount of rivalry behavior, for example, in their play activities, their motor dexterities and their scholastic accomplishments. Youth evinces the same behavior in its competitive sports, its proud loyalties, its readiness to defend, its school spirit, and even in its joking and horseplay. Grown up men and women manifest it in their business rivalries, their advertising, their "boosting" of club or town or city, their new cars, and in the parading of their accomplishments and their possessions. No small impetus is given to the work of the world by the intense rivalry with which men seek to find emotional gratification in their everyday activities.

11. *Display.* Display or "showing off" is not unlike rivalry as a form of expressive behavior. When one has achieved or acquired, he is tempted to display his good fortune so that others may be made aware that he has "arrived." This tendency to show off is an unmistakable evidence of one's longing for emotional gratification. By displaying his accomplishments, one demonstrates his cleverness and foresight, his talent and genius. In a world in which many fail, he has succeeded, and the temptation is strong to call that fact to the attention of all whom it may—or may not—concern. The small boy who displays his skating skill or perhaps a bandaged finger is bidding eloquently for the praise and admiration of his mates; so is the girl with the stylish party dress or the sparkling jewelry; and so, too, is the adult, who is proud of his town house and his country house or of the creditable showing which his son or his daughter is making in college. Display is sweet to everybody, though fortunately most of us succeed in learning that it is vulgar and offensive thus to set ourselves on parade before the eyes of others.

12. *Wanderlust.* Primitive people were compelled to rove up and

down the earth seeking food for themselves and pasturage for their animals. Roving was therefore an expression of the urge for self preservation. In civilized culture, the interest in new scenes and new places so characteristic of human beings has been transferred from the pain-escaping to the satisfaction-achieving drive, since it affords the restless, seeking mind of man a medium for self expression and expansion. The child who runs away or who thrills to tales of the "Wild West" or the buccaneers is projecting his personality either actually or in fancy upon some new or untried way of life. The wanderer, the globe-trotter, the hobo, the tourist, are all likewise releasing the force of their personalities upon new scenes and new places. Those who are denied opportunity to travel or who do not care to exert the effort often seek to experience similar satisfaction vicariously through the printed page, the screen, the lecture or some other second-hand source of information.

The Interrelationship of These Forms of Behavior. It should be obvious, of course, that there is no sharp line of distinction among these various expressive responses. Indeed, there is a great deal of overlapping among most of them. One should not be surprised at this, for after all the constant factor is the urge for emotional satisfaction: all these expressive mechanisms are but variables of it. In consequence, it is often difficult to say whether the reacting individual is deriving satisfaction through curiosity, or creativeness, or mastery, or fighting, or rivalry, or display or through several of them operating simultaneously. The significant thing is that he is searching for gratification in whatever channels of experience his surroundings provide.

Relationship of These Forms to Problems of Nursing. The nurse should understand that the sick person is temporarily restrained from the achieving of normal emotional pleasure. Because of his physical restrictions, he cannot direct his efforts upon material objects and upon other personalities as he can when he is in good health. Consequently he is apt to be in an impatient and often even irritable state of mind. Lamenting his present helplessness and his enforced idleness, he reflects cynically upon his lot, or upon the poor condition of his affairs; he worries over the advances which his competitors will make while he is himself inactive; he frequently, indeed, transfers his troubles from extrahospital to intrahospital events.

One rather common and somewhat amusing way in which the sick person seeks to achieve attention and satisfaction is by discoursing at length upon the nature of his ailment or upon the hazard of his operation. He does not soon tire of rehearsing to all who will listen to him—visitors, nurses and fellow patients alike—the details of his "case": the "worst of its kind the doctors had ever seen," or "the only operation of its type ever successfully performed in this hospital"; or "complicated by conditions" that were such as to lead the doctors to "despair of recovery." Items of this sort are told and retold by some patients after they find themselves safely through the crisis and on the road to convalescence.

Again, the patient may use his illness as the basis for excusing himself from meeting the normal demands and obligations of life, and so actually develop a satisfaction in his present state. This is particularly likely to be the case with psychoneurotic persons who feel themselves incompetent to impress their personalities flatteringly upon the environment. Their sickness—real or fancied—is an obliging thing which is seized on as a way of escape. Thus, the individual obtains sympathy for his illness and avoids at the same time all censure for his failure to achieve what he would like to do in his normal way of life.

For all of these and other reasons, the nurse has need to cultivate a great deal of forbearance and control and a boundless amount of intelligent sympathy and understanding. Only through a realization of the restrictions upon his ego which the sick person is suffering, with all the consequent worry and fretting and impotence, can she understand and excuse much which on the surface might appear to her extremely childish and silly.

THOUGHT PROBLEMS FOR THE STUDENT

1. List 10 different kinds of behavior under each of the following captions: Physical Reactions; Emotional Reactions; Organic Reactions; Intellectual Reactions; Moral Reactions.
2. Suggest several reasons why the psychologist should be so interested in the motives that lie back of human behavior. What is a motive, and what is the relationship of motives to behavior?
3. Suggest motives that might underlie each of the following types of behavior: a baby who is cross and fretful while company is present; a boy who refuses to "tell on" a mate who has done wrong; a girl who enjoys "wheeling out" an infant sister or brother; a high school student who studies hard in order to "make" the honor list; a collegian who shouts himself hoarse at a home football game; a man who practices diligently for months to improve his golf game; a woman who gives a party for some poor children.
4. How important a role do you feel the drive for release from organic discomfort plays in the lives of human beings? Does the drive gain or lose in its power over behavior as one grows older and more mature? Explain.
5. Think up numerous examples of behavior that appear to be motivated by the want of emotional satisfaction. How important a role do you feel this drive actually plays in our lives?
6. Suppose human beings were possessed of the drive to escape pain and discomfort, but were not also activated by the drive to derive satisfactions from

the environment: how would conditions of life and behavior among us differ from their present forms?
7. Carefully read "The Lost Commander" by Andrews; list underlying motives of Florence Nightingale's behavior.
8. List some of the "overintense" stimuli which you as a nurse have been able to guard your patients against, thereby maintaining their comfort.
9. What urges for satisfaction are gratified in the following illustrations:
    (a) Mr. Brown, who has both legs in traction, appears quite contented since he has been taught to do leather tooling. *creativity*
    (b) On the Surgical Ward the sun room is usually filled by 10 A. M. with patients gathering in groups, discussing their operations. *gregarious*
    (c) Miss L. removed her own dressing last evening in order to see the size of the incision. *curiosity*
    (d) Miss C. (who comes from a home with many cultural advantages) swears so constantly in her conversations that her classmates have dubbed her "What the ----- Cox." *display*
    (e) In theory, Miss H. favored socialized teaching methods; invariably, however, after introduction of the topic for class discussion, she monopolized the entire period for her own presentation. *possession & mastery*
    (f) Miss L. is the favorite nurse on the children's ward, because she can always suggest and direct the making of delightful things out of commonplace materials. *creativity*
    (g) For four years Miss V. had been nursing in four different states, spending a year in each position. Her fourth year she spent in Ohio; on its completion, she decided that she needed a change, so resigned her position and applied for staff duty in a hospital in California. *wanderlust*
    (h) As soon as Miss P. made a game of Mary's hand soak, Mary entered into the procedure eagerly. *display*
    (i) Miss Z. was never willing to participate in the extracurricular activities, unless she could be the chairman of the group. *mastery & poss.*
    (j) As soon as the patient in Room 10 was told that John had at last found a good position, she cooperated in every way possible to get well. She was one of the surprise recoveries; both nurses and doctors had almost given up hope of winning her cooperation, without which there was but slim chance of her cure. *rivalry*
10. Consider what would be the correct attitude of the nurse toward a patient who persists in exhibitionism or unseemly comments. Remember that dignity and understanding in meeting such situations are helpful to both nurse and patient.
    (a) Ignore such behavior on the part of the patient, by directing interest to other ward situations or topics; and then report to the nurse in charge what has occurred.
    (b) Frankly tell the patient that his behavior is not acceptable, and treat him as you would a patient who is momentarily irrational.
    (c) Leave the patient for a few minutes, call the head nurse, intern or orderly to assist in completing treatment or nursing procedure which you were doing.
11. Select one patient to whom you have given nursing care, make a careful study of her social, educational, emotional and physical history; in light of her present illness, list the physical restrictions, the social restrictions and the mental and emotional problems which appear to interfere with the present experience of normal satisfactions. For each problem appearing on your list,

suggest a practical substitute activity which should minimize the patient's dissatisfaction and discomfort and, in as many instances as you can, find substitutions which should make for constructive satisfactions.
12. Because fatigue definitely enters into hospital situations, suggest ways whereby its occurrence may be lessened:
   (*a*) For the patient.
   (*b*) For the student nurse.
   (*c*) For the head nurse.
   (*d*) For the intern.

SUGGESTED READINGS

1. Bullis, H. E., and Kelly, C. W.: *Human Relations in Action.* New York, G. P. Putnam's Sons, 1954.
    A good general book that will help you further to understand our human motivation.
2. Cruze, W. W.: *Psychology in Nursing.* New York, Blakiston Division, McGraw-Hill Book Co., 1955.
    Chapter 8, "The Motivation of Human Behavior," summarizes our psychological drives and purposes.
3. Karn, H. W., and Weitz, J.: *An Introduction to Psychology.* New York, John Wiley and Sons, 1955.
    Beginning on page 75 is a section entitled "Motivation and Learning," which may be read with profit.
4. Munn, N. L.: *The Evolution and Growth of Human Behavior.* Revised edition. Boston, Houghton Mifflin Co., 1955.
    This standard text will be found an excellent source book in the study of motivation. Cf. particularly Chapters 1 to 3.
5. Ruch, F. L.: *Psychology and Life.* 4th ed. Chicago, Scott, Foresman and Co., 1953.
    Chapter 5, "Motivation," presents a good survey of this subject. Chapter 6, "Emotions—Inner Springs of Action," provides further supplementary reading in the general area of motivation.

Chapter 6

> *Habit hath so vast a prevalence over the human mind that there is scarce anything too strange or too strong to be asserted of it. The story of the miser who, from long accustoming to cheat others, came at last to cheat himself, and with great delight and triumph picked his own pocket of a guinea to convey to his hoard, is not impossible or improbable.*
>
> HENRY FIELDING

HABITS, ATTITUDES, AND OTHER DETERMINERS OF BEHAVIOR

LEARNED AND UNLEARNED BEHAVIOR

Innate Drives as Unlearned Behavior. Psychologists commonly refer to that portion of our behavior which comes into functioning without previous opportunity to learn or practice as *unlearned behavior*. There are assumed to be preconnections in the nerve pathways which are ready to function in the new individual either from the day of his birth or else from the time when his stage of maturation is such as to call them into action. Thus, from the earliest weeks of life the infant manifests a definite tendency to avoid objects or situations which cause discomfort, annoyance or pain. He does not appear to have to learn or to be taught to recoil from such stimuli: the response occurs at the first contact. It is true, of course, that subsequent contacts will arouse somewhat modified responses due to the hangover effects of learning, memory and habit; the fundamental *innateness* of the avoiding or accepting behavior is, however, obvious.

Similarly with the urge to seek mental activity and emotional satisfaction, as we have seen. The baby is but a few weeks old when evidences that he is impelled by some internal compulsion to exert his will upon his surroundings come vividly into his behavior picture. The very circumstance that he squirms and reaches and grasps long before he is old enough to perceive relationships and meanings of objects is indicative of an inner urge to manipulate his environment in quest of satisfying experiences. The existence of a similar urge is indicated somewhat later on in his handling of his toys, his efforts to push chairs and other small articles of furniture about the nursery, and his interest in playing a simple game, or riding a "kiddy car." Consistently, year by year and stage by stage, as he grows older the child seeks without any direction or urging on the part of others to impose his will upon people, things and situations alike. Of course, as in the case of the pain-escaping drive, he is constantly learning new methods, new controls and new experiences, and these acquisitions, as they multiply, serve to modify and reconstruct most of the earlier concrete behavior patterns; fundamentally, however, the motive force that inspires and drives him in the conquest of his environment is the innate compulsion to seek pleasurable experience in controlling and organizing it.

Reflex and Automatic Behavior Are Also Unlearned. For purposes of logical completeness, it should be pointed out that the organism includes in its economy other and somewhat simpler forms of unlearned behavior, notably reflex action and automatic action. Examples of the former include winking the eye when a foreign object is thrust before it, sneezing when tiny gaseous particles bombard the nasal passages, coughing when irritating substances touch certain of the membranes in the pharynx, thrusting forward the foot when the patellar tendon is struck (knee-jerk reflex), and drawing back the hand from a piercing object. These protective responses are not only ready to function almost from birth without any learning, but they are not ordinarily subject to any great amount of modification through learning.

Somewhat similar to these forms of response, which we have termed reflex acts, and like them included here merely for purposes of logical completeness, are other internal responses deep in the organism that we may label as *automatic acts*. This type of organic response includes the regulation and pulsation of the heart, the circulation of the blood, the digestion and assimilation of food, the secretion of ferments and enzymes, and the excretion of body wastes. These processes are of vital importance to the maintenance of the health and efficiency of the body, and they undergo little modification during one's lifetime. Like the reflexes, they are ready to function from birth, or from the time when the maturation of the parts concerned is complete, and like them also they belong definitely and obviously in the category of unlearned behavior.

Disturbance of Organic Functioning in the Sick. While it is in the main true, as stated in the preceding paragraph, that the reflex and the automatic responses undergo a minimum of modification during one's lifetime, it must be appreciated that when the body is in a state of illness or deficiency there is commonly a considerable amount of malfunctioning in various organs—a fact which must be recognized by the nurse who would understand the mental behavior of her patient. Whenever the smooth and regular automatic functioning of the organism is interfered with, there takes place almost inevitably a "spread" from the physiological to the psychological, the patient manifesting pronounced psychic reverberations of his organic ills. This modification of the normal mental outlook and behavior occurring in times of physical disease or disability renders many an ill person a different individual, and one likely to be more trying to live with and to serve professionally.

It is to be observed that the ill person may be "jumpy" and irritable. His nervous system being more or less keyed up and his receptors frequently very acute, he tends not only to show an accelerated reaction time, but his reactions to quite ordinary stimuli may be exaggerated. Thus, he is likely to start at slight noises which would pass unheeded by the well person; the application of water or of dressings that may be a trifle above or below the comfortable temperature may produce in him a sharp circulatory or skin reflex; a twinge of pain, or even a bit of apprehensive reflecting may set his body into hot or cold shivers; certain odors, tastes, or the sight of blood or feces may nauseate him; dread over the withheld verdict of the examining doctor, the morrow's probing of a wound, or the prospect of a sleepless or painful night, may arouse superficial and internal muscles of his body.

In some physical conditions, on the other hand, there is a diminution in the acuity of the sense organs; in place of hyperactivity there tends to be a hypoactivity. This is, of course, the case when the patient is under the influence of opiates, when sensory anesthesias have developed or have been induced artificially, when the patient is unconscious, or when brain lesions occur. In such circumstances the nurse may expect the sick person to be mentally sluggish and to respond only moderately if at all to normal or even to considerably exaggerated sensory stimuli. Under such conditions, she will need of course to redouble her care in safeguarding the patient from stimuli that may be too strong for comfort or safety but against which his sluggish, hypofunctioning receptors cannot properly protect him.

In various stages or types of disease and defect, also, the automatic functioning of the internal organs may be affected. Digestive apparatus may be misbehaving; circulatory processes accelerated or inhibited, or perhaps incoordinated; respiratory action difficult or painful; assimilative capacities weakened; secretions slowed down, accelerated or chemically unbalanced; elimination blocked. In all of these and other conditions of organic malfunctioning or nonfunctioning, the nurse must expect the mental poise and serenity of her patient to be disturbed. While previously the sick person may never even have been aware that he *had* internal organs, so smooth and automatic were their functioning, he is now apprehensively cognizant of their existence and of the fact that organic comfort within the body cavities is, for the time being, at least, impossible. Awareness of this disturbing condition of his state of health serves to stir his emotions, color his thinking and precipitate aimless and restless physical and mental activity. Few experiences that an individual can have are so immediately connected with fretful mental and emotional behavior as are those arising out of physical malfunctioning or failure within his own organism.

Learned Behavior Characterizes a Vast Area of Human Experience. While in the last analysis everything we do could perhaps be shown to emerge directly or indirectly from one or the other of the two drives developed in the preceding chapter, we shall find it profitable to search for other motives connected with the experiences which we encounter in our day-by-day lives and the acquired viewpoints and attitudes which result from these experiences. For the mere circumstance that an individual lives, that he associates with other personalities, that he thinks and reasons, that he reads and converses and forms judgments, is evidence that he is piling up a fund of mind-stuff which differentiates him to a degree from every other individual and which represents definitely an area of learned reaction. In other words, the things which a person learns and the opinions he forms and the attitudes he develops in the course of the give and take of life all serve to motivate much of his contemporaneous and subsequent behavior.

Thus, human beings develop individually characteristic gait, style preferences, political affiliations, biases and prejudices, emotional likings and dislikings; they each form their peculiar and individual opinions and attitudes; they carry out their individual aims, ambitions, purposes; they cultivate their own individual sentiments, emotions and feelings. By virtue of our home training, our community and neighborhood training and the formal training of the schoolroom, we are fashioned into such behavior patterns and complexes as we represent individually and collectively; these learned or acquired traits and characteristics become themselves the motivating force for much of the subsequent evolution or involution of every one of us. It is to be our purpose in the present chapter to enumerate and define some of the more important and obvious of these forms of learned behavior in so far at least as they underlie and condition in us the further development of behavior patterns.

HABIT AS MOTIVE

We are all creatures of habit, so much so, indeed, that habit has been called "second nature" with us. Let a person react in a certain way to a given stimulus several times and he will, unless other inhibiting factors enter the situation, continue to react in the same way whenever that particular situation recurs. From the standpoint of nerve structure, it appears that functional connections are made among the nerve fibers by every act we do, and that once those connections have been made they continue to function thereafter until practice ceases. It is amazing, when one stops to think of it, how many of our customary daily acts are mere repetitions of the same acts of yesterday, the week before, and the year before. Think, for example, of the way we walk, speak, write, comb our hair, brush our teeth, carry ourselves, eat, and of the host of other purely physical reactions of the day's experience. Everybody is a slavish imitator of himself throughout most of his natural lifetime.

Close observation reveals the fact that we habitually dress one foot before the other; that we even button a button a certain way, and that if the relative positions of button and buttonhole were reversed, we would make a distinctly bungling job of buttoning; that we walk by preference upon a particular side of the street instead of upon the opposite side; that we use day after day the same speech forms, favorite exclamation, pitch and intonation of voice; that we think about the same things, criticize or condemn the same persons or things, seek the same diversions and pastimes; that we retire at the same hour, dine at the same hour, go to work at the same hour, relax in the same way at the same hour; that our life today is largely a replica of our life of yesterday and will be not vastly different tomorrow or next year. Such is the tyranny of our habits, and a necessary and constructive tyranny it is, for without habits we could scarcely hope to do smoothly and effectively the work we have to do; without them we would have no stability and no consistency, either of motive or of achievement.

How Habits Rule Us. Our habits, then, act as motives for much of our behavior. The housewife, for example, who is accustomed to wash the dishes at a regular time daily feels ill at ease or downright nervous if something intervenes to prevent her from performing this task. Witness the scandalized admission of Mrs. B—— that something unexpected happened so that "I didn't get my *dinner dishes* done until near five o'clock!" For her, the habitual practice becomes a motive for its continuance. So, too, with scores of other routine activities of our days.

So strong are our habit-motives that whenever something operates to interfere with their smooth discharge our temper may be all but ruined. The man who has mislaid his pipe is restless and ill at ease until he finds and lights it; if his newspaper is not at hand when he looks for it, he is similarly upset and his immediately subsequent emotional behavior is radically modified. Similarly, if he misses his car or bus, if he is late at his office, or if he is thwarted in the expected smooth running of the routine of his daily affairs, he may become cantankerous, and his associates or those who have dealings with him will be glad to give him a wide berth until he has regained his characteristic serenity. Our habitual daily round sinks deeply into our personalities and acts as a motivating force to keep us steadily and invariably in pursuit of whatever objectives we may have set for ourselves.

Life becomes, from this point of view, little more than a perennial following of the same schedule of working, resting, eating, playing and sleeping. Our daily pattern of activities comes ultimately to constitute our very personalities and beings: we *become* our habits, and they in turn become the motivating force that compels us to continue to be ourselves. Habit is transformed into second nature, indeed, and it succeeds in driving us with quite as much power and inevitableness as do the native urges themselves.

Habit and the Nurse. The psychology of habit concerns the nurse from two different angles: (1) from the standpoint of its relationship to her own character and proficiency as an individual and as a worker; and (2) from the standpoint of its relationship to the behavior of her patient.

As regards herself and her own personality and effectiveness, it is not extravagant to say that the efficiency and good standing of the nurse will be conditioned to a large degree upon the nature of her habit patterns. Cleanliness of body and dress; neatness and care of hands, nails and hair; erectness of posture; ease of gait; coordination and control of muscles; skill of hands and fingers; promptness of reaction; silence and alacrity of movement—these are all attributes which commend any nurse to her superiors and to observing physicians. It should be the strong and thoughtful purpose of every nurse who aspires to proficiency in the profession to cultivate habits of this order and not to rest content until they are at least approximated.

Habit Formation. Epitomizing William James' rules for forming habits, we may say that there are two essential things which one who purposes to form or break habits must observe: in the first place, he must feel the strong need of making the new habit a part of his equipment and be willing to plunge with determination into its formation. If one is only half-hearted or is inclined to temporize, he will never be successful in achieving a desirable habit. Postponement of practice or permission of exceptions operates to defeat the building of new habits. In the second place, one must *practice* the new habit. Mere resolutions to rise at five or to sleep eight hours nightly will never eventuate in the formation of habitual patterns of behavior. What is needed is faithful, persistent, day-by-day practice until the desired goal has been achieved. If all the good impulses and intentions in the world were actually to be objectified in transformed conduct and behavior, the millennium would be just around the corner.

If, then, the nurse tends toward the neglecting of her teeth or skin or nails or hair; if she has failed to cultivate gracefulness and ease of locomotion; if she appears to herself to be clumsy with her hands; if she habitually slouches in her walking or standing or sitting posture; if she has cultivated questionable personal health habits; if her voice is loud or uncontrolled; or if her bodily movements are slow, uncoordinated or heavy, she should look sharply to her shortcomings and defects of habit and set herself promptly upon the road to conquer them.

Modification of Habit Patterns in the Sick. From the standpoint of the behavior of the sick person, it is important for the nurse to know that everybody is a bundle of habits—habits of eating, sleeping, working, playing, doing, and the like. Consequently, when something occurs to interfere seriously with the smooth working of one's habit life, it must follow inevitably that the entire personality and behavior pattern of the individual are affected. Illness is a profound interrupter of one's established way of living. One cannot, when ill or suffering, eat what he will, when he will, or as he will; he cannot sleep as he has been wont to do; he cannot, it may be, rise, dress himself, attend his body demands, breakfast and dine and sup with his family, go and come as he is accustomed. For the time being, he must suspend certain of his regular habits—*i.e.*, he must submit himself and his affairs to a new routine. He finds himself under the necessity of establishing new habits.

If the nurse has ever personally striven to break a bundle of old habits and form several new ones in their place, she can understand how discouraging and often even disorganizing it is to the whole personality. She should sympathize with the sick person, who is forced by circumstance to make over established life patterns, and make them to conform to new conditions and new surroundings. She should respect his confusion and uncertainty, make the transformation of his habit reactions as easy as possible for him, surround him as far as possible with an atmosphere of encouragement, maintain a matter-of-fact attitude toward the formation of the new habits by the patient, eliminate suggestion of the awkwardness or restrictiveness of the new patterns by her own dexterousness of manual adjustment and by promptness of attention. By maintaining these attitudes and standards she will make easier for her patient the temporary disturbance which his entire habit system is of necessity undergoing.

ATTITUDES AS MOTIVES

Our attitudes fasten upon us with the tenacity of habits, and are as difficult to rid ourselves of. Contrary to the popular view, attitudes or mind-sets are not innate. Rather, we build them up ourselves. Some, we absorb passively and spontaneously from the social environment into which we are born and in which we grow up; others, we create more or less actively and consciously from our purposeful reflection and our intellectual contacts. Examples of the former uncritical attitudes that arise spontaneously include our attitudes toward customs, conventions, religion, nationalities, politics and other situations to which we early tend to react like our parents.

Some time since, a group of college freshmen were asked to write down the name of the political party to which they individually expected to belong. Every one of the thirty-eight persons did as he was bid. When they were asked a moment later, however, to write down the chief points of difference between the major parties, only three could respond intelligently. It was quite clear that most of them had adopted their political affiliations from the family environment.

Examples of actively constructed attitudes, which come about as the result of intellectual reflection, include those toward crime, unemployment, war, military training and other questions of the day about which there is constant discussion in our home circles, dining halls and in the public press. For every individual who has formed his opinions through calm reasoning and analysis, however, there are probably a hundred who have been molded unthinkingly into their present viewpoints by the forces which play upon them from their social and economic environment.

When we pause to examine the chief sources whence we derive our attitudes and mind-sets, we can identify several agencies as responsible. One is our favorite newspaper. Others are the books and magazines that we read; the movies, entertainments and theatricals that we patronize; the sermons, addresses and broadcasts that we listen to; the speech, examples and views of others with whom we live and have daily dealings; and the persuasive influence of social, business, political and spiritual leaders in our environment. These and a host of other external agencies are responsible for the molding of our mental attitudes.

Better Understanding Corrects Faulty Attitudes. It is a general fact that the rank and file of people look somewhat askance upon foreigners. Their mind-sets are favorable to their own nationals, and hostile to the nationals of other countries. This almost universal attitude of cultural provincialism is chiefly responsible for slowing down machinery for international cooperation and for delaying the progress of world amity and peace. Leaders in statesmanship, diplomacy and international relations have to reckon with the dragging influence upon their plans for building a commonwealth of nations which the popular attitudes of aloofness and suspicion exert. This is no new psychological development. The "phantom of the den"—as Francis Bacon called it—is as old as Holy Writ, at least. It is what led Naaman, captain of the hosts of Syria, to exclaim, when the Prophet of Jehovah bade him go and wash seven times in Jordan to rid himself of his leprosy: "Are not Arbana and Pharpar, rivers of Samaria, better than all the waters of *Jordan?*" It is what led the dubious Nathaniel to query suspiciously regarding Jesus: "Can any good thing come out of *Nazareth?*" It is precisely this same age-old provincialism of the American who, in his overpride of descent and background, manufactures the opprobrious epithets of "dago," "squarehead," "sheeny," "Chink."

Now the strange but fortunate fact is that when we come to take close-ups of those peoples who are not of our own bailiwick, we find them surprisingly and gratifyingly like ourselves. They love, hate, toil, sacrifice, give, worship, dote on their children, chat, shovel snow, mow lawns, wash dishes, and do a thousand and one other things exactly as we do them. They work to earn money to spend on necessities and luxuries just as we ourselves do. They have ideals, ambitions, jealousies, prejudices, much like our own. The attitude of provincialism is almost certain to be modified if and when one really becomes acquainted with those who bare their heads to other flags and bend their knees to other gods than ours.

We are eager and quick to adopt our attitudes, and often there is little justification back of them: perhaps some chance observation, some trivial occurrence, or some emotionally tinged inference. Once adopted, however, these mind-sets will resist wind and weather, even though reason and common sense and fairness will cry out against their continuance. Thus do our mental attitudes become motivating forces, like our habits, in the determination of vast areas of our behavior.

Attitudes and the Nurse. All that has been said in the preceding paragraphs regarding attitudes and mind-sets applies to the student nurse and to the graduate nurse. Since our attitudes are motivators of our conduct and behavior, we must insist that the nurse shall cultivate her mental attitudes with thoughtful attention. As a student nurse, she will find it valuable to develop a consciousness of these matters, for, as we have noted above, our mental attitudes grow much as our physical habits do, and if unfortunate or unhealthful ones get started they are bound to persist and become constantly stronger and more dominating. Some of the significant attitudes which the nurse should be cultivating throughout her student days in the school include among others the following: ambition to do her tasks well, willingness to work and to work with effectiveness, cheerfulness and optimism, interest in the problems and difficulties of other people, cooperativeness, industriousness, respect for the opinions and judgments of others, confidence in superiors, interest in increasing the fund of knowledge underlying effective nursing care, determination to continue to grow professionally. These are among the priceless personality assets of a good nurse. Each of them can be cultivated.

The graduate nurse will have need of all these assets we have mentioned. She will need, in addition, to maintain a consistent pride in her profession and a cheerful readiness to assume responsibility, to adapt herself readily to the temperament or personality of her individual patients, to maintain poise and self-control in all professional situations, to arise to the unexpected without undue panic, and to hold herself in readiness to respond promptly, sometimes instantly, to a call of need. All these and other professional attitudes indispensable to the nurse spell the difference between the successful and the unsuccessful practitioner of the art, between the reliable and the unreliable, the always employed and the rarely employed. They have a direct bearing not only upon the efficiency and employability of a nurse, but obviously also upon her own harmonious internal adjustment to and identification with her task. The intelligent nurse will make constant effort to maintain sane and healthy mental attitudes in all areas of her social and professional experience.

INTERESTS AS MOTIVES

Prominent also among the motivating forces that impel human beings are the interests and curiosities that they develop through contacts with their environment. These interests may or may not arise from obvious relationship to the vocational or professional activities in which we engage for a livelihood; frequently they may have no basis in the vocational background, but are touched off by some experience quite outside and unrelated to the daily walks of life. Regardless of their origin, our interests exert tremendous influence over us and not infrequently become so intimately and completely identified with us that they color and direct much of our behavior. A person who possesses a keen interest in anything tends to think and plan and act in accord with his interest-objectives.

The Collecting Interest as a Type. Possibly one of the most common and typical indications of their interest is to be found in the collections which so many people make of all sorts of appealing objects. The collecting hobby is one of the most universal evidences of the strength of a person's interest in the rare or the unusual or the inaccessible. Some collectors take the historical slant; others, the artistic or literary; others, the scientific; others, the personal and intimate. A university president has a rare collection of amber; a college professor, a fine one of first editions. An invalid woman has an unusual collection of cup-plates; another, one of mugs. The list of collecting hobbies which are popular among people everywhere is almost endless. It includes antique furniture, antique dishes, sculpture and paintings, pewter and old plate, china, glassware, candlesticks, books, nature specimens, autographs of celebrities, valentines, medals, vases, postmarks, stamps, coins, quilts, dolls, costumes, jewelry, maps, musical instruments, bottles, bookplates, Indian relics, ship models, letters, minerals, gems, and hosts of other objects too numerous to mention. Every one of these interests represents, it should be understood, not only the investment of many pleasant hours in search and study, but the outcome of a strong and driving motivation. Because a man is stamp-minded, for example, he is guided by certain definite purposes, and his personality is in consequence shaped and directed accordingly.

The Wide Range of Interests. Human beings have many other avocational interests besides those represented by collected objects. Here is a man, for example, who spends his free time over his microscope, studying the fascinating, invisible world of unicellular life; here is another who loses himself every evening in detective stories and mystery or adventure tales; here is still another who finds extreme pleasure in painting landscapes, and while he does not possess conspicuous talent, he is to be found every half-holiday with his brushes and palette on some sightly hillside indulging his fancy. This woman enjoys outdoor sports; that woman finds great pleasure in organizing visiting committees to call upon the sick. Some men find delight in their club, some in their vegetable gardens, some in their darkrooms. Some women find delight in their flower beds, some in their literary pursuits, some in their libraries, some in their kitchens.

There is no end, of course, to the things which have appeal and interest for men and women everywhere. Many of the satisfactions of life are derived from association with things that intrigue or allure our intellects, our emotions, or our need for physical expenditure. In seeking these satisfactions it is evident that our interests become strong motives to spur us on. *Interests* become *motives*, exactly as we have seen that habits and attitudes do.

Interests and the Nurse. It would be appropriate if the nurse were to find avocational interests in a field of activity related in some way or other to the subject of health. Following are some suggested interests: collecting postcard views of hospitals, including as many as possible from other lands; collecting autographs of contemporary nursing leaders, photographs of outstanding nurses and doctors; keeping a scrapbook to include such interesting items as science clippings from the daily press, accounts of superstitious beliefs relating to general problems of health and disease; photography of various steps in the recovery of patients who have had some unusual condition or operation. Scores of related topics of historical or present significance in man's struggle to overcome his greatest enemy, the microbe, might be suggested. Those mentioned are sufficient, however, to indicate how interestingly any nurse might select activities for many an off-duty hour that are directly related to the absorbing problem of personal and public health to which men in all ages have devoted attention. It is conceivable, too, of course, that any nurse who became thus interested in the investigation of some historical or cultural phase of her profession might in time so master it as to be in position to make a genuine contribution to the literature of the subject.

The nurse may well relate some of her free-time efforts to interests closely allied with her profession. Membership in social service clubs, assistance at social centers and in welfare movements and drives, identification with nursing organizations and active committee work, and attendance at meetings and conferences are examples of this type of activity.

Need for Extraprofessional Interests. It should be borne in mind by the nurse, however, that no professional person can be completely efficient and well adjusted to her job who has no recreational or avocational avenues of emotional release save such as are related more or less definitely to the profession she follows. Every normal and mentally healthy individual should feel the desirability of cultivating a few interests that are removed from the vocational field. There would be no point here in enumerating the interesting and intriguing hobbies that are available in any community or any environment. It is sufficient merely to suggest the desirability that every adult worker, regardless of occupation or profession, choose some one or more of the avocational opportunities that offer, and devote to it or them a substantial amount of her spare time and attention.

SUCCESS AND FAILURE AS MOTIVES

To any normal person, occasional failure is disheartening enough; continuous failure is overpowering. It is of course impossible for anybody to judge what percentage of those unfortunate individuals who take their own lives are driven to the act by an overwhelming conviction of their own failures and inadequacies, but it is probable that the percentage is high. Our personalities demand acceptance and recognition; denied them, they become morose and helpless—and hopeless. It is the rare and exceptional personality that will continue to spend itself against the forces and the other personalities of its environment without achieving the compensating satisfaction of awareness that it is making headway toward its goals.

It makes little difference at what age level or in what social setting we look; the painful truth is everywhere apparent that failure acts negatively as a motive to discourage further effort and to sour and antagonize the personality or the personalities concerned. We see it at the school level, where the pupil who is the chronic failer is the pupil who loses interest, stops trying, or else seeks for the satisfaction he craves in some compensating form of misbehavior which may be demoralizing or delinquent. The pupil who, on the other hand, feels at least occasionally the thrill of success and conscious achievement is the pupil who retains his interest, continues to try, and is in consequence motivated still further in the direction of more successes in his routine work. In like manner, the girl who is never popular and never receives the coveted attention of her friends of the opposite sex may be so negatively motivated that her work and outlook upon life are influenced unfavorably; whereas the girl who is modestly successful in securing the favorable attention of her mates is likely to be positively motivated by her success in the direction of normally extraverted and natural conduct and behavior.

At the adult level, evidences of this same motivating influence of success are to be observed. The artisan, for example, who acquires the reputation of doing efficient or clever work in his field is likely to find more jobs than he can accept, while the bungling, inefficient worker finds his patronage dwindling or disappearing completely. Similarly, the man who is known for the fairness of his dealings is likely to be the man who conducts a prosperous and successful business; the awareness that one is becoming socially accepted in the community or neighborhood motivates one to strive for continued favors; the man who has started a savings bank account is eager to see his balance grow, and to that end he will deny himself luxuries, or even necessities; ownership of a home inspires the possessor to modernize or beautify his holdings. All of these are illustrative of the strong driving power which the awareness of successful achievement exerts over the individual's subsequent efforts to achieve. The old adage "Nothing succeeds like success" is true, and it is equally true that nothing fails like failure. "To him that hath shall be given, while from him that hath not shall be taken even that he hath." The self-made man, so called, is after all merely the man who has gone forward slowly and perhaps laboriously from little successes to larger ones, until at length he has the comforting assurance that he has accomplished something worth while.

Success as a Motive among the Great and Near-Great. What is true with reference to the rank and file of people who succeed in a modest way at their daily pursuits is likewise true of the eminent people about whom we read or hear. Thus, the scientist who is able to push out the frontiers of human knowledge is encouraged by his success to redouble his efforts in the hope of bending the frontier still further outward. One thinks of the achievements of such notable men and women as Thomas Edison, Madame Curie, Louis Pasteur, and many others, who have gone on from conquest to conquest in the realms of their respective interests. So, too, the writer who produces a "best seller," the dramatist who produces a Broadway success, the artist who paints a masterpiece, the sculptor who chisels out of marble a notable piece of statuary, the discoverer who first sets eyes on a new land; all such creative workers aspire to repeat or surpass their previous successes. In this relationship, one thinks of a Booth Tarkington, a Rockwell Kent, an Admiral Byrd; and in the nursing field, of Adelaide Nutting, Annie W. Goodrich and Lillian D. Wald. The repeated successes of these individuals, well known in their various spheres, furnish striking evidence of the strong stimulus to continued achievement which success brings to those who write their names upon the rolls of fame.

Success and the Nurse. Success is just as sweet to the nurse, of course, as it is to anybody else; and failure is just as bitter. Since the degree of success which one obtains in her work from day to day becomes the motivation for the continuance of her performance at the same or at a higher level, it is obvious that everybody who aspires to achieve both for today and for tomorrow must seek to discharge her recurring tasks in such a way that she may feel the awareness of work well done, of performance approved by those in position to judge, and of each task met and carried through earnestly and effectively.

One who has not been disciplined to do the distasteful but necessary tasks about the hospital or the sick-room may not be relied upon to do the more technical and professional tasks later on. Meritorious conduct in the latter is likely to be conditioned upon meritorious conduct in the former. There are probably few men and women today in responsible positions of trust or influence who stepped directly into their positions; for most of them there were years of faithful, effective work at lower levels and in more monotonous tasks that preceded their elevation to the higher positions. Thus, from the standpoint of promotion in the profession as well as from the standpoint of one's own personal pride and mental hygiene, the basal virtue of effort sincerely and successfully expended should loom large upon the horizon of a nurse who has normal purposes and aspirations to rise higher in her profession.

EMOTIONAL DEPENDENCE AS MOTIVE

Some people around us never grow up, but remain infantile in their emotional evolution. Usually the fault is not theirs; rather, it is that of their parents, who have been either unwilling to encourage them to become emotionally independent or else have not known how to proceed to make them so. Such emotionally immature persons are unable to face life hopefully and aggressively; being conscious of their inferiorities, or preoccupied by the almost total identification of their personalities with those of their adult guides and associates, they are motivated in the direction of an introverted dependence and away from a normally extraverted independence and self sufficiency. Much if not most of their behavior is colored by this enslavement to the wills and the personalities of the narrow family circle.

Too many parents, by way of illustration, purposely and thoughtlessly, not to say selfishly, endeavor to prolong the period of dependence of their children beyond reasonable bounds. Sometimes this willful encouragement of an infantile reliance upon the parent springs from the dread which some fathers and mothers—notably mothers—have of seeing their children grow away from them and into new extra-home associations and interests. To this end, they may discourage normal efforts of their children to escape from the home circle, and may strive to protect their brood from harshness and unhappiness which might otherwise come to it.

Effects of Prolonged Infancy upon Personality. This attitude is human and understandable in a parent; its effect upon the progeny is, however, demoralizing. The child who is guarded from the everyday give and take of the play and community environment, who has his needs ministered to and his desires anticipated, who is taught to seek in the parents the satisfaction of his wants and aspirations, who becomes habituated to indulgence and endearment and easy forgiveness, and who is taught that the family circle is perfect and complete, is being poorly prepared to live his own life later on and to face with equanimity and determination the problems of adulthood.

There is not much place in the adult world of affairs for men and women whose personalities have remained infantile and who always look back upon their childhood experiences as representing the golden age of their lives. He who has been a "mama's boy" has more likely than not been abnormally motivated and will never become adjusted to the adult situations with which he will be continually confronted. Having been shielded and pampered and spoiled, he expects the grown-up world into which he is thrust to receive him, to continue to pamper him and to excuse or condone his every caprice. The normally evolved individual must face life and its problems "on his own," without the parental solicitude which sheltered him in his infancy. The infantile personality is motivated rather to run away from life, to avoid reality and actuality as being too harsh and unsympathetic to face.

As a child, such an emotionally dependent individual hesitates to stand on his two feet and meet his problems squarely, it being simpler to flee to the ever sheltering parent for defense and soothing. As a youth, he finds it impossible to emerge from beneath the family roof to find work, to go away to college, or otherwise to step beyond the family circle; homesickness and despair may be his portion, and he may forsake everything and flee to the sheltering and understanding environs of home. As a young adult, he is often unable to set up a new family circle of his own, either because he cannot transfer his infantile loyalties to another being, or because he is unable to find among women any one who appears in such glamorous light as his own mother; in consequence he may find himself wretchedly maladjusted to the normal drives of a grown-up individual. As an adult worker and an adult personality, he may rebel at the harshness of fate that has wrested him loose from the sure and easy moorings of childhood and set him adrift upon a turbulent sea, with no outstretched arms to succor him and no one to baby and pacify him.

Emotional Maturity of the Nurse. The adult individual is, as we shall see in Chapter 12, a person who has undergone psychological weaning from her earlier home and parental environment. This release from the childhood attitude of dependence is quite as essential in a nurse as it is in any other grown-up individual; perhaps it is actually more so. For the nurse will be, by the very nature of her calling, continually confronted with health-disease situations and conditions that will be tinged strongly with emotion. She cannot assume that all of her patients will be emotionally mature; indeed, even the emotionally mature often lose their courage and self control under stress of illness. The nurse must expect to find some of those whom she serves to have regressed temporarily to a somewhat infantile emotional condition. She will often encounter sick men and women who have "lost their nerve," who cannot envisage their lot with calmness and reason, who **become as dependent emotionally upon the nurse as they are physi-**

cally. To meet the demands which these situations impose upon her, if for no other reason, the nurse must be possessed of a completely mature personality. If she is herself childishly emotional, she will not only be a negative influence upon her childishly emotional patients, but she will find the emotional strain of her relationships with them dangerous to her own health and peace of mind.

There are, of course, many other reasons why an adult ought to be emotionally mature and self-regulating. Inasmuch, however, as Chapter 12 will be devoted to a discussion of the more important aspects of emotional maturity in individuals generally, it is not necessary to go further into them here. They apply equally to nurses as to all other grown-up individuals and workers.

THOUGHT PROBLEMS FOR THE STUDENT

1. Make a list of ten of your most important and constructive habits. Make another list of several habits you feel are not desirable and which you would be better off without.
2. Determine upon some particularly undesirable habit which you would like to conquer. Carry on for the next month an aggressive and purposeful campaign against it. Keep a day-by-day diary of your successes and failures. Try to allow no exceptions to occur in your struggle to overcome the habit.
3. What is your present attitude toward each of the following: (1) capital punishment, (2) racketeers, (3) kidnapping, (4) "soak-the-rich," (5) tipping, (6) disarmament, (7) labor and management, (8) revolution, (9) dictatorship, (10) survival of the fittest. Compare your own attitudes toward these concepts with those of other members of your class. Can you account for the status of your opinions?
4. What unhealthy mental attitudes have you observed in any of your friends or acquaintances? Are you able to account for their origin or development? How much influence do they appear to exert over those who possess them? How might each be changed over into a healthful attitude?
5. List your strongest personal interests. How have they been built up? Are you at present cultivating them? Are you forming or have you recently formed any new interest or interests?
6. Can you identify any individual from among your previous associates or contacts who appears to have made a failure of her life? Contrast with her some other acquaintance who has obviously been successful. What contributing factors can you cite to account for the sharply different personality outcomes in the two individuals concerned?
7. Write a brief case study of some individual known to you whose personality has been unfavorably influenced by a prolonged dependence upon the home or upon a parent. How might the present personality or emotional status of this person have been quite different?
8. (*a*) When your ward assignment is changed, on the first day with your new patients be cordial but not friendly; do not manifest interest, but give them good physical nursing care; keep your face expressionless.

(b) The second day be friendly, cordial, interested, cheerful in expression and manner. Note patients' gradually changing attitude toward you.

(c) List then the "bedside personality traits" which would distinguish the successful nurse.

9. Approach patients as if you expected them to cooperate, to get well, to make the best of their hospital situations. How does this expectant and interested approach influence the response that you get? Would you call this a subtle form of suggestion? Is it possible to be so positive in one's approach as to arouse antagonism? Experiment on different methods of approach to people, keeping a record of those which elicit best responses; analyze those which are unsuccessful and find out why.

10. Make a study of the early settling and development of the community or city where you are located; visit historic sites, read available literature, talk with life-long residents, compare growth and chief interests of the city by decades.

11. Start a collection of picture postcards showing hospitals at home and abroad; classify them according to the style of architecture, or some other criterion.

SUGGESTED READINGS

1. Blair, G. M., Jones, R. S., and Simpson, R. H.: *Educational Psychology*. New York, The Macmillan Co., 1954.

    Part III includes good treatment of "Motivation: The Forces Which Energize and Direct Behavior."

2. Cruze, W. W.: *Psychology in Nursing*. New York, Blakiston Division, McGraw-Hill Book Co., 1955.

    It is suggested that the student refer to the index to locate discussions of "habits," "attitudes," "interests" and "emotions as motives." There is good treatment of each of these topics.

3. Garrison, K. C., and Gray, J. S.: *Educational Psychology*. New York, Appleton-Century-Crofts, Inc., 1955.

    The student is referred especially to Chapter 8, "Interests, Attitudes and Values."

4. Munn, N. L.: *The Evolution and Growth of Human Behavior*. Boston, Houghton Mifflin Co., 1955.

    Chapters 2, 3, 4 and 5 particularly should be scanned carefully by the student interested in broadening her understanding of the foundations of unlearned and learned behavior.

5. Weiss, M. O.: *Attitudes in Psychiatric Nursing Care*. New York, G. P. Putnam's Sons, 1954.

    Discusses general and specific attitudes essential in the nurse, especially when dealing with nervous or disturbed patients. "In the modern psychiatric hospital, more important than her feet, or her hands, or her brain, are the manifestations of the nurse's heart."

Chapter 7

> The nervous structure is like a grand orchestra, in which one instrument alone out of time or tune disturbs the harmony of the rest, and the finest musical composition in the world is entirely spoiled by its discord.
>
> FORBES WINSLOW

THE NEUROMUSCULAR MECHANISM AS MOTIVATOR

PSYCHOLOGICAL BEHAVIOR RESTS upon the continuous interaction of three separate and distinct processes: sensory, or receiving; nervous, or connecting; and muscular, or responding. Throughout the life of the organism this trilogy of physical conditioning underlies and implements all our conscious experience; it likewise regulates the internal automatic functioning of every organ in the body.

We shall consider first, in order, the role played by the sensory organs in this tripartite process. It is the assumption of the authors throughout this chapter that the student has already had, or is currently having, courses in anatomy, physiology, biology and related subjects, and hence has some foundation in the structural basis of behavior. The present discussion is limited to certain relevant psychological and nursing aspects of neuromuscular and glandular activity.

THE SENSE ORGANS AS GATEWAYS TO THE BRAIN

What sort of task would it be to teach a child born without eyes, ears, sense of touch, sense of smell and sense of taste? What sort of teachers and tutors would be required for the task? How successful would be the combined efforts of home and school in transforming such a handicapped individual into a finished educational product? Could she, by any conceivable means, be taught to understand language? To talk? To recognize faces and voices? To know night or day, good or bad, false or true? To make her wants known to others? Could she learn to walk, sit, run, play? Would she know affection? Ambition? Could she reason? Will?

A child born into the world without any functioning sense organs would be doomed to a lifetime of complete helplessness. Fortunately, it is rare that a child is completely lacking in all of them. It does happen occasionally, however, that one is born deaf and blind. Parents face an almost impossible task in attempting to teach such a child. If, like Miss Helen Keller, her eyes and ears are normal at birth, so that she has opportunity to build up in her early years a background of normal visual and auditory patterns of response, it may be possible for her to continue to progress educationally if she becomes blind and deaf in subsequent childhood years. Even in the case of Miss Keller, however, continuing mental evolution would have been extremely unlikely but for the patient and resourceful tutoring of a friend and companion who devoted much of her life to the task.

Our sense organs are the gateways to the mind, and when any one of them is blocked the mind cannot receive the particular kind of sensory data which the nonfunctioning organ was designed to deliver; if all of them are blocked, the mind can receive no data of *any* type from the outside world. In the latter event, the brain would remain forever locked in its bony skull-casket, much like a radio receiving set that has no means of being "tuned in" to the myriads of wave frequencies bombarding it from the surrounding ether.

Some Phenomena of Sensory Experience

1. Visual. One of the most obvious and universal of these forms of sensory bombardments is the visual experience of color. Everybody knows that some colors are "warm" while others are "cold"; that some suggest cheer and contentment, while others are somber and funereal. Popularly, we speak of a person "green" with envy, of a face "red" with anger or "white" with fear, of a "true blue" character, of a "yellow coward," of the "blackness of despair," of the "white heat of rage." Popularly, too, we associate red with courage, blue with fidelity, white with purity, purple with royalty, yellow with riches, and red with anarchy. The emotional reference of color is almost proverbial among most civilized peoples. Among savages, too, there is a strong color consciousness; even children have a dawning color sense, being usually able to recognize and use consistently when only four years old at least four or five common colors.

Influence of Colors upon the Sick. A small amount of experimental work has been done upon the effects of various colors upon the emotions. One investigator finds yellow a stimulant of hope and ambition; red, inciting to great uneasiness and even violence; blue, soothing and quieting. There should be for the nurse some suggestion in this of the possibilities of using color as a curative, or at least as a quieting medium with her patients. If colors react upon the mentally ill, they may be expected to have definite emotional influence upon those who are mentally and emotionally disturbed over their physical impairment. Flowers cheerfully arranged on the table in the sickroom; clean uniforms; subdued lights and colors for those who need sedative influences; warm, bright lights and colors for those who need stimulation and encouragement—these things are many times subject to the nurse's control. Somewhat outside her control, but not outside her needful information, are such relevant environmental appointments in the sick-room as plain, cheerful walls, plain covers and spreads, harmonious hangings and decorations. All these things undoubtedly have a psychological effect upon the sick person.

Ocular Aberration and Discomfort in the Sick. Intimately concerned as they are with carrying to the brain much of the sensory information from our environment, the eyes play a major role in the drama of consciousness. So long as they are keen and continue to function smoothly and without noticeable irritation, eyes rarely become sources of worry or apprehension. When, however, as is frequently the case with unwell people, the functioning of these important organs is impaired by reflex disturbances occurring elsewhere in the body, when they are inflamed or distended by excess blood in their membranes and muscles, when they smart from sleeplessness, or when for these or other reasons they fail to focus properly, they may arouse in the patient great distress and alarm.

Ocular discomfort is frequently associated with bodily disease or deficiency, as may be noted by the dullness and lack of luster of the eyes of a sick person, by their redness, twitching, or staring. These are conditions commonly observed in patients. It is important for the nurse to realize how sympathetically the eyes mirror the state of one's bodily ill health and often of his mental and emotional suspense or fear. Careful attention to shades at bright windows, to nearby lights and bed lamps, to bathing, to cooling applications, and the like, is always indicated when a patient's eyes cause him additional distress. Often a cool hand lightly pressed over them, and a few comforting words of reassurance, will have good psychological effect upon the sufferer.

2. Auditory. We live in an age of noise. The advance of our machine civilization has brought with it all manner of noise that tends to be trying upon our nervous system. One has but to consider the loudspeakers that blare at us, the sound-advertising trucks that boom through our city streets, the screaming sirens of emergency and patrol wagons and fire-fighting apparatus, the annoying horns that honk at us from all directions, the shouts of hawkers and of newsboys, the exhausts of motors, the grinding of iron wheels upon iron rails, the screeching of whistles, the roar of shovels and drills and air compressors used by street gangs and sewer gangs; the rat-a-tat-tat of riveting, and the din of machinery in our factories to realize that modern industrial civilization has its decided drawbacks from the viewpoint of reasonable quiet and peace in our communities.

There is a question as to how much nervous energy is used up by the average individual in counteracting surrounding noises. While it appears to be true that complete quiet does not provide the ideal surroundings for efficient mental performance, a moderate amount of auditory stimulation being favorable to the maintenance of effort and attention to the work in hand, it is true that too intense auditory distraction operates to reduce efficiency. It is the generally accepted opinion among psychologists and psychiatrists that the strain and the wear and tear upon the nervous system inflicted by exposure to long and intense noise are bad. Man's auditory receptors were intended to be used upon the prairies and in the wide open spaces, where the stimuli that might get to them were produced chiefly by the vocal cords of animals and of other human beings rather than by the vocal cords of machines.

Noise as a Nuisance. In 1925 and 1926, in New York City, a survey of the sources and intensity of city street noises was made. Similar surveys have been made in Chicago, Boston, Washington, and other cities. The corner of Sixth Avenue and Thirty-fourth Street, in New York City, was found to be the noisiest street area recorded up to that time anywhere in the world. The din at this point, where three main streets, three surface-car lines and a double-track elevated line intersected, was estimated to be sufficient in intensity to make the normal individual about two-thirds deaf. A two-month survey conducted in 1949 by the Van Der Scholie Laboratory, as reported by the Associated Press, listed the ten noisiest cities in America, in order, as Pittsburgh, Chicago, New York, Boston, Philadelphia, San Francisco, Cincinnati, Houston, Miami and St. Louis. On the average city street in America, the daytime noise is estimated to be sufficient to render the normal individual one-fourth to one-third deaf.

Much of the noise that is pounded into our ears in the modern community is needless; that is to say, it could be either eliminated or else reduced if public opinion were to demand it. Some cities have realized the needlessness of the noise nuisance and have enacted ordinances to attempt to control it.

Recently in our own country, a national Noise Abatement Council has been formed to deal with this whole problem. Among other things, the Council has set up an annual Noise Abatement Week during which, in April 1954, some twelve or more cities turned their attention to ways and means of controlling excessive noise in streets, offices and homes. The cities of the United States are not alone in becoming conscious of needless urban noise which might be reduced sharply if society became interested in it. Thus, in Marseille, France, and in Lima, Peru, to mention only two foreign cities, determined anti-noise campaigns were underway during the summer of 1954.

Taking our cues from the staccato of the machines about us, we are tending to become a restless and noisy people, unable to enjoy calm and quiet. There will undoubtedly be found to be a limit to the amount and intensity of noise which the human nervous system can safely bear. While it possesses enormous powers of adaptation to disturbing agents, it is doubtful if it can ever adjust without great nervous strain to continued and half-deafening noise.

Noise and the Sick. The irritability of the receptors in the unwell individual is commonly much greater than it is in the well person; consequently, a given constant volume of noise which would cause no apparent annoyance to a normally healthy person may disturb the same individual when he falls sick. Therefore, the nurse needs to exercise thoughtful care to reduce noise in and about the sick-room to a minimum. Especially important is this during the hours of sleep, for sick people are often aroused easily from their slumbers.

3. Olfactory. Odors play a considerable role in our lives. Esthetically, they may be dischared from natural objects, such as flowers, herbs, grasses, and the like; they may also be combined in synthetic perfumes. Gastronomically, they are closely allied with appetite and hunger, as any lover of roast meat knows who has found it difficult to restrain himself during the last half hour before the roast was taken from the oven and placed on the dining table. Socially, unpleasant body odors serve as important means of making us aware of the need for bathing, for putting on fresh linen, for improving a poor physical condition often responsible for foul breath, and the like. Commercially, some manufacturers have found it easier to sell products such as stationery, glue, oilcloths, raincoats, and even silk stockings, if a little perfume has been imparted to them during the manufacturing process. From the standpoint of health and safety, certain odors, like escaping gas, frequently warn us of the imminence of danger.

The Olfactory Sense and the Nurse. The nurse should understand that the sense of smell plays a rather important role in the sickroom. Quite obviously in a hospital or other environment where there are sick people, disagreeable odors will be present: from the body eliminations and discharges, from the foul breath of the patients, from stale bandages, from coagulated blood, from certain medicines, from anesthetics. Unless care is taken in the handling of such materials and situations as these, the nurse may find her patient uncomfortable or even nauseated. She will therefore need to look to such matters as keeping certain doors closed, certain other ones open, controlling window ventilation, manipulating deodorants and removing wastes. These may appear small matters on the surface, as indeed they are; but they may easily make the difference between a sensorily comfortable and a sensorily uncomfortable patient.

A word must be said, too, regarding the personal cleanliness of the nurse. The intimate associations which she has continually with her patients require that she be meticulous in this matter. It is unpleasant for anybody, sick or well, to be made aware of the odor of stale perspiration from the clothing or body of one's associates. There is one way, and one way only, to avoid offending others in this regard: that is through strict attention to bathing and personal cleanliness. To counteract the lingering traces of disinfectants and anesthetics about her hair and uniform, the nurse should seek by means of deodorants to keep her clothing and herself always as wholesome as possible when on ward duty or in the sick-room.

4. Gustatory. Taste, like smell, plays a strong role in our lives. The sense of taste and the sense of smell are closely coordinated. If a person holds or plugs his nostrils and asks a friend to place on his tongue a cube of some raw vegetable, *e.g.*, potato, turnip or onion, without his knowing which it is to be, he will experience considerable difficulty in attempting to identify the vegetable he is chewing. He will correctly conclude that when taste is not reenforced by smell, food does not possess its usual pleasing flavor. It is a common observation that when one has a head cold, which blocks the olfactory cells with mucus so that odorous particles can not reach them readily, food tastes flat and insipid. Much of the satisfaction we derive from our food lies in the pleasing odors that we experience while it is being prepared and while it is being eaten.

Adaptation to taste and to smell takes place quickly; that is to say, a persistent odor soon becomes so weak as to be barely if at all noticeable, and a particular taste is soon jaded. This is probably because the sense organs fatigue quickly and require a brief resting period in which to recuperate. A rose smells sweet only at the first two or three sniffs; shortly, its fragrance is reduced. A food that is too salty becomes more palatable as we continue to eat it; so with sour, or sweet, or bitter tastes.

Bearings upon Nursing. Because of the operation of this principle of adaptation, the nurse should realize that odors from the surgery or from dressings and anesthetics to which she is exposed may be strong enough to annoy or nauseate a patient, yet be imperceptible to herself. She should therefore at all times give thought to the ventilation of the ward and rooms which her patients occupy. They will be grateful for this thoughtfulness on the part of those who take care of them. Disagreeable tastes are less inevitable in the experience of sick people than are disagreeable odors. It is true, however, that in many types of illness the mouth "tastes bad," and food is not relished. Frequent attention should be given by the nurse to rinsing the patient's mouth and to serving food that is fresh, clean and tastily prepared.

5. Skin Senses of the Sick. The skin senses of the sick person are extremely likely to be oversensitive; this is notably the case with the temperature organs. In those who are ill, uncomfortable skin reflexes are set off readily by slight changes in the surrounding temperature, or even by the thoughtless touch of a cold hand or of cold articles of clothing. In certain kinds of illness, merely to move the body in bed or to uncover any part of it is sufficient to arouse unpleasant sensations of cold. Even in a warm room or a well heated ward, patients will frequently wish for more covers to the bed than may appear needful to the nurse; the nurse should realize the abnormal condition of their skin receptors and be prompt and willing to see that they are kept warm and comfortable. In general, elderly people feel the cold more acutely than younger people do; the circulation of their blood being more sluggish, they will usually require a somewhat higher temperature for comfort.

Then, too, the patient's skin may be irritated by dressings or by long and painful confinement in bed. A little attention on the nurse's part to massage, to the use of soothing lotions, and to smoothing out the wrinkles from sheets, pillow slips and garments will often greatly relieve the discomfort. Finally, the nurse's hands should be kept as soft and smooth as possible, since they come in contact with the skin surfaces of her patient; rough, harsh hands may hurt the oversensitive skin of a sick person.

6. The Vestibular Sense. From the standpoint of nursing, the patient's vestibular, or static, sense assumes considerable importance. It is not alone in elderly and aged people that dizziness and poor balancing of the body are experienced; even the younger individual is likely, during certain types of illness and the recuperative period following, to suffer from vertigo, particularly when he changes his position. Even the simple matter of being turned over in bed or of being raised to a sitting posture from a prone one may set off disagreeable and nauseating reaction in the semicircular canals and the auditory vestibules. In prolonged illness, and in certain febrile conditions and digestive and circulatory disturbances, this functional phenomenon may be disconcerting. Even after convalescence is well under way and the patient has become ambulatory, care must often be exercised by the nurse to guard him against stumbling and falling from sudden recurrences of dizziness and nausea.

Not infrequently, older people, aware of what they commonly term their "light-headedness," develop a timidity in going up or down stairs, or even in walking about the room or the house, that attending nurses may find hard to understand but must nevertheless accept as inevitable in their patients. Fear of falling and of breaking bones is omnipresent in many aged people. Along with failing eyes and ears go also a dimming and faltering of the equilibratory mechanism which no available mechanical device comparable to glasses and hearing aids can rectify. To patients thus afflicted, the understanding nurse becomes a pillar of strength.

7. The Kinesthetic Sense. Easy operation of an automobile or airplane and similar coordinated physical movements of all types would be impossible were it not for the constant sensations of strain, position and tension which the kinesthetic receptors report to the central nervous system. Acts of skill of all varieties are possible only after one has learned to coordinate his muscles and hence is aware of the "feel" of the correct move. The golfer, the baseball player, the tennis player—all become proficient to the degree that they can reinstate the feel of a correct play when they are about to make it. The bungling player merely fails in "feeling" the coordination that must be achieved if a graceful play is to be had.

Kinesthesis and the Nurse. The nurse in the sick-room needs a highly developed kinesthetic sense. It makes a great difference to the patient whether the nurse's fingers are deft or clumsy in manipulating a dressing, whether her touch is light or heavy in adjusting a bandage or disinfecting a wound, whether her movements are jerky and incoordinated or whether they are smooth and effective. Erratic handling of a clinical thermometer, a catheter, a syringe, or bed pan; aimless pulling at a quilt or cover; clumsy insertion of a tube or the needle of a hypodermic; spasmodic and irregular muscular control in moving a patient or in changing his garment; bumping into the furniture and jarring the bed—all of these things may be very trying to the delicate nerves of the sick person. If the nurse is conscious of any abnormality of muscular coordination, she should forthwith put herself through a serious course in self training in order to correct this defect. The general environment of a hospital ward or sick-room is a poor environment in which to demonstrate the imbalance and incoordination of her muscles.

8. Visceral or Organic Senses. Everybody who has ever experinced distress from the stomach or intestines during an attack of indigestion realizes that the internal organs of the body are able to transmit on occasion unpleasant sensations. Whenever any of the visceral organs in the thoracic or the abdominal cavity are thrown out of normal functioning, they discharge sensory impulses which serve as warnings that something is amiss; incidentally, these impulses may be disconcerting and painful. Microscopic examination of the internal organs reveals that fibers pass from them to the nervous system, thus conveying to the brain information as to the internal state of the body.

Prominent among the sensations arising from internal structures are of course hunger and thirst, the former being due in part to rhythmical contractions of the stomach walls, and the latter to a reduction of the amount of water in the body tissues and a consequent drying of the throat. Other organic sensations commonly experienced from malfunctioning or diseased mechanisms include those associated with nausea, dysentery, "heart burn," palpitation, pleurisy, neuritis, headache and toothache. All organic or visceral sensations of this order are unpleasant, and they may be distressing.

We are not so apt to think of the milder sensations which proceed constantly from these same organic structures in times of health and proper functioning. Much of our day-by-day serenity and good spirits, however, is to be attributed to the regularly smooth and integrating operation of the internal mechanism. When one is in good health and feels "fit for anything," he may be thankful that the nervous discharge over the sensory fibers that connect the various structures of the body with the correlating and interpreting nervous system is pleasant and agreeable rather than the reverse. This continuous and smooth passage of sensory current from the viscera to the brain is responsible for our general feeling of well-being; interruption or modification of it is, by the same token, responsible for the feeling of ill-being and malaise that we often experience.

Relationships of Organic Sensations to Nursing Problems. The discomfort of being physically helpless and bed-ridden, and having certain body functions suspended or performing abnormally, could be borne by the sick person if it were not for the nausea and internal pain that accompany these conditions. The nurse herself has experienced enough short periods of illness, no doubt, to understand how disagreeable these organic sensations may be; she can fancy how disconcerting and disorganizing to the sufferer they must be when prolonged over a period of months, as they not infrequently are in the person whose health has been undermined by disease or deficiency.

The nurse must understand that when a patient appears to be exacting or crotchety, when he fusses and frets, when he sighs and moans, he is not purposely trying to make all his neighbors and attendants uncomfortable and does not wish to make them hate him and his troubles; rather, she should appreciate the fact that a series of uncomfortable and unfamiliar sensations is passing from his bodily structures into his consciousness, and that he is in consequence in a disconcerting mental condition.

Far from treating such a patient with animus or derision, she must rather treat him sympathetically and understandingly. This does not mean that she is called upon to aid and abet him in his misery by sentimental display of pity and over-sympathy; what she is called upon to do is to understand the nature of his discomfort and try to do everything within reason to cheer him and make his burden as bearable as possible. Irritation and loss of patience or display of temper have no place in those who care for the sick; neither have sentimentality and identification. One of the most helpful rules of conduct to cultivate in handling the sick is the maintenance of an objective, detached, business-like attitude, tempered with kindness and cheerfulness.

THE NERVOUS PROCESSES

Importance of Association. We come next to the second of the three interacting physical processes that constitute the organic basis of psychological experience: namely, the nervous or connecting process that brings sensory experience into contact with responding apparatus. In the preceding section we made frequent mention of the fact that the sense organs of the body serve as gateways to the central nervous system, and that were it not for his receptors man could never succeed in learning anything about himself or his environment. We may say with equal certainty also that but for his nervous structures man would likewise continue in complete ignorance of himself and his environment. By standing as outposts at the periphery of his body and as sentinels within his visceral organs, the sensory gateways are able to admit whatever messages and dispatches are clamoring for attention and adjustment; but it is only through the intermediary of the spinal cord and the brain that all this mass of incoming stimulation can register in consciousness. Receptors would be useless without a central nervous system to receive and coordinate the information they pick up; the central nervous system would in turn be useless without receptors to bring it something to coordinate; responding organs would be helpless without a nervous system to innervate them and make them react, and there would be nothing to react to if the receptors did not pick up the stimuli adequate to arouse them. Thus do sense organs and nervous structures cooperate in regulating and presiding over our human behavior. Make a pass at a person's eye, and he will blink; throw pepper into the air, and he will sneeze; spray tear gas about him, and his tears will flow. These are specimens of first-level, physical responses.

But it would be a mistake to infer from these examples that all or even the most significant of man's responses are muscular or glandular. By all odds, the more characteristically human of our responses are *mental*. They involve paying attention, recalling, thinking, reasoning, judging, deciding, imagining, and the like. Man is most typically distinguishable from the animals by his mental reactions, not by his muscular or glandular ones. It was not by mere chance that the upper brain developed more in him than it did in the animals below him; the human cerebrum and cortex have achieved their size and complexity for the simple reason that man has striven to react to his environment with intelligence and insight, whereas the animal has been satisfied with achieving gross physical satiety. The former has thought, planned, reasoned, invented; the latter has followed instinct and remained animal. Man has willed to project and extend himself creatively and transformingly into his surroundings; the animal has submitted to its environment and has been in considerable measure dominated by it.

The cerebrum controls, then, the most essentially *human* behavior. Relatively very small in most animals, the cerebrum is the largest part of the human brain. To it come ultimately all information and the apprehension of all conscious experience; in it takes place all deliberate reflection; from it proceed all voluntary and purposeful reactions. Within its millions of cells and across its billions of fibers are initiated and projected all of the elaborate and complicated higher processes of thought and consciousness.

Through the potentialities of the cerebral structures it is possible for Michelangelo to conceive and execute a masterpiece of art, for Beethoven to produce a great sonata, for Harvey to discover the circulation of the blood, for Pasteur to induce a brilliant theory of disease, for Florence Nightingale to initiate worldwide hospital reform. It is this same cerebrum that makes possible for all of us the enunciation and the understanding of language written and spoken; the recognition of a face, a symbol, a principle or law; the planning, experiencing or recalling of an event; the awareness of the self and of the egos of others around us.

Something of the miracle of cortical association may be appreciated if the nurse will think now, for example, of her first days in the school of nursing. Forthwith a long chain of ideas is released in her mind. She recalls the early impressions that the hospital made upon her, with its uniformed nurses and interns, its rows of beds, its wards and rooms and patients; she recalls also the new personalities, her roommate, perhaps also her feelings of temporary loneliness and dismay. And from any one of these individual words or phrases another long string of associations is readily set off.

Integration. Still another related miracle of the central nervous system is observable in the complete integration of our reactions, both mental and motor. The entire organism, under the directing and co-ordinating influence of the brain and cord, works together as a unit. It is not, on the surface of things, apparent to the casual observer, for example, that the skilled baseball pitcher is using when he delivers the ball over the plate no fewer than 200 bones, more than 500 skeletal muscles, unknown thousands of involuntary muscles, and probably millions of neurones and nerve fibers.

Supplementary Conditions of Nerve Functioning. 1. *Facilitation.* It is a commonly observed fact that when two or more stimuli, any one of which is adequate to arouse a response, are presented simultaneously they cause a more prompt and vigorous response than one of them alone would have caused. The term *facilitation of nerve impulse* has been applied to this phenomenon. Holding out food to a dog and calling him at the same time by his name will bring him more promptly and eagerly than would either stimulus alone. Awareness that it is time for dinner, that pleasant odors are issuing from the kitchen, and that the dining table is set and ready, facilitates a hearty response in the hungry person.

2. *Prepotence.* Some of the stimuli that pour in to our consciousness are of such a nature that they tend to block other competing stimuli and sidetrack them effectually, at least for the time being. Such stimuli are said to be *prepotent*. In general, prepotent stimuli have the right of way through the nervous system because they are related to the survival or preservation of the organism. Thus, a sudden twinge of pain from any part of the surface or interior of the body shatters its way into our consciousness and compels attention; similarly, a sudden flash of light or a loud detonation will bring us to our feet and drive out all other and lesser competing stimuli from present consciousness.

3. *Summation.* Sometimes a given stimulus is inadequate to arouse a response because it is too weak or transient; when, however, several such stimuli are presented simultaneously or in succession they will often be found so to reenforce one another that the subject responds. This represents *summation, or convergence, of stimuli.* It may be illustrated by the following: a whisper in a room where someone is sleeping may be so low as not to be detected by the sleeper; a gentle "tucking-in" motion may also pass unnoticed; so may a light touch upon the cheek. If, however, all three stimuli are applied serially, the

sleeper will be more likely to be aroused. It appears that stimuli coming in over several receptors may thus "converge" upon a single responding organ and set off a reaction.

4. *Diffusion.* At the opposite extreme of convergence is *diffusion of nerve impulse.* Theoretically, at least, a single incoming stimulus from a single receptor may be intense enough to cause every responding organ in the body to react. In other words, single sensory experience may set off motor reactions at every level of the nervous system. A prolonged tickling of the sole of the foot, for example, which at first elicited only a drawing up of the knee, may become eventually so unpleasant as to evoke widespread explosive reaction throughout most of the muscular and glandular structures of the body. Similarly, a sick person may become suddenly so nauseated by an odor to which he has become negatively conditioned that his entire reaction system is thrown into a paroxysm. While this widespread reaction of the responding organs to a single incoming stimulus occurs only in unusual circumstances in which either there is persistence of the stimulus or else a strong disturbance of the organism, the fact that it can and does take place is indicative of the further fact that every one of the millions of neurones in the body is connectable, and may be connected when the occasion demands, to any other.

5. *Reciprocal Innervation.* When one group of muscles in the body is working, other muscles antagonistic to them are idling. Thus, when an object is grasped with the fingers, the muscles of the palmar side of the forearm exert a tension that flexes the fingers; conversely, when the fingers are straightened out, the muscles on the opposite side of the forearm exert their tension and extend them. This sort of nerve discharge is called *reciprocal innervation.* Through their coordinating functions, the cord and lower brain level send out reciprocal motor impulses, now to one group of muscles (the flexors) and now to the other group (the extensors). In such functions as walking and swinging the arms, these reciprocal impulses are sent out rhythmically and in alternation so that when one foot or one arm is flexed, the other is extended.

In the operation of many machines used in industry, in writing with a pen or a typewriter, in chewing food or in shaking or nodding the head, this alternate innervation of various antagonistic muscles is carried out smoothly and for the most part unconsciously. The information switched by the working muscle to the central nervous system becomes the stimulus for the discharge of the next motor impulses into the poising antagonistic muscle, which, when it reacts, supplies the stimulus in turn for a new motor impulse to be discharged into the first muscle, and so on in series as long as the situation calling for such reciprocal action lasts. When the coordinating muscle group is not reacting, there being at that instant no motor impulse discharging into it, it is said to be *inhibited*. Contraction and inhibition are therefore equally forms of reaction.

Abnormal Functioning of the Nervous System in the Sick. When a person is ill, most if not all of his bodily organs and functions may be upset, and his whole system may react more or less abnormally. His digestive organs may be inefficient; his kidneys and his circulation may be disturbed; his legs may ache; his head may ache; his appetite may be gone; he may have an elevation of temperature; and he may say mournfully that he feels as if he had been "pulled through a knothole." Of all our body systems, the nervous mechanism is perhaps the most profoundly disturbed by illness. Serving as it does as the great coordinator and regulator of our behavior, the nervous system could hardly escape being placed under excessive strain by serious malfunctioning of the organs under its control.

1. *Certain Thresholds Are Lowered; Others Are Raised in the Sick.* Illness of the body brings about sometimes striking changes in the levels of thresholds in the nervous system. Reactions that were, during a previous state of health, easy and matter-of-course become now difficult; those that were then difficult become now easy and natural. One patient, for example, when visited by his wife after a minor operation at a hospital, threw his arms about her neck and wept like a child: it was probably the first time in twenty years that he had shed tears.

This matter of lowering or raising of thresholds is interesting. Ordinarily it is easy for the patient to talk about himself, about his pains, about the precariousness of his condition when he was operated upon, about the slimness of his chance of surviving the surgeon's knife, or about his present delicate status. Often, too, a person who has devoted little attention to himself before his illness becomes when sick selfish and self-centered. One patient may be made irritable and sulky or querulous by his illness; another may become almost painfully altruistic and considerate of those who wait upon him. Some patients fall into attitudes of pessimism; others develop a new serenity and optimism. Some who, before they were ill, were tyrannical toward their friends and associates, now grow tractable and considerate. One elderly man who had not spoken to his brother in thirty years began, when his health failed, to cultivate him actively.

Sometimes a patient is resentful of the attention given by the nurse to other patients on the ward, deeming it his own personal right and need to have her ministrations exclusively for himself, and becoming peevish and fretful when her professional attentions are given to others. Frequently it is difficult for a male patient to submit to the professional ministrations of his nurse, especially with reference to bathing and caring for his body; other male patients have no such inhibitions. Another interesting evidence of the change in thresholds in the sick is furnished by the circumstance frequently observed that one has more time for self analysis and for contemplation, and in consequence turns his thoughts upon spiritual values. Thus, he who has been a scoffer may surprise everybody with his faith.

2. *Many Reflexes Are Intensified in the Sick.* The normal reflexes are likely to be intensified during illness. The skin may be drawn up into goose-pimples and the patient may shiver as with an ague if a slight draft reaches his body, if a sponge is too hot or too cold or too rough, or even when his position in the bed is changed by the nurse. His auditory nerves are likely also to be on edge, and he may react abnormally to such stimuli as the rustling of the nurse's uniform, the squeaking of casters or trucks, and other noises that are unusual. So, too, unshaded light from a window or lamp may be almost unbearable to his eyes; odors that suggest anesthetics or body discharges may produce violent and persistent nausea. Pain or the anticipation of pain momentarily may be reflected in wry face, groanings, and in a general jumpy or tense muscular condition.

3. *The Rate of Cerebration in the Sick Is Modified.* In connection with certain diseased conditions there is often observed to be a speeding up of the associative processes. Vocally expressed or vocally unexpressed, the patient's thoughts may run on and on without apparent direction or end. There is so little demand upon him to use up his energy physically that the sick person, especially if his malady is functional rather than organic, finds his mind to be very active. This arousement of the cortical neurones may render sleep difficult and fitful, and so may retard convalescence. On the other hand, in certain other diseased conditions, cerebral activity may be slowed down and the patient remain for long periods quiescent and mentally detached. In either case, the rate and persistence of cerebration will vary with the individual patient, with the nature of his malady, with his general attitude, with the time of day and with the degree of fatigue present. The nurse must expect wide individual variation in this regard.

4. *There Is Faulty Integration in the Sick.* The normal individual when in a state of health behaves in an integrated manner. That is to say, he has no difficulty in coordinating his movements, in focalizing his efforts upon the task and in holding his entire organism to smooth and efficient performance. The sick person, on the other hand, particularly if he stays sick for some time, experiences difficulty in integrating his behavior. On the motor side, he may find it awkward

to feed himself, to get out of bed, to walk, to handle his body with customary skill. On the sensory side, he is likely to over-respond to some stimuli and under-respond to others; he exaggerates sounds, brightness, weight of clothing and variations in temperature. He is apt to magnify his pains and handicaps out of proportion to their actuality. Instead of maintaining a philosophical and serene attitude, he worries about his condition and his affairs, and he experiences inner turmoil and conflict over matters past, present and future. Thus, instead of preserving a unified and integrated personality, the sick person may be disturbed and perplexed, with the confidence and aggressiveness that characterized him when he was well now dissipated in worrying and apprehensiveness. It appears that the cortex has lost something of its unified and effectual control and that energy is expended in purposeless and untoward cerebration.

RESPONDING MUSCULAR AND GLANDULAR PROCESSES

Role of Muscles and Glands. Finally, as we indicated earlier, the muscles and glands are brought into action. These organs, constituting the responding mechanism of our bodies, make it possible after sensory perception has occurred and appropriate neural connections have been established, for the individual to react by walking, turning, manipulating, vocalizing, or by any or all of the innumerable conscious neuromuscular adjustments that may be indicated by the situation of the moment. Deeper in the organism, too, these structures underlie the regulation of the automatic or reflex body processes which take place largely or entirely without involvement of consciousness or will. These include the subtle changes in glandular secretions that constitute the organic basis of our emotions in time of stress or emergency.

Muscle Tonus. If one will note the position of his fingers at any moment, he will observe that they are not extended straight outward but that they are slightly flexed, or bent; that is to say, the flexor muscles maintain a slight pull, even when the subject is relaxing or resting. When one is lying down, it is not comfortable to keep the legs completely extended continuously: to do so would be to innervate the extensor muscles, whereas nature inclines to keep the flexors slightly innervated. In conditions of good health and vigor, the cerebellar cells are continually discharging a mild current into the flexor muscles of the body. This results in a condition of *tonus*, or *muscle tone*. It keeps the muscles of the body in a state of readiness to contract, and harks back for its origin to the time when our primitive ancestors, living in imminent danger of molestation by animals or by other human beings, maintained their skeletal muscles in a continual state of readiness to defend the organism either by flight or by attack. In modern civilized society, while the need for such readiness to protect oneself from physical dangers has largely disappeared, our motor equipment has not lost its fundamental emergency set-up; we continue muscularly alert to some degree at all times whether waking or sleeping. In general, good muscle tone in a person means, in addition to the tendency for a slight tension to be exerted upon the flexor muscles, the awareness of a feeling of muscular well-being and fitness which imparts to him a potential spryness in sharp contrast with the manner and the potentials of the individual whose musculature is flabby and whose movements are sluggish and ponderous.

Health and Muscular Exercise. Whenever a muscle contracts it uses up a modicum of food and produces a modicum of lactic acid and carbon dioxide. A working muscle is warmer than an idle muscle because more blood is being sent into it to provide for metabolism. People who work hard with their muscles require more food and produce more fatigue poisons than do people who remain idle or who work little. To maintain a condition of health and tonicity, muscles require exercise. "Soft" muscles are an indication that one leads a somewhat inactive life; "hard" muscles, on the other hand, are associated with the active, muscular life. It is normal for the muscles of our bodies to use up a considerable amount of food and to throw off a considerable amount of toxins in the course of a day. Discomfort and ultimately danger come only when the expenditure of energy is so prolonged that each night's sleep fails to restore the body completely.

Exercise of all our muscles is essential if we are to remain in good health and in a state of readiness for life and its daily tasks and problems. The healthy person is not afraid of good, stiff muscular work; rather, he thrives upon it. Witness our athletes and the ever-growing numbers of those who find delight and refreshment in sports and strenuous outdoor activities. Exercise replenishes the oxygen in the lungs, inundates the muscles with fresh blood, stimulates the eliminative and excretory organs to react vigorously and effectively, improves the tone of striped and visceral muscles alike, and probably helps to keep the brain clear and active, not to mention other psychological benefits that are associated with the physically active life.

Application to Nursing Problems. 1. *Modification of Muscular Tone in the Sick.* In our daily life we do our tasks most efficiently and with the least amount of neuromuscular wear and tear if and when the tonicity of our muscles, striped and unstriped alike, is at its optimum. Illness is likely to affect muscle tone both directly and indirectly. Directly, it may influence it through the cerebrospinal system and the mental states and attitudes which express themselves through the innervation of muscles that respond to the central system. Thus, one finds ofen in the ward a patient whose muscles are in such a state of hypertonus that he "cannot let go"; his body is tense and uncomfortable from this constant innervation; his mind may be overactive and his senses over-acute, as we have seen; such bodily functions as digestion and elimination may be seriously impaired by this incessant tension; the heart and circulatory system may also be placed under considerable strain; the patient may have difficulty in relaxing his keyed-up muscles and going to sleep; repair and regeneration of his tissues may be impeded by this condition.

On the other hand, the nurse will also observe patients who manifest an abnormally relaxed or hypotonic musculature. This condition may be confined to an isolated group of muscles, as for example, certain of the postural muscles, or it may prevail generally throughout the muscular structure, as in the individual who has passed through the crisis of a serious illness and is left weak and helpless. During certain febrile conditions, the muscles may be hypertonic, while during subsequent conditions of allayment of the fever they may manifest an abnormal relaxation and hypotonus. In some forms of illness there may be a hypotonus during critical stages, while in others a reverse condition may obtain.

Indirectly, illness may interfere with normal muscular tone through the effect which it often has upon the endocrines and upon the emotions. Take, by way of illustration, the patient who is frightened about his condition and will not be reassured. Fear and apprehension place a heavy burden upon his visceral functions and upon the organs that underlie them. There may be a hypertonus throughout the digestive tract so profound that ferments cannot be manufactured or discharged normally and peristalsis is inhibited. Reflex reverberations of this alimentary condition are likely to be felt widely throughout the other organs and systems of the body, notably perhaps in the kidneys and throughout the circulatory system, the muscles of which are kept in an abnormal condition of tension. The production of fatigue toxins is favored under these conditions, of course, and the effect of these may be felt in every organ and tissue of the body.

Hypotonic reactions in the smooth muscles may also be an indirect result of illness, as may be seen in the occasional patient who has no desire to get well, no wish to live. This psychological condition may be best observed in those individuals who have missed the ordinary satisfactions and securities in life while they were in a state of health and who now, when they have been stricken by disease, lack those returning enthusiasms and purposes that comprise so essential a part of the will to live. While the number of such patients in the general hospital is relatively small, nurses may expect to find them commonly in the mental hospitals. Wherever they are found, there is likely to be observed by nurse or physician a pronounced hypotonicity of the musculature that is often chronic and forms one of the real obstacles to the efficacy of therapeutic efforts.

2. *To the Organism, Sickness Is an Emergency.* A man faced with the necessity of running away from a wild animal that has escaped from his cage at the zoo is a different man from the man who is confronted with no such emergency. Certain of his glands suspend their secreting functions immediately while certain others increase theirs enormously; certain blood vessels constrict while certain others dilate; blood pressure rises, digestion stops; sugar is released; the red corpuscles in the blood are augmented; the whole muscular mechanism becomes more sympathetically toned. All of these organic changes make it possible for the man to make his escape from the pursuing animal. The entire emergency mechanism is set into functioning in order that the individual may escape with his life.

Sickness and disease should, from the standpoint of organic functioning, also be looked upon as emergencies, the only distinction between organic dangers and environmental dangers being the fact that the former are internal. The presence in the body of a spreading colony of microbes is the stimulus to the defensive mechanisms of the organism to rout the invaders and save the host from destruction. This means that the major task of the body is, for the time being, the development of counteracting agents in the blood stream to fight the microbes. Everything else becomes secondary. Such food as the patient can take must be selected so as to yield its nutriment economically and readily to the blood; rest and sleep must be promoted and safeguarded in order that the accumulation of wastes in the blood may be reduced to the minimum; air and sunshine and massage must be utilized in order to aerate the blood and speed its circulation through affected parts; negative or exciting emotional states must be guarded against in order that certain irritating glandular hormones may not be released into the blood.

In consequence of all this great preoccupation of nature with the safeguarding and enriching of the quality and potency of the patient's blood stream, it is obvious that the functioning of all the organs and systems of the body has to be modified toward this end. The patient may grow weak; his flesh may waste away; his muscles may grow flabby and shrunken; his mind may become delirious. These things are of relatively minor consequence when compared with the necessity for fighting the invading microbes; when victory is assured, nature may undertake the repair of these secondary conditions. Sickness is an emergency, and to meet it the entire organism girds itself. The nurse is a co-worker with nature throughout the crisis, it being her task to facilitate the struggle by keenness of perception of the moment's need, promptitude in her ministrations, and the maintenance of a demeanor that is calculated to encourage confidence and serenity in the patient.

3. *Illness Is Fatiguing.* Fatigue in the healthy individual is due physiologically to the accumulation in the blood of toxins thrown off into it by contracting muscles. In the sick person, in whom skeletal muscle activity is reduced almost to the zero point and in whom perhaps smooth muscle activity is not ordinarily greatly increased, a new source of toxins comes into existence; *i.e.*, the poisonous invading microbes and the dying white corpuscles that are struggling to engulf the germs. The presence in the blood of these toxic substances appears to be in effect not greatly different from that of true fatigue toxins. We may infer, then, that illness is fatiguing, and we may expect the patient to feel physically tired from the internal struggle going on between his tissues and the enemy that they are harboring. In serious illness he may barely have left over from the struggle enough strength to raise his hand or turn his head; in less serious illness and during recuperation, he will of course have a greater residue of physical energy. The nurse should understand, however, that illness is fatiguing, and that the patient must in all kinds and degrees of illness be guarded from overdoing.

Needless traffic, heavy covers, clumsy books or bulky magazines to hold, too many visitors, even too much solicitude from the sympathetic young student nurse, may be tiring to the convalescing patient who more than anything else needs rest and peace. The thoughtful nurse will be on the alert to promote physical quiet and mental serenity in her patients through whatever opportunities may offer in the way of adjusting reading stands, back rests, knee rolls, and the like, and through discouraging prolonged visits, whispered consultations and monotonous conversations.

4. *The Convalescing Patient Needs Exercise.* The convalescing patient needs exercise of a sort adapted to his particular present capacity to benefit from it. Returning health brings with it a new restlessness of muscle and a new eagerness to assay motor coordinations and controls that the weeks of illness have disrupted. In some patients or at some stages of disease, merely to be raised up in bed, or to sit up for a few minutes in a chair beside it, will be exercise enough for the day, and the prospects of it will be looked forward to and anticipated with almost childish zest. For other patients, or at other stages of recovery, to walk the length of the corridor on the nurse's arm, to be

wheeled for a half hour into the sunlight, to walk unaided to the toilet or the bath or sun-porch, or to "visit" down the ward, will be adventures fraught with keen anticipation beforehand and sheer delight in the realization and in the memory afterward. The nurse should understand how much these simple bits of daily exercise mean to people who have been confined for a period in bed, and she should be as faithful and methodical in making them available for her patients as she is in giving them their medicine, taking their temperature, or performing the scores of other professional functions of the nurse on ward duty.

5. *Exercise and the Nurse.* In her own interest, the nurse should expect to spend a considerable amount of her free time every day in the prosecution of some sort of relaxational or recreational activity that will call for regular muscular expenditure. This does not need to be strenuous, but it should be of such a character as to set the blood in vigorous circulation and dispel something of the fatigue and monotony that the day's work commonly brings.

Some professional workers in the nursing field make the mistake of assuming that the walking about and the lifting and the manipulating that go with the performance of the daily round provide the muscular activity that is necessary. Possibly all that is *necessary*—yes, but not of the type that the body needs to promote its resilience. The nurse needs extravocational exercise in order to keep her muscles in good tone, speed up her circulation, stimulate her reflexes, sharpen her senses, open her pores. A brisk walk, a short hike, a game of tennis, or some other activity in the open air ought to be included in the day's agenda for every nurse. If one gets into the habit of indulging regularly in some moderate forms of exercise such as these, she will do much to keep her physical body in trim, to keep her mind interested and alert, and to relieve the daily tasks of their sameness and monotony.

Glands as Responding Organs

We have referred to muscles and glands as responding organs. The particular responses which glands make are *chemical* in nature; those which the muscles make are *mechanical*. That is to say, when a motor impulse discharges into a gland, it causes that gland to increase, to hold constant or to decrease the rate of production of the chemical substance which it is charged with manufacturing, and which is essential in varying amounts and in varying situations to the adequate functioning of the organism in general. A gland may be thought of as a chemical laboratory whose product is indispensable to the continuing existence of the subject. Each gland produces a specific secretion or *hormone* which serves a specific function in the maintenance of the body economy.

Glands are of two types: *duct* glands and *ductless* glands.

Effects of Emotion on the Duct Glands. One may sit down at the dinner table, hungry and in good spirits at the outset, but because somebody at the table scolds him, worries him, or makes him angry or resentful, suddenly he finds his appetite gone and his spirits dampened. His food has lost its appeal, and he shortly excuses himself with the remark that he is not hungry. Other common experiences are breaking out in a cold sweat when terror grips one, or bursting into tears when grieved or mortified. In all of these and dozens of similar forms of reaction, duct glands are thrown into modified activity: the appetite is lost because the gastric and other digestive glands suddenly stop manufacturing their secretions; the person has a cold sweat because his perspiratory glands become more activated under stress of fear; the tears come because the lacrimal glands are overstimulated by the emotional state. All of these and other illustrations that might be cited indicate the close and intimate connection between states of strong emotion and the rate of secretion of the duct glands.

A number of highly interesting experiments have been performed by LeComte, Bickel and Sasaki, Oechsler, Cannon and others which have demonstrated this relationship in animal subjects. When a dog, for example, is eating his food and his gastric juice is flowing freely from the gastric glands, if a cat is suddenly introduced before him, he flies into a fury and his glands stop secreting; even the pancreatic juice and the flow of bile may be checked under these circumstances. These demonstrations in animals (notably in dogs, cats, rabbits and guinea pigs) corroborate the naïve observation of similar relationships in human subjects between emotional states and duct gland activity. The smell or sight of one's favorite food, a psychic state of happiness or content, pleasant or agreeable surroundings—these conditions are associated with normal flow of the digestive juices; on the other hand, a condition of anxiety, worry, fear, anger, suspense, discord, excitement, and the like, tends to suppress the normal flow of these juices. Gastric distress, heaviness in the stomach, vomiting, diarrhea and "emotional dyspepsia" Cannon finds to be associated with inhibition of normal functioning of the digestive glands.

Modern physiology has demonstrated conclusively the fact that good digestion must wait on appetite, and that when emotional states of a negative sort are present, both appetite and good digestion take flight.

Ductless Glands. More elusive are the *ductless glands* commonly called the *endocrines*, or the *glands of internal secretion*. It is only comparatively recently that we have come to understand much about these organs. Today, while there is some tendency to attribute to them more mystical power than perhaps they actually possess, there is a dependable science of endocrinology with the chief teachings of which the nurse should be familiar.

The endocrines act more or less as a unit, tending to some degree at least to counterbalance one another. The thyrotropic hormone of the pituitary influences the activity of the thyroid. The adrenalin stimulates the liver gland to release its sugar, and the thymus and pineal glands probably hold in check the gonads during childhood. Exactly to what extent there is further interaction among the endocrines we do not know. Cannon found that the presence of excess adrenalin in the blood hastened coagulation only when the liver gland was intact and was contributing sugar to the blood. Physicians are called upon frequently to deal with glandular imbalance, in which a deficiency of one type of hormone appears to cause others to be too heavily drawn upon in an effort to compensate, or in which excessive secretion of one may stimulate others to abnormal activity. Thus, a hyperthyroid condition may be the result either of overactivity of the adrenals or of underactivity of the pituitary; a similar known relationship exists between the adrenals and the pancreas, and between the gonads and the thyroid. Awareness of this interaction and interdependence among the endocrines is a development in modern medicine which has convinced endocrinologists and physicians that the whole matter of endocrine balance is of considerable importance. Within certain limits the hormones of one endocrine control, stimulate or compensate for the hormones contributed by other endocrines.

Relationship of Glands to the Problems of Nursing. 1. *Good Cheer with the Patient's Meals.* From the standpoint of nursing, a most interesting and important relationship between glandular functioning and the behavior of the patient is to be noted in connection with the activity of the duct glands concerned with the digestion of food. The research work of Cannon and others has indicated that a close correlation exists between emotional states and digestion. The normal flow of saliva and of the other digestive fluids is fostered by affective states of pleasurableness and is inhibited by unpleasurableness. We say that the mouth "waters" at the mere thought of food; Cannon has demonstrated that the stomach "waters" also; that is to say, there is an initial psychic secretion which occurs all along the digestive tract when food is anticipated, or is actually set before a hungry person, *provided* he is in a pleasurable state; if his affective condition is the reverse of this, the secretions do not flow and food, if introduced at such a time into the alimentary canal, cannot be digested.

The state of feeling likewise effects a modification of activity in certain of the endocrines, notably in the adrenals, as we know. Unpleasant states of anger, fear or pain cause widespread inhibitions of digestive functions through a withdrawal of blood from the stomach and intestine. It should be apparent, therefore, that mealtime for anybody ought to be a time of cheerfulness and pleasurableness rather than the reverse. For the sick person this is of the utmost importance, since his appetite is likely to be somewhat capricious; moreover, his malfunctioning organism is causing him pain and apprehension, which circumstance in itself tends also to retard the process of digestion. Consequently, the patient's food should be served daintily and attractively; portions should not be discouragingly large; dishes and linen should be scrupulously clean; odors should be fresh and savory. Through these means the fickle appetite of the patient may be subtly encouraged.

2. *Avoidance of Emotion in the Sick-Room.* Strong emotion fitted man properly enough for a primitive environment in which he might be called upon momentarily to meet physical emergencies; man's organism has retained the emergency mechanisms embodied in the autonomic nervous system and the endocrines, and hence man finds himself in modern civilized society with their force undiminished. To the arousing situations to which he formerly reacted physically by fighting, by rage, by flight, by bloody struggle, he can now react only physiologically; that is to say, when he is angry, afraid, in a temper, or in pain, he does not clench his fists and join in mortal combat; nor does he run blindly and with pounding heart through the forest to safety; instead, he merely stops digesting his food, narrows his eyes, throws adrenalin and liver sugar into his blood. Instead of *doing*, he merely *prepares to do*. This general arousing of the organism places a strain upon it which, unless the pressure can be relieved by vicarious forms of physical expenditure, is inimical not only to comfort and serenity but also to the performance of visceral functions.

In the sick-room care should be exercised to keep the emotional tone of the patient as healthful and normal as possible. The mere circumstance that the organism is malfunctioning disturbs the autonomic and visceral functions; the nurse should so order and control the stimuli that play upon her patient that the depressing and the arousing emotions, *e.g.*, apprehensiveness, anger and fear, will be reduced to the minimum. In general, the following of a regularly established routine in the physical care of the patient will be helpful from this standpoint, as will also the maintenance of an equable disposition and a good-natured patience. The nurse who tends to discourage the anxious but often mute questions of the patient by an affectation of crispness or aloofness and unconcern, or who otherwise tends to "get on her patients' nerves" or allows them to "get on hers" to the extent at least that she exhibits before them an unpleasant personality—such a nurse can hardly expect to keep the spirits of those dependent upon her calm and unruffled.

3. *The Nurse's Own Emotions.* Any person who works professionally among the sick is subjected to emotional strain. In contact intimately with suffering, with discouragement, with ebbing life, she is a rare nurse whose own personal emotions remain unruffled. From her constant association with those who are preoccupied or fearful over their condition, any nurse will tend to experience something of the depressing influences in her own organism. From her care of some patients who may be exacting and selfish, she experiences something of annoyance and resentment. Fortunately, from contacts with good numbers of her patients who remain calm and cheerful in adversity, she is motivated in the direction of satisfying and agreeable states of feeling.

In any case, the nurse should seek outlets for the emotional tensions that arise from the peculiar nature of her work. These outlets should include agreeable and stimulating associations with people who are both physically well and mentally well adjusted.

It is observed in mental hospitals that attendants themselves sometimes become morbid after a few months or a few years of service unless they take precautions to counteract the depressing influences about them. While not so spectacularly the case with nurses in the general hospital, the condition is analogous, and the need of adequate outlet is no less important. Let the nurse then cultivate congenial friendship with other nurses, and better still perhaps with people in wholly different occupations and professions from her own; let her interest herself in wholesome avocations and hobbies that will provide a medium for self-expression; let her devote herself to activities that call for physical expenditure in which experiences of pleasurableness and mild competitiveness are fostered. Fortified by frequent contacts with such beneficial influences as are represented by these activities and relationships, the nurse will be able to go back to her patients with a new strength and a new wholesomeness that will be of benefit not only to herself but also to those who must look to her for the example of encouragement and cheerfulness which they need.

THOUGHT PROBLEMS FOR THE STUDENT

1. Why is it a very difficult task indeed to teach a child born blind and deaf? Did you ever personally know such an individual?
2. List situations in which you have experienced definite interference with your sense of balance or equilibrium. How are the resulting sensations to be accounted for?
3. List situations in which you have experienced kinesthetic sensations of strain, movement, coordination, and the like.
4. Cite evidence from your own past or continuing experience to prove that visceral sensations play important roles in our lives. List a number of visceral sensations.
5. (a) Blindfold yourself for one hour when you feel wide awake; talk with friends, also spend some time alone.
   (b) How does this give you a better understanding of the patient who has both eyes covered with eye pads?
6. Plan a color scheme for a private room in the hospital; for your own room in the home.
7. Why are signs erected close to hospitals reading "Hospital—Quiet"? Outline a plan whereby an effective drive might be made against unnecessary noises *in* the hospital.
8. List objectionable odors found in hospital situations and suggest how they might be lessened.
9. Prepare a 250-word discussion on "How the Nurses Give Special Consideration to Patients' Sense Organs."
10. Name five disease conditions in which disturbances of certain receptors are characteristic symptoms of the disease.
11. Write a brief paper to indicate that you understand the meaning of *integration*, using an appropriate example of your own choosing to illustrate the process.
12. Suggest additional examples of *facilitation;* of *prepotence;* of *convergence, or summation;* of *diffusion;* of *reciprocal innervation.*
13. By diagram, illustrate various structures involved in the development of the movement patterns called nursing skills. Will many repetitions of one procedure eventually become so mechanical that the initial movement of the procedure may serve as a stimulus to bring in its wake the other movements which are needed to complete that particular procedure? Discuss.
14. Consider the nurse who gives an effective bath and at the same time carries on an interesting conversation with the patient on other topics. Would this constitute good nursing care? Give reasons for your answer.
15. List six stimuli which would be prepotent in hospital wards. Give your reasons for selecting those you have chosen.
16. What would be some stimuli you could add to the ward situation to facilitate favorable responses from patients? Favorable response from the head nurse?
17. List varying conditions of muscle tone that you have yourself experienced under different circumstances of alertness, fatigue, illness, excitement, anger, fright, and the like.
18. Have you ever been ill? For how long a time? How ill? To what degree has your personal experience with illness made you aware of the fact that illness is fatiguing?
19. Describe peculiarities in behavior or in appearance which you have personally

observed in some individual presenting one of the following grandular abnormalities:
   (a) Cretinism.   (d) Addison's disease.
   (b) Exophthalmic goiter. (e) Acromegaly.
   (c) Myxedema.   (f) Dwarfism.
                            (g) Gigantism.
20. What are the procedures you are taught in Nursing Arts which have as their objective the maintenance of muscle tonus? Discuss in a 100-word paragraph.
21. List the occupational therapy exercises which are available in your hospital for the maintenance and stimulation of patients' muscle tonus. Match these with the diagnosis where you think the doctor would permit and encourage their use.
22. Sketch an ideal tray for the convalescent pneumonia patient; if equipment and food permit, give actual demonstration. Stress points which you believe would make special appeal to the patient. How does this tray compare with those served to the patients in your hospital? Make practical suggestions that you believe would improve the food service, from the patient's point of view; from the point of view of the hospital administration.
23. Discuss one habit you have developed which serves as an adequate emotional outlet for you.

SUGGESTED READINGS

1. Crow, L. D., Crow, A., and Skinner, C. E.: *Psychology in Nursing Practice.* New York, The Macmillan Co., 1954.
   Chapters 4 and 5 deal with the physiological bases of behavior (sense organs, endocrines, muscles and the nervous system).
2. Cruze, W. W.: *Psychology in Nursing.* New York, Blakiston Division, McGraw-Hill Book Co., 1955.
   Cf. especially Chapter 5, "The Receptors and Their Functions," and Chapter 6, "The Nervous System," for germane material in both these areas.
3. Karn, H. W., and Weitz, J.: *An Introduction to Psychology.* New York, John Wiley and Sons, 1955.
   Chapter 9, "Personality," has good material on ductless glands.
4. Munn, N. L.: *The Evolution and Growth of Human Behavior.* Boston, Houghton Mifflin Co., 1955.
   Contains a wealth of material in the field covered by the present chapter, easily located by using the excellent index.
5. Orr, W. H.: *Hormones, Health and Happiness.* New York, The Macmillan Co., 1954.
   Discusses the origin and nature of hormones in the human organism from childhood to old age.
6. Pfeiffer, J.: *The Human Brain.* New York, Harper and Brothers, 1955.
   A popular book, accurate and understandable. Well worth reading by any layman interested in understanding something of the marvels of the human brain and nervous system.
7. Ruch, F. L.: *Psychology and Life.* Chicago, Scott, Foresman and Co., 1953.
   Chapter 9, "The Special Senses," is particularly good for supplementary reading.

Unit 4

How We Learn

Chapter 8

> Wisdom is the principal thing; therefore get wisdom; and with all thy getting get understanding.
>
> PROVERBS, 17:7

LEARNING: STAGES AND PROCEDURES

THE FIRST STAGE IN LEARNING: ACQUIRING THE INFORMATION

As WE OBSERVE the multitude of objects, situations, people, principles and conditions that make up the world around us, we can hardly fail to be impressed with the miracle of mind which makes it possible for us to take them all into consciousness and become intellectually aware of them. Beyond this miracle is the still more striking one of the ability we have, after the observation has been made, to retain them and to reinstate them in memory.

These three processes—perceiving, retaining and recalling—comprise true *learning*. Only if and after one has extended her mental processes through each of these stages can she be said to have *learned*. It is not sufficient for one to have seen or heard or otherwise sensorially been aware of a fact or a situation or event: one must also have retained the experience in her brain cells or nervous system well enough to be able to recall or reinstate it when it is needed, and with sufficient clarity to satisfy her that her memory is not playing her false. *Learning* that a pneumococcus, for example, is a spherical bacterium, associated causatively with pneumonia, has been completed only when the learner can promptly recall what she has learned about this particular microbe and can recognize the remembered material as belonging with pneumococcus and not with meningococcus, with tubercle bacillus, or with the spirochete.

The first step toward intellectual mastery of anything becomes, therefore, the *impressing of the data upon the mind; i.e., paying attention* to what is to be learned and retained. We must have had our attention called to the material and have been made perceptually aware of its actuality before we can proceed with ultimate and complete learning of it. This circumstance suggests the important role played by *attention* and *perception* in learning.

Voluntary and Involuntary Attention. To some objects or events, we pay attention actively, purposefully, with the desire and the mind set to understand them, even though they may be difficult and may require a great deal of hard and consuming mental effort. Examples of this sort of active or voluntary attention are to be seen in such behavior as keeping at one's work persistently when one would prefer to substitute something more interesting, or in forcing oneself to study, to do what is expected of her, to follow her line of duty. A pupil pays this sort of attention to a difficult or uninteresting explanation by her teacher, to words of parental admonition or reproof, to explicit instructions as to what she is to get for her mother at the store, and the like. One ordinarily pays voluntary attention because she has learned that it is the expected or the profitable thing for her to do.

On the other hand, there is a tendency to pay passive or *involuntary* attention to certain situations. Common examples are: attending to a brilliantly sparkling electric sign, to the cry of "Fire!" or to the smell of escaping gas, or to the screaming of automobile brakes. These are all suggestive of involuntary attention, that is, of attention which we are forced to pay because the stimulus is novel, sudden, intense, interesting, or otherwise compelling enough to draw our thoughts away from our present tasks and direct them, at least for the moment, upon the stimulus. Advertisers, showmen, manufacturers, chambers of commerce, and the like, depend upon the power of involuntary attention to direct the minds of potential buyers or investors to their offerings. The psychology of advertising devotes itself to a study of the laws underlying the arousal of involuntary attention; if it pays to advertise, it is because when people have had their attention directed to a specific brand of merchandise, they are very likely to call for that brand when they next go marketing. The influence which color, noise, display, motion, suspense and exaggerated statement have over our minds is tremendous. To such compelling stimuli as these, psychologists apply the term "factors of advantage."

In our everyday life experiences, we shuttle back and forth continually between those stimuli to which we choose inwardly to attend and those which are thrust upon our receptors externally, as may be illustrated in the following situation. A student is sitting at her desk preparing a lesson in psychology, to which she is devoting her full attention, since the topic she is studying at the moment requires thoughtful concentration. Let somebody call her name, however, or start conversing, and forthwith her thoughts are drawn involuntarily away from her textbook and directed upon the speaker. Or let the radiator nearby begin to pound; let the electric lights waver, grow dim, and then become bright and stabilized again; let an incipient twinge from a sensitive tooth or a fleeting cramp in her back smash its way into her consciousness; let a stray thought of what she will have for dinner or where she will go this evening pass the citadel of her consciousness; or let any other of the hundreds of extraneous and irrelevant occurrences that are always taking place about one assail her: gone are her studious attitudes and her good intentions and her present ambition to get her psychology lesson; she is at the mercy of circumstances. True, the interruption caused by the foreign stimulus may be only fleeting, but at least it sufficed to draw her attention

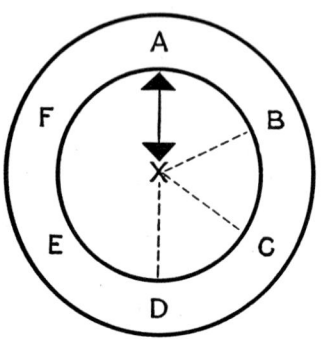

Fig. 6. Sketch to illustrate marginal and focal ideas at any conscious moment. X represents the focal series; A, B, C, etc., represent marginal stimuli, any one of which may at any instant drive out X and replace it with a new focal series.

momentarily to it and away from the task which she had set herself voluntarily and purposefully to accomplish.

Psychologists often refer to the intruding ideas or experiences that break in upon our work as *marginal ideas* and to the central task as the *focal idea*. Figure 6 represents schematically the structure of our consciousness at any given waking moment, the focal idea being held in the foreground only until some marginal idea becomes strong enough or insistent enough to drive the focal idea out into the fringe and to replace it in the focus. The conscious life of all of us during any given period of time becomes largely a succession of exchanges between focal and fringe or marginal ideas. Almost everyone can will to keep the important, needful idea series in the focus fairly continuously, but we are all at the occasional mercy of the competing marginal stimuli. The good student, while she cannot keep the latter from intruding, can and does bring back the focal series promptly and is not inclined actually to welcome every distraction that comes knocking at the door. The good student is able to *select and control the stimuli* to which she wills to attend and to *neglect* others. Attention is therefore both a selecting and a neglecting process.

What is commonly termed *inattention* does not exist: there is no such thing; the inattentive student is merely paying attention to the wrong things, *i.e.*, to the marginal ideas rather than to the focal series. When John's teacher warns John that he is "not paying attention," what she means is that he is not paying attention to what she wishes: he is rather paying attention to what *he* wishes, *e.g.*, to the ball game that is to take place after school, to wishing it were summer, or to any one of the innumerable other things which interest him.

Perception. We attend to a situation in order to perceive it clearly, to derive *meaning* from our experience of it. Hold before a baby a radio tube, and he cannot *perceive* it for it has no meaning for him; all he can do is to look at it. Seeing an object, *i.e.*, receiving sensory impressions through the eyes or experiencing it through any other receptor, is not necessarily perceiving. In order to perceive, one must have had enough experience beforehand to give meaning and significance to the present stimulus. Laborious concentration and vacant stares of complete bewilderment are to be observed in the infant as he endeavors to make some semblance of order out of the chaos about him. Only very gradually from the sure vantage point afforded by his mother's arms can he learn the essential *meaning* of *puppy, toy, grandma, papa, bottle, hand, nose, house, yard, automobile*. And slower still is his acquisition of meanings of abstract concepts, such as *happy, afraid, naughty, comfortable, asleep, good, bad*.

We who are grown up have been able to establish surprisingly satisfactory order and meaning in our universe. Through retained memory of our past experiences, and through the use of the analytical powers of our minds, we are in a position not only to recognize former percepts but also to ascribe meaning to new objects and situations and thus fit them into our scheme of comprehension. We seek to classify, to make meaningful, to catalog, whatever new objects or experiences come to us, and to place them in their proper relationships with other objects and experiences. In all these processes, it goes without saying, *attention* is fundamental, since it makes it possible for the individual to receive into his focal consciousness the stimuli that surround him.

Illusions of Perception. Sometimes, however, we do not see or hear, or otherwise sense, experiences as they actually are. Ichabod Crane, when he was returning from the fair Katrina Van Tassel's, mistook the rubbing together of birch branches for the groaning of witches, and the disguised Brom Bones galloping behind him at midnight for the terrible "headless horseman of Sleepy Hollow." The reader herself, no doubt, has mistaken for an intruder her own coat hanging carelessly over a chair in the darkened room when she entered; she has misinterpreted some sound nearby as somebody calling her name; she has perhaps mistaken some disturbing noise that awoke her for the voice of one of her patients calling; or she has been sure

Fig. 7. Size and perspective. In spite of appearances the figures of the boy and the man are the same height. (Cameron: Psychology and the School. D. Appleton-Century Company, Publishers.)

that her companion addressed her and has inquired what she said, only to be assured that she had not spoken. The mistakes that all of us make in estimating distances, perspectives, height, weight, durations of time, and magnitudes are proverbial, since our sense organs do not always register accurately the stimuli that fall upon them. We are prone to see or hear what we expect to see or hear, or what we are mentally *set* to experience. Thus, misprints will sometimes get past the most experienced proofreader; the ordinary reader will rarely notice any except the most glaring errors in type. The desert traveler, half-dying of thirst, experiences commonly the illusion of "seeing" in the mists upon the horizon the palms of a green oasis and splashing waterfalls.

Perception and the Nurse. The more scientific the task in which one is engaged, the greater becomes the necessity for accurate observation on the part of the worker. The practice of medicine and surgery is fundamentally a scientific technique and necessitates the greatest

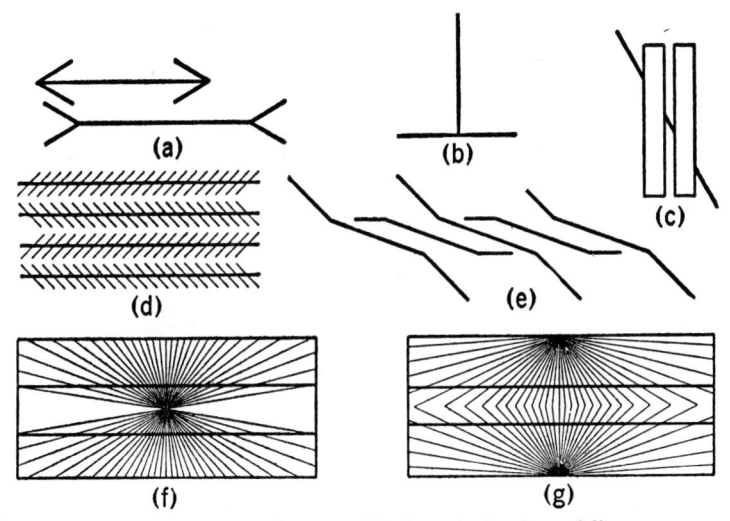

Fig. 8. Optical illusions. *a*, Müller-Lyer illusion: the horizontal lines appear to be of unequal length; *b*, overestimation of the vertical; *c*, Poggendorff illusion: the transversal appears to be out of alignment; *d*, Zöllner illusion: the horizontal lines do not appear so; *e*, Lipps parallels: the middle sections of all the lines are parallel; *f* and *g*, Hering illusion: the horizontal lines appear to curve in the middle. (Trow: Introduction to Educational Psychology. Houghton Mifflin Company, Publishers.)

accuracy on the part of all who are in any way concerned with it. The nurse must realize that she is being prepared to carry on a prominent and essential role in the application of the healing art, and hence must school herself to be as accurate in her essential relationship to it as is the physician in his. Life and death depend every day in the hospital upon the accuracy with which a nurse observes or perceives. Numberless routine details are left to her to administer, and no guesswork can be permitted about her performance of them.

Consider, for example, the following simple tasks which are commonly assigned to the nurse: reading a thermometer; recording a reading upon a chart; graphing a record; reading and following a prescription; and making reports, oral or written. These are routine matters, it is true, and some of them may after a time appear to the student to be of slight importance. Accuracy in discharging them, however, is demanded of every staff worker who is charged with the

Fig. 9. This picture is an old engraving of the first vaccination against smallpox, performed in England in 1796 by Dr. Edward Jenner. It is included here as a simple perception test for the student. Study it carefully for about 15 seconds; then turn to page 153 and see how many of the questions based upon it you can answer without referring back to the picture. Check your accuracy afterward by reexamination of the picture.

day-by-day care of the sick. Eyes and ears and fingers must *report conditions as they are*, not as they *probably* are, as they were yesterday, or as they *ought* to be. The emotions must not be permitted to stampede the perceptual faculty; scattered attention must not make it possible for error to creep in; the pressure of "a dozen things on one's mind" must not be an excuse for failure to observe and record or execute carefully each individual item assigned or expected of one. The young nurse must learn to discount emotion in a health-disease situation, and to rely solely upon the testimony of her senses which she has trained to avoid distortion and exaggeration. The nurse who mistakes phlegm in the throat for the death rattle, or who records 98.9° as 99.8°, is obviously not a good perceiver or a good recorder.

THE SECOND STAGE IN LEARNING: RETAINING THE DATA

Forgetting. As soon as we stop using what we have learned, we begin to forget. Many studies of the permanence of retention of facts learned in the schools have been made by various investigators, with the general conclusion that the ordinary person forgets within a few years a great many of the things of a factual nature which he learned or was drilled upon in school and college. About all our schooling appears to do for us is to provide the setting wherein we may sharpen our minds and discipline them to attend, to think, to reason, to judge, and the like. Almost everyone who has been out of school for some years would find it extremely difficult to write a character sketch of Cassius, or to outline the early history of the Jamestown colony, or to give the details of the Lewis and Clark expedition. The fact of the matter is, we have forgotten much of the relevant information we once had about these persons or events, and we would wish to review them before hazarding the task proposed.

Following the classic research of Ebbinghaus, we discover that within an hour after practice ceases we have forgotten 50 per cent of memorized data; within twenty-four hours, two thirds of it; by the end of a week, three quarters of it; and by the end of the first month, four fifths of it. About the only crumb of comfort one can find in this fact is the circumstance that while forgetting proceeds rapidly at first, it continues more and more slowly after the first initial loss, reaching a point after several weeks where the amount retained from month to month remains substantially constant over a long period of time. Figure 10 represents the general appearance of the curve of forgetting for ideational data. Motor skills alone remain tolerably constant and intact, regardless of somewhat prolonged disuse.

Other experimenters have found that after practice stops the rate of early loss proceeds less precipitously. Thus, Luh demonstrated that 50 per cent of learned material was retained two days after the initial learning. Ebbinghaus's more striking loss may be due to the fact that he was his own and only subject, and that he failed to control adequately the possible factor of fatigue. Moreover, forgetting is now known to depend upon many variables: *e.g.*, kind of material, idiosyncrasy of the learner, nature of the in-between activity, method of measurement used by the experimenter, etc.

It must be understood, however, that this matter of forgetting is not quite so disconcerting as appears on the surface. If it is true that we forget many if not most of the facts we learn in school, it is also true that we retain most of the skills and attitudes that were developed during the years of our formal schooling. In the very process of studying a unit of material we achieve training in using the mind analytically and thoughtfully, and this is a discipline that carries over

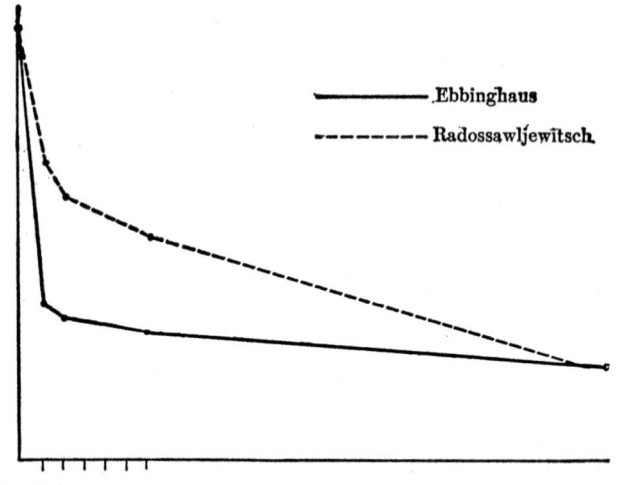

Fig. 10. Curves showing rate of forgetting. Ebbinghaus used nonsense syllables, which he memorized to the point of just recall; after the elapse of varying intervals of time, he relearned the lists, using as the measure of rate of forgetting the time required to relearn a series. Radossawljewitsch repeated Ebbinghaus' experiments with twenty-seven observers, and while he found the former's general conclusions to be valid be demonstrated that forgetting proceeds much less rapidly during the period immediately following the learning than Ebbinghaus had found. The curves in the figure indicate the relative findings of these two experimenters. It is drawn to represent loss over a period of thirty days. (Averill: Elements of Educational Psychology. Houghton Mifflin Company, Publishers.)

into subsequent learning situations. After all, the acid test of learning lies not in the perfection of exact memory but rather in the degree to which what has been learned transfers to life situations, supplies a basis for grasping and evaluating new experience, builds in a rich background of interpretation, and equips us to attack new learning experiences with improved form and technique. These are ends to which most of our studying leads, even though much specific and exact information is lost in the process.

Overlearning. There are some things that we have memorized, however, that we shall never forget: *e.g.*, our names, the Lord's prayer, and the poems and memory gems and nursery rhymes of childhood. We retain these things indefinitely because they were *overlearned;* that is to say, practice of them did not stop at the end of a

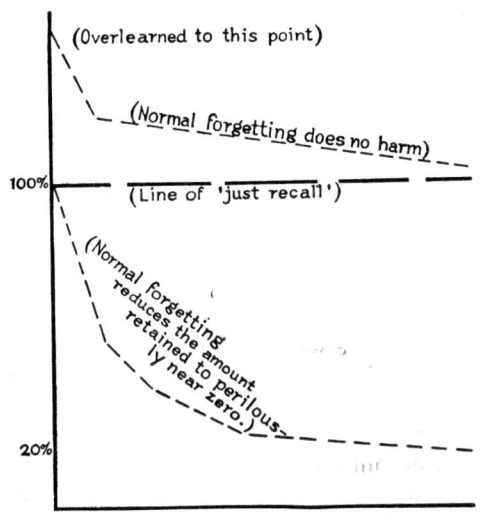

Fig. 11. Sketch to illustrate the importance of overlearning.

school day or a school unit of work: it has continued off and on most of our lives. Any material which is thus repeated well beyond the point where it can just be recalled for immediate purposes is said to be overlearned. Overlearning becomes highly important to anybody who purposes to retain particular facts over long periods of time.

Questions on the picture, page 150
1. How many people appear in the picture?
2. How many women are in the picture?
3. How many women are wearing hats?
4. Which arm of the boy is being vaccinated?
5. Is the boy wearing low or high boots?
6. Is the boy grasping the arm of a man or a woman?
7. Is the doctor wearing a hat?
8. Who is holding the doctor's horse, a boy or a man?
9. How many windows in the house are visible?
10. How many doorways are visible?
11. Is the chair on which the boy sits an arm-chair or an armless one?
12. Is there a bucket visible?
13. Are the blinds open or closed?
14. How many pillars can be seen supporting the balcony?

In the light of this principle, it is obvious that we should not be content with the minimum amount of study or practice required; we should rather be anxious to drill ourselves beyond the bare amount needed for immediate recall. In this way we may escape the embarrassment and vexation of needless forgetting of materials that were only half learned. It is far wiser to *learn to overlearn* than it is to be content with *underlearning*.

Thorndike's Law of Exercise. Thorndike's *Law of Exercise* is a formulation of this same principle, thus: *the strength of a stimulus-response connection is increased by use or exercise;* and conversely, his *Law of Disuse* states that *the strength of such a connection is decreased when it is not exercised during a period of time*. There are numerous other factors in good learning and in poor learning to which we shall return in the next chapter.

Retroactive Inhibition. Certain interesting experiments have shown that if one would retain effectively something that he has just learned, he should keep his mind inactive for a period following the learning, notably by sleeping. Undoubtedly much of our forgetting would be eliminated if we were not compelled by program and school routine to turn immediately from the study of one subject to some other, without giving the brain cells time to assimilate the former material. As it is, the new datum appears to be retroactive upon that previously practiced, inhibiting its best retention. It is a familiar fact that the mind retains overnight with clarity and faithfulness the thing studied just before retiring. It would be a splendid habit for anybody to insist upon keeping his mind fallow and his attention as unfixed as possible for at least a five-minute interval after he has finished one mental task before engaging upon some other task of a different type or content. It is almost as though, using the otherwise absurd analogy of a dish of gelatin, the brain cells must be given a little time to "set" after new material has been poured into them if they are to retain it.

Periods of sleep or mental inertia, however, can rarely be alternated with periods of mental work. Programs and appointments and the general nature of our waking life will hardly adapt themselves to such an arrangement, desirable as it might be ideally. The student can, nevertheless, hope to hold retroactive inhibition at a minimum by striving for comprehension of each block of material as it is interpolated upon the preceding, by searching out similarities among materials studied in successive periods of application, and by the realization that materials sometimes "get in each other's way" and have to be frequently reviewed and carefully integrated.

THE THIRD STAGE IN LEARNING: RECALLING THE DATA

Mere retention of material learned is, of course, not sufficient: one must also be able to reinstate or recall it when it is needed. Casual and incidental though many of our experiences are, they tie together in mind in accordance with certain definite and long-understood principles which Aristotle first enunciated more than two thousand years ago. The same principles which operate in the original impressing of the experiences operate also in their recall when needed. As at present understood, these classic explanations of recall are contained under the primary *Law of Association* and the secondary *Principles of Association*.

The Law of Association. The Law of Association may be stated as follows: *Of two things previously experienced together, the entrance of one into the mind tends to draw in the other also.* This is Aristotle's old *Law of Contiguity*, and upon its operation is based all learning and all recalling. If a thing is to be remembered, it must be associated contiguously with something else; if it is to be recalled it must be recalled contiguously with the former associated idea. From this point of view, all that teaching consists of is setting the stage of learning in such a way that those things which are to be remembered shall be *experienced together* by the pupil. Thus, the teacher must bring the following ideas together in the child's attention, and the child must so experience them: "coffee" and "Brazil"; "8 $\times$ 7" and "56"; the "boiling point" and "212°"; "insects" and "*Lepidoptera.*" In recall, according to the Law of Association or Contiguity, "coffee" suggests "Brazil," "Brazil" suggests "coffee," etc. The more rich and numerous the associations, the more varied and elaborate the mental life becomes. In our discussion of conditioned learning, we shall find likewise that the adequate and the neutral stimuli must both be experienced together. Thus we may say with equal truth: all learning is conditioning, and all learning is associating.

The Secondary Principles of Association. 1. *Recency.* The more *recently* two associates have been experienced together, the more likely is the presence of one of them in the mind to draw in the second than it is any of the scores of other associates that have been connected with it at various times and under various circumstances in the past. Students make use of the principle of recency when they "cram" at the last minute for an examination, trying to associate together in an hour the hosts of associated ideas that they have been considering for a semester.

2. *Frequency.* Of several ideas previously experienced together, when one is in the mind it will tend to draw in the one that has been most frequently experienced. The purpose of drill work in our schools

is to lower the neural thresholds by repetition of ideas or concepts that belong together and are to be made permanent. The more the drill, the better the recollection. This is Thorndike's *Law of Exercise* or *Use*. If one associates "9 $\times$ 8" with "72," and not with "76," it is because the former association has been made most often.

3. *Primacy.* This principle states that the first or earliest association formed between two ideas sometimes operates preferentially, even though other associations have been made more often or more recently. It is because of the operation of this principle that we sometimes find our first impressions to be lasting, and our earlier experiences to be most vivid.

4. *Intensity.* Sometimes an experience is so intense or emotional that whenever any element in it is subsequently present in the mind, other elements that were associated originally with it tend to come plunging back into consciousness. Thus, a certain old soldier refuses to eat any kind of canned meat, for it reminds him of the abhorred "bully beef" that he ate in the trenches, and that brings back to him poignant memories of the horrors he experienced in the First World War. Teachers continually make positive use of this principle when they try by means of elaborate motivation or device to make a new association vivid in the mind of the learner. In the exercises in application at the end of this chapter, the student nurse will find some examples of the role played by association in the mastering of her own particularized kind of knowledge and information.

Other Determiners of Association. There are many other factors which influence the sequence of ideas in our minds. Among them we may distinguish here the *mood of the moment,* the *mind-set* or *attitude,* and the *similarity* or *identity* of experiences. The mood of the moment will often determine our train of thought or will favor the arousal of one chain of associates instead of some other. Thus, when one has a headache or a touch of indigestion, the world may look "blue" to him, the sun being too hot or the cold too penetrating. The mind-set or attitude of the moment plays a prominent role likewise in determining the nature of our associations. If one is set to study history, his fund of historical knowledge is readily available; if geometry, his fund of arithmetical knowledge. If he is set to add, then the situation

$$\begin{array}{r} 87 \\ \underline{79} \end{array}$$

leads him to add 9 and 7, to carry one, and to add it to 7 and 8; if, on the other hand, he is set to subtract, a wholly different series of associates between 9 and 7 and between 7 and 8 is called into operation.

Certain features of similarity or of identity between our experiences often determine our associations. Thus, Mr. B. reminds one of Mr. C. because the two individuals have certain features in common—possibly eyes that are similar, or a similar gait or facial expression. Consequently, when one sees Mr. B, he is reminded of Mr. C. Much of the social conversation that we carry on with our friends is projected upon the often repeated words: "That reminds me . . .," and one often notes that a member of the group in which friendly conversation is going forward can hardly wait to contribute to the circle some incident of which he is reminded by some associative cue that the conversation has given him.

Recognition. There are, of course, all degrees of recall, ranging from a vague consciousness that the situation presented to the mind has been experienced before to a complete recognition of it in time and space as it was originally experienced, or as it may have been modified by subsequent experience or reflection. It sometimes happens that one has a bothersome "feeling of familiarity," and is half persuaded that he has "been in that same place before," or has "seen this person somewhere before." This is an elementary and incomplete recognition in which some of the details are re-presented while others are missing. Thus, a snapshot of a landscape which one has never actually seen may contain certain combinations of trees, sky and elevations which one has himself experienced in a wholly different setting. Partial recall of this sort represents a simple form of memory and presupposes far less drill and a much lower order of logical comprehension than is true in the case of true recall.

Consider, by way of illustration, the following questions from an objective-type examination:

1. The cotton gin was invented by
 FULTON   HOWE   WHITNEY   McCORMICK   MORSE
2. The Federal Reserve Act was passed by Congress to_____
_____. (Complete the statement.)

It is a simpler matter to *recognize* the name *Whitney* in connection with the invention of the cotton gin than it is to *recall* the facts underlying the passage of the Federal Reserve Act. The former calls for mere elementary selection of one from among several alternatives; the latter calls for precise memory. The one may be established somewhat casually and may be revived with a minimum of mental effort; the other must be established thoughtfully and analytically, and can be revived only by the employment of voluntary and logical principles of association. The student should strive in his learning to form associations sufficient to insure that what he recalls shall as far as possible wear the stamp of definite and sure identification. The degree of overlearning will relate directly to the degree of recognition.

THE MOTIVATION OF LEARNING

Importance of a Feeling of Need in Learning. The hungrier the man, the more ravenously he eats. About the same laws govern the intellect as the stomach. One of the most ignominious of all the sources of weakness in our schools and colleges has been the neglect of the fundamental principle of learning which this truism implies. Often the only animated person in a schoolroom is the teacher: the pupils are passive and quiescent. The former may be flushed, warm, even excited; but unless the boys and girls feel some kindling desire or feeling of need to learn what she would impart, they will imbibe but little. If the student feels no interest in the work assigned, but looks upon it as a task to be accomplished merely because it has been set by a taskmaster, he generally reacts with a passive attitude. Such learning experiences leave the learner cold and indifferent, if not actually rebellious. Unless illumined with a feeling that it is worth while, a learning situation tends shortly to degenerate into a bore and a grind. When the feeling of need exists in the mind of the teacher only, there is likely to be no avid and eager response on the part of the learner.

This sort of learning situation contrasts sharply with one in which there exist consciously in the mind of the learner an awareness of his need for the material which appears on his educational menu and a readiness to attack it. In this latter type of situation, learning becomes interesting and challenging. At its best, all learning is of this sort. Let the task be one whose solution is needed by the learner, and learning becomes a joy. Even though it may be difficult and may tax the best ingenuity and patience of the pupil, such learning is likely to be of high quality and to be satisfying.

All Strongly Motivated Learning Is Tension-Reducing. Not all learning, of course, is thus conflagrational; only in spots and at times does it approach fire heat. In our best learning moments we feel something of the consuming power of mind when it is set at work upon a task that is meaningful and intriguing. All learning that is strongly motivated proceeds dynamically until the tension that has been developed by curiosity or by the necessity of arriving at a solution has been reduced. Give Mary a new bicycle and dangle before her the prospects of riding with Henry and Sue, and you have set in order a learning process that will be likely to persist against all bruises and bumps and falls and tears until Mary has learned to ride. Give Ann a pretty new doll to dress, and some pieces of lace and cloth, and you have challenged her with a learning process that knows no faltering or discouragement, in spite of needle-pricks and bungling handiwork, until she has produced a dress in which to clothe her treasure.

There is literally no end to the indefatigable practice that boys and girls will put forth in their determination to master the skills and processes that fill the environment of childhood outside the school. One has but to call to mind the persistence which children will manifest in such situations as learning to skate or ski, to yodel, or to build a radio receiving set, to realize how strong is the urge to cultivate new skills and develop new motor controls in youth. This phenomenom is demonstrated by the persistence with which a child will apply himself in learning to pitch a good "curve," master a clever tennis stroke, or send wigwag signals across a hillside or lake.

In all these situations, as long as the art or skill sought for remains unmastered, the organism experiences a definite tension which is released only when successful completion of the process is achieved, This tension or restlessness is present in the neuromuscular system whenever one is confronted with a problem for the solution of which he feels strong desire or need. Why is it that schoolroom tasks so rarely express themselves in this way?

Conditioned Emotional Learning. Dr. J. B. Watson, a number of years ago, did some pioneer work in this country in the study of emotional learning through *conditioning*. We shall have a great deal more to say about conditioned learning shortly. At this point, however, it will be helpful to note how peculiarly our emotional responses arise out of conditioning experiences. Before Watson's now classic investigation of this phenomenon was reported, it had always been supposed that we are born with certain "instinctive" fears, such as fear of snakes, rodents, darkness, strangers, and the like. Then came Watson, in 1921, to demonstrate that such fears are not to be thought of as being innate but may be accounted for rather as being *learned* through conditioning.

In a most interesting experiment, Watson used for his subject an eleven-month-old boy, named Albert, the child of a wet-nurse in the Johns Hopkins Hospital. The boy had lived an unusually well adjusted existence, never having been taught to fear anything, and perhaps never having seen an animal at the time when the experiment with him was begun.

Albert was placed on a mattress on the experimental table. Presently a white rat was released beside him. Interested and curious, he reached out for it, but at the instant when his hand touched it, the experimenter struck a resounding blow upon an iron bar behind Albert's head. Now a sudden loud noise is, for anybody, an auditory shock, and adequate to produce a fear reaction. Albert jumped violently, withdrew his hand from the vicinity of the rat, and fell forward on the mattress. After seven repetitions of the two simultaneously presented stimuli, given on succeeding days, Albert manifested violent fear whenever the rat was shown him. This conditioning is diagrammed in Figure 12.

As a result of associating simultaneously the loud noise and the white rat, Albert was *conditioned* to fear the rat, and would henceforth be afraid of rats whenever and wherever he met them. Subsequent observation of Albert showed that his fear of the rat had transferred to all other furry objects, notably to a rabbit, a dog, some cotton wool, a Santa Claus mask, a fur coat. Obviously the child had learned to be afraid.

Early Emotional Conditioning. The possible application of the concept of conditioned emotional learning to the whole gamut of our

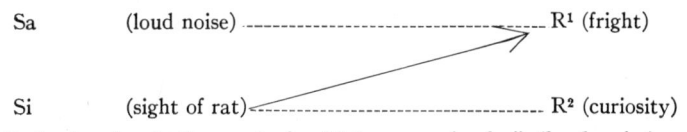

Sa   (loud noise) ------------------------------ R^1 (fright)

Si   (sight of rat) ------------------------------ R^2 (curiosity)

Fig. 12. In the sketch, Sa stands for "Adequate stimulus" (loud noise), which logically results in R^1 (fright). Si stands for "Inadequate stimulus" (sight of the rat), which should logically lead only to R^2, *i.e.*, to curiosity about the rat, but which, after being associated with the simultaneously occurring loud noise, illogically leads to fright. The two stimuli were experienced by Albert in the same instant of time, *i.e.*, they were associated contiguously.

human fears is limited only by one's imagination. It becomes apparent that we have in conditioning a valid explanation of most if not all of our fears and aversions. Thus, a child grows up afraid of electrical storms because he was frightened in very early life by noting fear in his mother, or in some other person, during a storm; he grows up afraid of the dark because he was threatened with the dark closet, or the "bogey man," or with some other disciplinary djinn conjured up by thoughtless adults; he is afraid of dogs because he has been warned that they will bite him if he goes near them; he dislikes a certain kind of food because his initial contact with it was associated with something unpleasant; he experiences aversion to this person or that person, to this activity or to that activity, because of early conditioning.

And most unfortunate of all, as in the case of Albert's derived fear of all furry objects, one may transfer a fear which was originally conditioned as a single emotional response, to a host of other stimuli that are related only vaguely if at all to the original conditioning one. Most of us are harassed and disconcerted by a variety of negative emotional reactions suggestive of fear or anxiety or dread, most of which could be traced back to conditioning experiences of early life. The fact that the original experience may have been completely forgotten only makes the presence and the power of our negative emotional responses the more baffling and distressing. Their beginnings forgotten, and their original dimensions tending to expand to include other vaguely related experiences, conditioned emotional attitudes of a negative sort come eventually to play a strong role in the lives of most people.

Experimental Extinction. Sometimes it is necessary that several simultaneous repetitions of the two stimuli be presented before the conditioned response is built up; sometimes, however, a single vivid experience may be sufficient to condition a child permanently: being scratched by an angry cat, or falling overboard and being half-drowned, occurrences which suffice to drive him to fear all cats, all water. Fortunately, most conditioning experiences tend to fade out with the passage of time and, excepting the most vivid of them, are forgotten.

A classic example of the extinction of a conditioned fear response is that reported by M. C. Jones, in which a child who had been conditioned to fear a rabbit that had nibbled his finger came gradually to lose his fear. Each day, while the child was eating his dinner, the rabbit was brought into the room, but was kept at first unobtrusively in the background. The child's eagerness for the food was sufficient to keep his focal attention upon it rather than upon the animal. Little by little the animal was introduced nearer to the child, until eventually the fear was extinguished and the former attitude of interest was substituted for it. The inhibition, fear, had been itself inhibited by wise reeducational procedures. The difficulty with many a child's fear reactions is that they are either misunderstood by the parent or else are made still more poignant by poor handling. Thus, to laugh at a child who is afraid of the dark, or to scold him for his fear of strangers, is more likely to make matters worse than it is to uncondition the fear response.

Conditioned Learning in the Home. Much of the learning of childhood, both in and outside the school, is conditioned learning. In infancy, the baby is conditioned to the sound of his mother's voice, to the sight of her face bending over him, to her encouraging presence in the general environment; he learns when to expect his food, to recognize the preparations for it, and to apprehend its source; he learns whether to cry or to smile; he learns to like this and to dislike that, to seek this and to avoid that; he learns to read warnings, approval, reproof in his mother's face; he learns to recognize his toys long before he can call them by name; he learns to fall asleep at the accustomed time and in the accustomed surroundings, to gurgle with expectancy at sight of his bath and his floating toys, and to do other things that have been associated repeatedly or impressively with adequate stimuli. He forms his food habits and aversions as a result of conditioning; he learns similarly to love his mother, to sleep alone in a darkened room, to feel loyalty to and security in his home, to avoid common dangers, to associate names and sounds with objects and events, to talk, to read, to recognize.

Conditioned Learning in the School. Basally, the tools at least of learning appear to be acquired by the pupil in the primary grades through a process of conditioned learning. Consider, for example, how he comes to recognize words in reading. The teacher presents to him

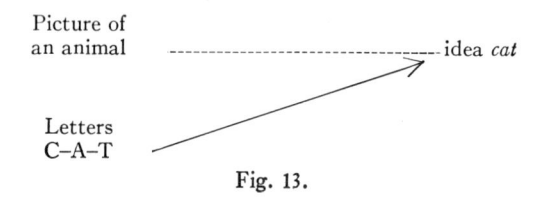

```
Picture of
an animal    ----------------------------idea cat
                                       ↗
Letters                               ↗
C-A-T                               ↗
```

Fig. 13.

on the blackboard or a flash-card the picture of a small animal with the symbol C-A-T beside it. Before practice, there is no connection whatever between these three letter-symbols and the idea *cat;* after practice, however, the picture of the cat may be dispensed with, and the mere presentation of the symbol C-A-T will arouse the idea *cat*. We may diagram the process (Fig. 13).

So it is with all the other common nouns and descriptive adjectives which the child is taught to recognize. In elementary number work also, early learning proceeds from simple conditioning of the child's reactions to the concrete, recognized stimuli until the associated ideas are fixed in his mind. Mastery of other tool materials of learning which cannot be so readily pictured in concrete form is of course a more difficult process for the young learner, who must fall back upon sheer repetitive memory as a means of learning to recognize and use the symbols involved.

Conditioning and the Nurse. Some persons are accustomed to faint at the sight of blood. Such an emotionally conditioned individual could hardly aspire to a profession in which the sight of blood is a part of the routine experience. One who is to become a nurse must have been conditioned favorably to the work which nurses are called upon to do; at least, she must not have been conditioned unfavorably to it.

If we were to ask the members of a class of student nurses how it was that they individually had decided to take up nursing as a career, we should probably receive some such replies as the following: "I admire a certain nurse, and hope to become like her." "I fell in love with a nurse whom I once had when I was sick, and have wanted to be a nurse ever since." "I was brought up in a family where there was much sickness, and I have enjoyed helping to care for the ill." "Nursing is a kind of service, and I should like to make my life count for something constructive." "The education of a nurse is valuable not only now but later on if and when I become a home maker." All of these reasons for embarking upon the profession suggest that the students concerned have been by some experience or other conditioned favorably to the work of the nurse.

Not only, however, should the student have been favorably conditioned to the idea of nursing; she should also become now progressively conditioned to all the details of the practice and exercise of the art. As her nursing education proceeds, she will find herself becoming conditioned, for example, to the manner and technique, even to the facial expression and muscular set of the physician or the surgeon whom she is assisting; to the mental attitudes and the requirements of the head nurse, supervisor or director; to the general professional atmosphere of a hospital; to the following of a strict schedule; to the significance of suddenly changing symptoms in a patient; to the facing of great human emotional crises in the sick—and all with the minimum of emotional disturbance personally. Other things being reasonably equal, the nurse in whom the physicians and the supervisors have the greatest confidence is the nurse who has conditioned herself positively and sanely to these eventualities and to other routine or emergency situations that make up the daily experiences of those who minister to the sick, the suffering and the dying.

The learning process for the student nurse is, in considerable measure, a progressive self schooling in keenness of observation, in cooperativeness, in adaptation to circumstances, and in emotional control. Often the difference between a student nurse who is a failure and one who gives good promise of success and perhaps of distinction is merely the difference in self schooling in these fundamental conditioned attitudes which each has achieved.

Providing for Transfer. Late nineteenth century psychologists, following the classic notion that the mind is a series of separate faculties, *e.g.*, the *memory* faculty, the *reasoning* faculty, the *judging* faculty, and so forth, understood that certain difficult subjects of study like Latin and mathematics trained the mental faculties and hence made one better able to learn other things. They looked upon the mind as somewhat analogous to a muscle which is made stronger by gymnastic exercise. If one applied himself to the study of Greek, he trained his mind to be keener in learning any other subject, much in the same way that if one trains his muscles in playing football, he will be better able to move furniture or climb a ladder. In other words, according to the older psychology, study of certain "hard" subjects had disciplinary value for the general training of the powers of observation or of judging, which transferred to subsequent situations in which mental activity was required. This belief has long been the essence of the theory *of formal discipline,* and has accounted for the persistence in the curricula of high school and college during the last century, and to some extent down to the present time, of Greek and Latin. Such subjects as these have been required not principally because of their content but because of their alleged formal values in *disciplining the mind.*

Since 1901, when Thorndike and other experimentalists began scientific inquiry into the whole question of transfer of training, there has come about considerable modification and revision of the old formal discipline theory. The most important conclusion which the modern investigators have reached is that there is no such wholesale transfer from one subject to another as had been supposed. Following Thorndike and others, it is now rather generally accepted that transfer takes place between two situations only in so far as the two situations possess "identical components." If there is in both an *identity of content,* such as facts and words; if there is an *identiy of procedure,* such as technique in using a dictionary or vocabulary or the employment of an habitual method of attack; if there is an *identity of ideals or attitudes,* such as earnestness, determination to master, thoroughness, then transfer will be likely to take place from one field or subject of study to another, or from the schoolroom situation to life situations beyond the school.

Surely, unless there is transfer of some of these identities from school to life, we waste our time in teaching and learning in the schoolroom the principles and ideals of good conduct upon which so much emphasis is being placed today. We teach children to be honest in school, in the hope that this attitude will become an integral part of their character make-up; we teach them to think logically, to be unprejudiced, to maintain an open mind and to be industrious, because we want them to exercise these virtues in the extra-school life and years. We anticipate that there will be considerable actual carry-over from school to society.

Among the conclusions arrived at by the scientific investigators of this matter of transfer, none is perhaps of greater significance for the student than that which states that transfer does not take place, to any great degree at least, *automatically.* The circumstance of there being identical components will not guarantee carry-over from one to another situation or setting. It is of importance that the individual learner shall himself be indefatigable in his search for identities and for generalities that will transfer, as Judd has pointed out. He needs to be on the alert to note general principles that can be "lifted" from the present setting and applied in others; he should be alert to keep his mental content fluid so that it can be permeated with new ingredients as they are come upon; he should beware of pigeonholing, isolating, or sectioning his fund of knowledge into separate and watertight compartments; he should be constantly concerned to organize his knowledge as it accumulates from day to day and from experience to experience.

The good learner will search actively for valid conclusions, for universals upon which to hang the particulars, and for relationships among facts. If, for example, he learns that the American colonists set large store by the principle of liberty and the right of self determination, he should find that fundamental culture-idea permeating his subsequent study of our national history, and it should be a helpful concept to carry through the interpretation of the historical events of the past two centuries. The story of our country, when interpreted in the light of this activating principle, becomes a far more interesting record than it does if the learner sees in its sweep only the piling up of one isolated event upon another. The evolution of our democracy is possibly more the story of the imprint of this fundamental philosophy upon the ambitions and the purposes of men than it is of any other single motivating influence.

Transfer and the Nurse. Nursing is distinctly an *applied* art. The work of a nurse is concerned with bringing to bear upon the present patient or the present hospital situation such wisdom, insight and skill as she has achieved in her training and her experience. This means, obviously, that she will have to "lift" from her book study, lectures, demonstrations and therapeutic participations common and universal principles and procedures that will have validity and practicality in her subsequent sick-room and ward duties. As her experience increases with training, and afterwards as a practicing nurse, she will become more facile in transferring the fruits of yesterday's theory and practice to today's and tomorrow's problems as they arise individually with patients.

From the present psychology course, for example, the student nurse is deriving a fund of practical knowledge about people, both sick and well, that must find its way into actual practice if it is to function properly. The justification for the inclusion of psychology in the crowded curriculum of the school lies principally in the extent of its transfer to professional growth and performance and to personal development. It is not without design that the title of this textbook is Psychology *Applied* to Nursing. From a professional point of view, there can be no greater objective for psychology as a curricular subject in the school of nursing.

So we might refer to other courses which the nurse is carrying, or will carry at some time during the training period: to sociology, in which is presented a background for the better understanding of patients and their families and the communities from which they come; to *materia medica,* in which are stressed the understanding and use of drugs and their physiologic effects upon the human organism; to microbiology, in which is developed for the student the role of the microscope as an indispensable modern aid in the study, classification and understanding of cellular and intercellular action and reaction in health and disease; to anatomy, in which is learned the structure of the human organism and its component parts, to the end that basal understanding of regularity and irregularity or defect may be built up in the nurse's mind; to chemistry, in which are traced the composition and nature of matter, especially of organic matter, in order that the nurse may be familiar with the principle chemical elements and with the normalities and abnormalities of body chemistry. In these and other scientific subjects in the nursing school curriculum, the student will be mastering technical materials rather for their transferability and applicability to her professional practice than for intrinsic academic information.

THOUGHT PROBLEMS FOR THE STUDENT

1. Collect from illustrated magazines several advertisements that you think would challenge the involuntary attention of readers. Analyze each of them to determine what are the "factors of advantage," *i.e.,* what is the specifically compelling quality of the stimulus in each case?
2. List in parallel columns two sets of situations: one set in which an individual would probably use voluntary attention, and one set to which he would probably tend to be attracted involuntarily. Do the two processes ever overlap? Explain.
3. Give examples of illusions which you have personally experienced.
4. Find in a magazine or book a picture presenting some detail, and ask one of your classmates to look at it intently for ten seconds. Be accurate about keeping the time. Then instruct her to answer ten factual questions about the picture that you have previously devised for the purpose. Account for the results.
5. Illustrate each of the principles of association by examples of reactions taken from your own everyday experience or contacts. Which of the principles appear to be the more commonly occurring ones for most people?

6. During the first week that you spent on the wards, did you feel any *needs* for learning? What were they? List some of the items of knowledge and some of the skills which you have since mastered that have given you a gratifying feeling of effectiveness. Would you say that these acquisitions have had a tension-reducing effect? Discuss some learning needs which you experience when you are assigned to a new ward.
7. Give an illustration from your nursing experience where insight suddenly produced a solution to your problem.
8. What are the focal stimuli to which you attend during the care of a first day postoperative appendectomy? To the care of a pneumonia patient who has been ill only two days?
9. Do you find that your observation of patients is more accurate now than it was two months ago? Why? In what way would knowledge of a patient's diagnosis influence your perception?
10. Upon what factors does perception depend when you are taught nursing procedures?
11. Identify each of the principles of association with a personal learning experience that has taken place during the past month.
12. Discuss five procedures which you have overlearned. Summarize five facts in relation to health and disease which you meet daily in hospital situations. What is your reaction to them, now that you have so thoroughly overlearned them?
13. From personal experience, cite examples of sudden insight or "repatterning" in learning. Did trial and error figure at all?
14. Collect as many instances as possible of emotional conditioning of children. Suggest several personal conditioned emotional attitudes that you yourself possess, indicating if possible how and when they were established.
15. Can you give any examples of extinction (unconditioning) of conditioned fears or other emotional attitudes in children?
16. Cite several examples of transferred learning experiences that you can consciously identify with the original acquisitions.

SUGGESTED READINGS

1. Blair, G. M., Jones, R. S., and Simpson, R. H.: *Educational Psychology*. New York, The Macmillan Co., 1954.
    Part III contains good chapters on "Organization of Learning" and on "Transfer and Application of Learning."
2. Karn, H. W., and Weitz, J.: *An Introduction to Psychology*. New York, John Wiley and Sons, 1955.
    Refer to the authors' discussion of attention, page 65; of perception, Chapter 3; of transfer, page 82; and of conditioning, pages 83 ff.
3. Rotter, J. B.: *Social Learning and Clinical Psychology*. New York, Prentice-Hall, Inc., 1954.
    Pages 365-372 contain considerable material on transference written from the point of view of the nurse's handling of patient therapy.
4. Ruch, F. L.: *Psychology and Life*. Chicago, Scott, Foresman and Co., 1953.
    Chapter 11, "The Learning Process," will provide excellent parallel material to the present chapter.

Chapter 9

The sweetest and most inoffensive path of life leads through the avenues of science and learning; and whoever can either remove any obstruction in this way, or open up any new prospect, ought so far to be esteemed a benefactor to mankind.

DAVID HUME

LEARNING: SOME COMPARISONS AND PRINCIPLES

EXPERIMENTING WITH ANIMAL LEARNING

Before we inquire further into the human learning process, it will be worth our while to digress briefly in order to study some of the interesting features of learning in animals. In so doing, we shall discover a number of significant facts about learning that are found to be common to human and animal subjects alike. Most of us have observed the development of some skill or "trick" in an animal pet, but few of us have set out to study the growth of such learning processes experimentally.

The Problem Box. Experiments with animal learners have been illuminating from the standpoint of aiding us to comprehend something of the strength of motives and of the amount of tension present when a problem is presented for solution. A hungry cat is placed in an experimental problem box (Fig. 14), escape from which can be had only after the animal performs some simple preliminary act, such as pulling at a loop over its head, stepping on a platform, or nosing up a button. A ration of food is placed just outside the box and the animal can both see and smell it through the bars of its cage. Immediately the animal begins to react. The strong motive to satisfy its hunger impels it to behave in a manner characteristic of all hungry animals. It jumps about from side to side of the box; it claws and bites at the bars; it tries to squeeze its body through the openings; it thrusts forth its paws in a desperate effort to clutch the food. Finally, after some minutes it *chances* to make the proper preliminary contact, and the door of the box swings open. Forthwith, the animal leaps through and proceeds to devour its ration.

In subsequent trials with the same box, the cat requires less and less time to make the appropriate response; ultimately, after days and perhaps weeks of practice, it eliminates all random movements and proceeds instantly to make the needful response as soon as it is placed in the box. To this kind of learning in which there is assumed to be at first nothing but random, aimless reaction, but in which there emerges after a time a chance correct response that finally is stamped into the neuromuscular system of the animal, experimenters have given the appropriate name *trial and error learning*. Various animals

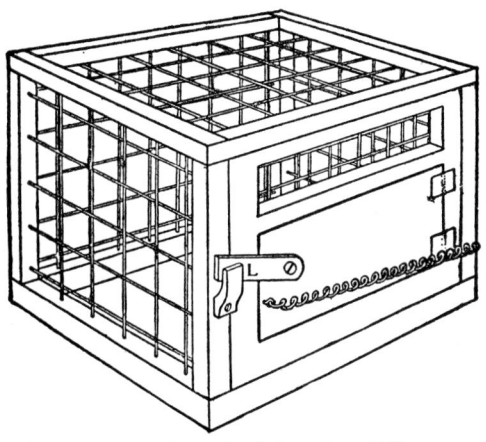

Fig. 14. A puzzle-box to study animal learning. When one of the random movements of the animal proves successful in lifting the latch, a spring gently opens the door. (From Watson.)

besides cats have been used in problem box experiments: when the motive is strong enough, almost any animal will attempt to learn and will keep trying until either it is successful or else gives up from exhaustion or frustration. The restlessness and tension in the animal's organism are apparent to the observer.

The Maze. Another device used in animal experimentation is the *maze*, a piece of apparatus which comprises a labyrinth of blind alleys leading to the food chamber (cf. Fig. 15). At first when introduced into the maze, the subject runs aimlessly through the passages, coming frequently back against the same blank wall. It may wander about helplessly for a long time, arriving eventually by chance within the food chamber. As it continues to run the maze day after day, however, it begins to make fewer false turns and to proceed more directly along the correct pathway. Thus, an experimental group of thirty-four thirsty rats that averaged eight errors the first day in running a simple maze were runnning the same maze after three weeks of daily trials with a daily average of but a single error.

While various animal subjects have been employed in maze-learning experiments, rats have been used most extensively, hundreds of individual experiments having been conducted with rats as learners since maze experimenting began. The motive used may be hunger,

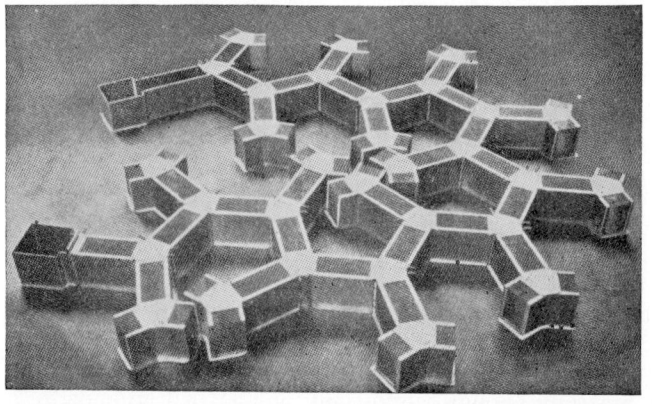

Fig. 15. Warner-Warden unit maze. Upper figure shows the four types of unit of which the maze is constructed; from left to right, entrance box, pathway unit, cul-de-sac, goal box. Lower figure shows one of the possible patterns—an arrangement including fifteen culs-de-sac.

thirst, shock or pain, punishment, the presence of an animal of the opposite sex, or some other appealing stimulus.

Although two general conclusions have been drawn from all these experiments: (1) the animal will not attempt to learn unless it is activated by a strong motive or feeling of need, and (2) animal learning is typically trial and error, recent developments in animal experimentation have made it appear that under certain conditions the learning of animals may not be completely blind and random, but may suggest something of the nature of insight or plan. (See page 172 ff.)

TRIAL AND ERROR IN HUMAN LEARNING

But let us see whether the human learner makes any use of the trial and error method of the animal subject, and if so, whether it is blind or whether there are associated with it reasoning and insight.

A human subject is given a typical mechanical puzzle and directed to "take it apart." Let us suppose the puzzle to consist of two interlocking rings which can be separated from one another only when each has been manipulated into a particular position. The ordinary human subject will be found, like the animal, to make a great many initial random trial and error movements, which may appear but little if any more intelligent than those of the cat in the problem box or the white rat in the maze. He proceeds more or less blindly to twist and pull and turn and shake the rings; he may make the same false moves a dozen times. Careful observation of his performance may indicate that he is doing *some* thinking, that he pauses occasionally to scrutinize the device, turning it thoughtfully about, and appears to be *searching for a clue*. The fact that he possesses a language and can carry on a running conversation with himself aids him in analyzing the moves to be attempted.

While much of the behavior of the human puzzle-solver is trial and error, the human learner soon perceives where to apply his efforts; the problem is not entirely meaningless; he may discover a notch here, a groove there, or an aperture elsewhere. Mentally, he is alert and restless, just as he is alert and restless physically. Suddenly, whether by chance or as a result of insight, he succeeds in detaching one link from the other, and his tension is reduced. Perhaps he does not sense how he achieved the solution, and it may take him almost as long to take the puzzle apart a second time as it did the first. In any case, however, he retains from his first trial some vestiges of memory that will help him in the second. Random trial and error moves are reduced in number in subsequent trials in human subjects.

We have used the solving of a mechanical puzzle as an illustration of trial and error learning. We might just as well have used tennis playing, learning to typewrite, or any other motor skill which cannot be immediately achieved. In all these performances trial and error appears to combine in the human learner with insight and conscious control to promote mastery.

Frequently the human learner who is practicing the acquisition of a motor skill like typewriting finds himself suddenly employing a new and improved technique which may have been in existence for several days before he becomes aware of it but which when he notes its existence he finds himself consciously adopting as a valuable adjustment. There appears to be no question that it worked itself out unconsciously, or that progress in a learning situation is something more than hit or miss, random acquisition: the whole organism is reacting, promoting unconscious gains and short-cuts as well as irrelevant motor responses and occasional insight during the learning process.

LEARNING AND INSIGHT: GESTALT

Several psychologists, working with higher animals such as cats and apes, have demonstrated that, like, human subjects, they show insight in learning. Notable among this group of psychologists should be mentioned Dr. W. Koehler, of the University of Berlin, who did significant work with apes at Tenerife. In one of his experiments with Sultan, a male anthropoid ape, Koehler placed the animal in a commodious cage in which the only objects were a box and two hollow bamboo rods, one smaller in diameter than the other but of approximately equal length. Beyond the bars of the cage he placed some bananas.

Sultan is hungry for the bananas, and for some time he thrusts first one stick and then the other between the bars in a vain attempt to draw toward him. Sultan tries various other random methods of obtaining the food objective, but without success. He even pushes one of the sticks out on the ground toward the bananas as far as it will go, and then moves it cautiously nearer with the other stick. The first stick actually touches the bananas, and Sultan immediately shows great delight: he has made contact with his objective, although he cannot draw it toward him. For more than an hour he repeats this procedure, or variations of it. Finally, he retrieves both sticks and climbs up on the box and begins to play carelessly with them. All at once, the two rods chancing to lie in a straight line, Sultan pushes the thinner one into the thicker one, appears forthwith to have an "idea," and is off on the run to the railings. After some effort to insert the smaller rod in the larger one firmly enough to hold, Sultan is rewarded by being able to draw each one of the bananas, one after the other, to the side of the cage, forgetting even to take time to eat, so great is his delight at what he has wrought.

Here is learning which unquestionably suggests a sudden repatterning of the baffling elements comprising a total situation. To this sudden clarification of a problematic situation the psychologist gives the name *insight*. Koehler and others of his school of psychological thought—known as the *Gestalt* school—reasoning from such observations as the one just cited, do not agree with the theory that accounts for animal learning as the operation of blind trial and error. They see in animal learning something more than an ultimate chance success which becomes stamped in by satisfying repetition. The Gestalt psychologists insist that the subject experiences a new perception of the situation in which what was a moment before *ground* (*i.e.*, background) becomes suddenly *figure* (*i.e.*, foreground) and the animal perceives a new *Gestalt* or patterning of the stimuli before him.

Fig. 16. Animal learning. (Koehler: The Mentality of Apes. Harcourt, Brace and Company, Inc., Publishers.)

Thus, to apply the Gestalt interpretation, the cat in the problem box did not at first direct its effort to the latch or to the door, but made random trials at every part of the box; after a time, however, the latch and the door and the meat outside are "seen together" in a new patterning. Thus also Sultan, the ape, suddenly "saw" a new possible relationship between the two sticks, and then between the combined sticks and bananas outside the cage. Thus, too, the human subject has turned a puzzle picture aimlessly about in his hand without being able to "find the bear" or the "shepherd's dog," until certain lines and certain hitherto meaningless areas suddenly repatterned themselves, *i.e.*, suddenly emerged from *ground* into *figure*, and forthwith he exclaimed: "Oh, I see it now!" In all these examples the Gestaltists would say the tension is reduced through the *establishing of an equilibrium or closure*, where a moment before the entire situation was open and what would bring satisfactory solution of the need was anybody's guess.

There is no essential reason for rejecting either the trial and error explanation or the Gestalt explanation of learning of this sort. In all learning—both human and animal—there is a great deal of random, pointless manipulation of objects (or of ideas in the case of humans),

Fig. 17. Ambiguous figure and ground. Different forms will be seen depending on whether the black or the white appears as figure. (Modified from E. Rubin, taken from Murphy: General Psychology, by permission of Harper and Brothers.)

regardless of whether the situation is in the nature of solving a puzzle or (again in the case of humans) of reasoning out a baffling intellectual problem. In both human and animal learning there is at times evident, in the midst of trial and error indirection, a sudden repatterning and insight which suggests a new move or relationship. Fortunately, we do not have to become partisans of either the trial and error or the Gestalt viewpoint; we may accept both and apply each individually as it seems to offer an explanation of a specific learning response.

ANIMAL LEARNING AS CONDITIONING

The Pavlov Experiments. When somebody gives an intimate description of a sumptuous feast, or when our attention is otherwise

LEARNING: SOME COMPARISONS AND PRINCIPLES

called to the subject of interesting and delectable viands, we have the experience of a gush of saliva and a "watering" mouth. Most people have observed often enough this reaction to the perception or the imagining of food. It remained, however, for a Russian physiologist, Dr. I. P. Pavlov, to investigate the nature of this curious phenomenon, and from his experiments on the salivary reflex has come one of the most helpful and promising viewpoints in modern psychology. For Pavlov, learning is neither trial and error nor repatterning: it is *conditioning*, *i.e.*, it is the result of associating a neutral stimulus with an adequate one so that henceforth a new or *con-*

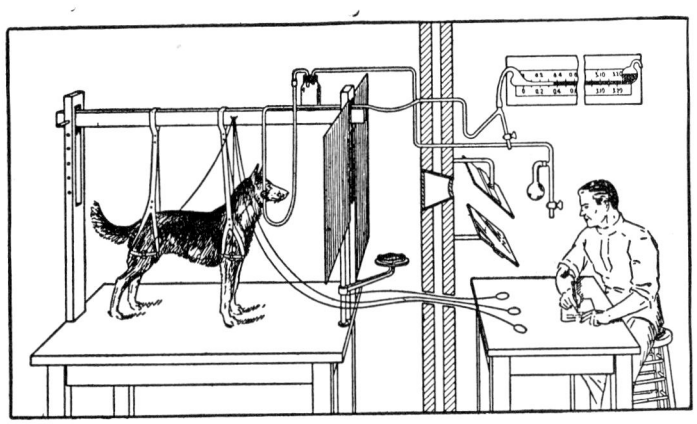

Fig. 18. Pavlov's arrangement for a salivary conditioned reflex in the dog. (From I. P. Pavlov: Lectures on Conditioned Reflexes. International Publishers, 1928.)

ditioned response takes place. We have already referred in Chapter 8 to emotional conditioning in human learners.

Let us briefly describe one of Pavlov's experiments. For his subject, he uses a dog; the laboratory in which his studies are carried on is a series of sound-proof rooms, in one of which the animal, harnessed lightly and comfortably, stands on a table "ready" for the experiment. A tube has been inserted into the opening of a salivary gland in his mouth, and the saliva as it is secreted flows drop by drop from the tube into a graduated glass; it is automatically counted as it is discharged. In an adjacent room, completely insulated from the room where the dog is, so that there may be no uncontrolled cues to motivate the animal, the experimenter sits at pneumatic or electrical controls; a periscopic mirror device makes it possible for him to see plainly the entire scene in the adjoining room. It should perhaps be added that the dog and the experimenter are on the friendliest of terms and that the former has no fear of his master.

How Conditioning Takes Place. Suddenly a bell rings in the experimental room. The dog pricks up his ears, but there is of course no salivary response. Promptly after the bell stimulus, a dish of powdered meat appears before the dog. Forthwith, the saliva flows copiously into the glass, and the animal devours the food with much relish. This, of course, is to be expected. The presence of food before a hungry animal, or a hungry man, starts the salivary reflex. We understand that food is a biologically adequate stimulus to the flow of the digestive fluids. As the experiment proceeds from day to day, however, we find a peculiar and quite unexpected development. After a few repetitions of the bell stimulus, followed immediately by the presenting of the food, Pavlov discovers that it is possible to evoke the salivary reflex by the mere ringing of the bell, *without the giving of food.* Here is a surprising discovery. There is no logical relationship, of course, between the stimulus *ringing bell* and the response *flow of saliva.* Illogical though the connection is, it is there, and

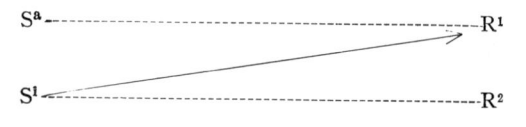

$$S^a \text{-----------------------} R^1$$
$$S^i \text{-----------------------} R^2$$

Fig. 19.

Pavlov concludes that the dog has been "conditioned" to the ringing of the bell by the mere circumstance of *its having been experienced simultaneously with a logical or adequate stimulus.*

We may diagram this conditioned learning as in Figure 19, in which S^a stands for the adequate stimulus (presence of food) and R^1 for the logical or unconditioned response to it (gush of saliva), and in which S^i represents the inadequate stimulus (the sound of a bell) and R^2 the logical response to such a stimulus (pricking up the ears). The arrow from S^i to R^1 indicates that after practice the presentation of S^i (ringing bell) brings about the conditioned response (gush of saliva). Thus may a response ordinarily connected with one situation become associatively attached to or conditioned to a wholly different situation.

The experiment above outlined is typical of many carried on by Pavlov in investigating the phenomenon of conditioned learning. Other physiologists and psychologists, impressed with the possibilities of approaching the study of behavior from the angle of conditioning, both in animal and human subjects, have followed Pavlov's technique. Krasnorgorski and Mateer have investigated the salivary response in human beings; Bekhterev, Bernstein, Cason, Hilgard, Watson, and others have investigated conditioned human muscular reflexes of various sorts; and other experimenters have studied the conditioned response as attached to visceral and glandular functioning.

Conditioning in Animal Training. Anybody who has ever trained a dog to "beg," to "play dead," or to "lie down and go to sleep," when told to do so, made use of the conditioning technique, whether he was aware of the fact or not. Anybody who has trained a cat to jump through his arms used the same principle. In the training of circus animals the stage must always be set so that the animal will experience an associated stimulus at the same time that it is given an adequate stimulus, such as praise, punishment or food. By this method a lumbering elephant can be taught to kneel at the tap of a circus girl's whip, a seal to balance a ball, or a horse to dance. The significant thing is that the animal must *want* something; a well defined purpose must activate it if any appreciable effort is to be put forth by it.

SOME IMPORTANT PRINCIPLES OF HUMAN LEARNING

1. **Importance of a Definite Goal.** There is no question that much of our educational practice in the past has been content with assigning tasks to be done by learners who themselves had no clear idea of the meaning or end of the tasks. To them, "school" was synonymous with the blind following of directions and the pursuit either of vague or else of unperceived goals. Fortunately, the modern school is a different sort of institution, with its motivated tasks, its concise units of work, and its measuring instruments to determine the progress of the pupils toward their goals.

In any kind of learning, it is important that the pupil have a clear and tangible goal in view. Psychologists have measured the effects of knowing the objective as opposed to being in a state of ignorance regarding the objective, and invariably they find that those who have the goal clearly in mind learn better than do those who work in the dark. Goals and objectives vary, of course, with the nature of the general task. Some goals, such as searching for an explanation of why the automobile industry in the United States centered in Michigan, are achieved by inductive methods; others, such as the winning of a bachelor's degree or a nurse's diploma, may be somewhat remote and realizable only after a great number of intermediate and lesser goals have been won. The fact remains, however, that regardless of the immediacy or the delay in reaching our goals, we are willing to study and apply ourselves faithfully only when we are aware that we are working toward a definite and sure purpose. Aimlessness, indecision and idleness characterize those individuals who are without worthwhile objectives; for those who have in mind a pot of gold at the foot of some near or far rainbow, these characteristics are likely to resolve themselves into precision, determination and hard work.

2. **A Reassuring Knowledge of Progress.** Awareness of a goal is not enough, however; one must have a conscious assurance that he is making progress toward its achievement if he is to exert himself intellectually to the limit of his capacity. Experiments have indicated strikingly that, at the grade school, the high school and the collegiate level equally, frequent and regular check-up of the amount of progress being made toward the goal acts as a strong motive to promote continuing effort on the part of the learner. Suppose, for example, that the goal of a given elementary grade in spelling for the year is mastery of 200 new words. With this objective before him and with interesting standardized spelling tests to record his gain, it becomes a simple and challenging matter for the learner to keep a graphic record of his progress from week to week toward his goal. At the same time, he has a measure of his errors and learns where he must put forth additional drill effort in order to keep his curve rising normally and encouragingly.

Increasingly, the materials of elementary education are coming to be included within definite and tangible units of minimum essentials of knowledge, and their rate of mastery by the learner is coming to be objectified through practice tests, achievement tests and graphic recording by the pupil himself. He knows where he stands relative to where he stood yesterday and last week, or last month; he knows wherein he is lacking and wherein he is strong; and he knows the rate at which he is moving toward the grade goal in all subjects.

3. **Optimum Length and Distribution of Practice Periods.** Let us suppose that a student is given a typewriter for a birthday present and is eager to learn to write with it. Which of the following distributions of nine hours of practice (540 minutes) would be the most economical in establishing the rudiments of this new skill:

30 minutes a day, for 18 days
20 minutes three times in the course of each day for 9 days
45 minutes three times in the course of each day for 4 days
60 minutes three times in the course of each day for 3 days
90 minutes in the forenoon and 90 minutes in the afternoon for 3 days
270 minutes in the forenoon and 270 minutes in the afternoon for 1 day
540 minutes (9 hours) of continuous practice?

A number of experiments conducted with both human and animal learners seem to have demonstrated that shorter practice periods are more economical than longer periods, and that when distributed over several days they yield better returns than when they are concentrated into a single sitting.

Of the several alternatives proposed above for learning the elements of typewriting, it is probable that the best returns from the 540 minutes available would be achieved by practicing at the machine for thirty minutes a day for 18 days. The alternatives included probably grow increasingly less desirable as they stand in the list. A law of diminishing returns operates in many kinds of learning as the length of practice periods is increased much above twenty or thirty minutes, or as the interval between them is diminished or increased much from twenty-four hours. There is some evidence that an interval of twelve hours between practice periods is satisfactory in certain kinds of learning. Of course where only a little time is available, the length of each individual period may have to be short, but even so it is desirable to spread the periods over several days or several half-days.

In certain kinds of learning, as in the intellectual study of content subjects like history, psychology and economics, where there is not demanded a repetition of the same mental or motor skills (as is required, for example, in handwriting, arithmetic drill and typewriting), the principles enunciated in the above paragraph do not apply. With materials that are constantly changing and presenting new viewpoints and new angles of intellectual approach, the law of diminishing returns from study may not begin to operate until after several hours of continuous application.

4. Whole or Part Method? Naïvely, most persons who have a selection of poetry to memorize will proceed by the part method. That is to say, the individual learner will say over and over again the first two or three lines, or perhaps the first stanza, until he can repeat it without looking at the copy. Then he will proceed to the second stanza and do likewise, coming back when he can just say that stanza through to the first one and joining it to the second. He tends to follow this so-called *part method* throughout the poem.

There are several objections to the use of the part method of memorizing. In the first place, the subject overlearns the first few stanzas, since with the addition of each new stanza he goes back and repeats the preceding; as soon as he can just say through the last stanza, his practice of it stops, and when he subsequently gets up to recite his poem he goes swimmingly through the first lines, but hesitates and stumbles in the later ones. Second, *by going back from the end of one stanza to the beginning of it, or to a preceding one, he tends to associate backward instead of forward;* this will cause confusion later when he wishes to go straight through the selection.

Everybody has noted the difficulty which youthful "piece-speakers" have of proceeding consecutively through the maze of stanzas. Third, the mental attitude of the part-method learner is likely to be a casual one; he tends to regard his learning as a series of disconnected applications in which he learns one stanza now, and another one sometime later when he happens to feel like it.

Several experimenters have been able to show that the most economical method of learning a poem of moderate length may be to employ the *whole method;* that is, to read the entire poem through again and again, from beginning to end, without cutting it up into parts. In this way, the logical sequence of ideas is maintained, there are no backward associations, each portion has the same amount of drill as every other portion, and the mental attitude fostered is one of active and thoughtful reaction. One difficulty in inducing youthful learners to use the whole method rather than the part is the fact that they have always tended to use the latter, since they could note *some* progress, even though slight, from the first practice minute, whereas in using the former method a learner may spend fifteen minutes reading and rereading his poem without being able at the end of that time to recall even the first word. It might well be, however, that after one or two more practice minutes he would be rewarded by finding himself able to recite the entire poem without error. Like all other workers, learners like to see results and are impatient when required to put in a somewhat prolonged initial period in which no returns are apparent.

A few investigators have failed to note any preference for the whole over the part method. To some extent, this may be because their practice subjects had mind-sets against the former and in favor of the latter. The senior author has found with college students as subjects a strong predilection for the part method and has been able to demonstrate at least to his own satisfaction that those learners who did poorly when they used the whole method tended to attack their task with an attitude of defeatism, and so did not give it a fair trial. One experimenter demonstrated that the whole method was more economical for gifted than it is for the average run of children.

Of course, for some kinds of material, whether they are to be learned by rote or mastered logically, the part method has its place. In a particularly difficult assignment, for example, the student should first probably read the entire assignment for the author's general orientation and point of view, and then proceed to isolate those sections of the lesson that are particularly involved or abstruse for special analytical study by parts. Then, after he has ironed out the difficulties, a final rereading by the whole method, with the mind being definitely active and analytical, should leave him with a stable and tenacious memory of its content. Some psychologists have termed this method of learning the *whole-part* or the *part-whole* method; one investigator calls it the "progressive-part" method when rote material is sectioned into units of several stanzas and the learner proceeds to learn each unit, progressively, until he reaches the end of the selection.

5. **Logical Learning and Rote Learning.** In this section we have used incidentally the terms "rote learning" and "logical learning." A few additional words need to be said regarding them. Rote memorization means the actual *verbatim* learning of a passage of poetry or prose so that the learner can repeat it exactly as it stands in the book. Logical learning means the intellectual mastering of the ideas contained in a passage, without any attempt to retain the author's language. The former type of learning is legitimate in the memorization of selections of verse or of fine prose which are worth remembering, as, for example, *The Daffodils*, the *23rd Psalm*, and the *Declaration of Independence*. It has little place, however, in the conventional learning of the content subjects of the schoolroom. The student who mistakes *memorizing* for *studying* makes a serious blunder. The mastering of schoolroom assignments calls for the use of logical memory, *i.e.*, for the use of the mind analytically and thoughtfully in digging out the meaning of the materials being studied and in assimilating them without the burden of retaining the phraseology in which they are couched.

Logical learning calls for a disregard of the author's language, as such, and for an earnest and aggressive effort to grasp meanings and ideas, and then for the logical arrangement and assimilation of those ideas in the mind. Logical learning calls for a determined search after relationships, for the classification of facts, and for their unification and integration. It does not depend upon the ability nor the intent to reproduce exactly. Material learned *verbatim* remains in isolation in the mind and does not assimilate with anything else. Material learned *logically* gravitates, by the very force put forth in its acquisition, to relevant mental materials, and hence unification and ordered integration tend to become almost matter of course.

6. **Role of Mental Fatigue.** A certain small boy in the fourth grade arrived home after school "dead tired," as he expressed it when his mother bade him run an errand for her at the store two or three blocks away. Because of his condition of extreme fatigue (?), the lad voiced his opposition to doing any more work. There had been at school some sort of timed arithmetic drill in the morning and a "mean old examination" in the afternoon. This was the general family

situation at 4 P.M. At 4:20, after he had returned from his errand at the store—to which he had been at length reconciled by the reward of a nickel "to buy what he wanted"—and while he was sitting idly playing with his dog's ears, his attention was drawn to a peculiar yodel issuing from somewhere down the street. Straightway both boy and dog dashed off in the direction of the yodeling. At 6:20, two good hours later, the boy's father had literally to go across to the vacant lot and impound his son's baseball in order to get him home to supper. Tired? Oh, no; he was not tired: two hours of running and shouting and yelling had left him warm, happy, and *rested,* so it appeared.

Of course the boy was not "dead tired" at all when he arrived home from school; instead, he was suffering from boredom. The arithmetic drill, the geography examination and other tasks that had filled his school day had bored him; they had not fatigued him. His subsequent behavior on the vacant lot proved that eloquently enough. He was tired of being bored, tired of sitting still, tired of not having any opportunity to tire himself out muscularly. Paradoxical as this seems, it is true. Most of the so-called "fatigue" about which people commiserate with one another is not genuine fatigue. It is rather *pseudo-fatigue, which is principally a state of mind resulting from uninteresting tasks, from confinement, from repetition of the same movements, from poor motivation or no motivation at all.* Change the environment, vary the nature of the task, inject a powerful motive, and your erstwhile "tired-to-death" person will carry on for hours and feel rested and refreshed afterward.

When due allowance has been made for the fact that there is considerable expenditure of muscular effort in the schoolroom and in the performance of any sort of mental work—*e.g.,* the taxing strain upon the ciliary and the recti muscles of the eyes, upon the muscles of the back and shoulders in holding the body erect and quiet, upon the muscles of the arms and hands in writing or holding a book—the fact remains that most mental workers do not experience a resulting accumulation of fatigue toxins from these sources sufficient to account for the "tiredness" which they feel after a small amount of application. The explanation of what passes for mental "dead-tiredness" is to be found rather in jaded attitudes and lack of interest in the routine tasks. Only in rare cases of individuals who actually exhaust themselves mentally by prolonged and usually *perennially* prolonged application, without compensating and adequate periods of proper rest and sleep, does true mental fatigue come about. Even so-called "nervous breakdowns" may be more often due to faulty mental attitudes, worry, apprehensiveness, and the like, than they are to overwork.

7. **Mnemonic Devices to Be Used Sparingly.** Everybody makes some use of artificial aids to memory. If we are asked how many days there are in the month of May, we very likely find flashing through our minds the old doggerel: "Thirty days hath September . . . ," and by means of its aid we report with confidence that there are thirty-one days in May. Or we may have learned the notation on the musical staff by combining the spaces into the word f-a-c-e, and the line notes into the mnemonic: "Every good boy does finely." So with the spectral colors, the first letters of which, taken in order from the red end, form the name *Roy G. Biv*, red, orange, yellow, green, blue, indigo, violet; so too with the perplexities of the correct spelling of words containing the diphthongs *ei* and *ie:*

> "I before e, except after c
> or when sounded as a,
> as in neighbor or weigh."

In our early learning of the rudiments of knowledge in various fields, the occasional employment of simple mnemonic devices is helpful. Those mentioned above have been boons to millions of pupils who have found it difficult to remember certain serial or connected relationships by the tenacity of memory. Learning the spectral colors, for example, by means of the simple Roy G. Biv mnemonic, requires but five or ten seconds, and once thus learned they are never forgotten; learning them by repetition and drill requires a great deal of time and does not guarantee the likelihood of their being retained and recallable at will. Probably all of us find ourselves constructing other mnemonics occasionally that will aid our retention of some serial information that we wish to remember in exact order.

Mnemonics, however, may be overdone. If one were to attempt to construct mnemonics for everything he had to learn, he would be hopelessly confused in his own devices. Most things that are to be learned can best be learned logically and analytically in their own setting, without lifting them out of it and tying them up with something wholly extraneous or irrelevant. It is far more sensible and economical to associate together things that logically belong together than it is to introduce artificial associates to aid in reinstating them. Too many mnemonics clutter up the memory and become more of a nuisance than a help. Even simple "crutches," such as putting down in the next column to the left, as one adds, the number to be "carried"; counting on the fingers; tracing in grooves to learn the formation of letters in writing, and the like, may prove uneconomical in the end, for the victim must sooner or later discard them if he is to progress confidently and unhampered. A mental crutch, like a wooden one, may give early support, but one can never go fast or far so long as he leans upon it.

8. **Memory Cannot Be "Trained," but One's Learning Is Improvable.** Magazine advertisements often purport to interest people in improving their memory. There may be a picture of two men meeting in a hotel corridor, one of them extending his hand familiarly to the other while the latter looks mystified and dubious. The caption runs something like this:

> 1st man: "How do you do, Mr. Granville Grayson. I am delighted to see you again."
> 2nd man: "Er— how do you do? —er— why, yes, that is my name—er—but you've got me. I can't seem to place you at all."
> 1st man: "Why, my dear Mr. Grayson, don't you recall that in the Pennvania Station seven years ago last Friday we chanced to be waiting for trains, and had some conversation as we stood at the information window?"
> 2nd man: "Er— er—"

No doubt the advertisement carries in bold-face type some such intriguing guarantee as this: "You, too, can have as tenacious a memory as this man. Send us no money; just drop a card and we shall be glad, . . ." The gullible are often taken in by this type of misrepresentation.

Most memory training systems that one sees advertised are likely to be valueless. Ability to learn any kind of material comes from practicing that kind of material, and not from practicing the intermediate and often grotesque mnemonic systems that are advertised by their clever promoters. The student is warned to avoid such memory systems, and is urged rather to strengthen her own learning technique. Materials that have not been actively and carefully attended to when they were presented cannot be readily recalled. In order to cultivate a keen memory, the student should train herself to pay better attention to the things she wishes to retain. She should select judiciously, organize carefully, and be zealous to overlearn. She should form the habit of getting clear and vivid impressions, whether it be of the names of strangers to whom she is introduced, or of the significance of some of the important principles of learning which we are discussing here: *good retention depends always upon good learning.*

9. **Use of Imagery and Language Symbols.** In an earlier chapter (cf. Chapter 7) we suggested that all the information one can possibly acquire must come through one or another of the sensory gateways

to the mind. Experiences that are thus received appear to remain stored up in the mind as *images:* e.g., we may recall in our "mind's eye" in *visual imagery* the face of a friend, or of a neighborhood scene; in *auditory imagery,* we may hear still in our "mind's ear" the shriek of a locomotive whistle, or the buzzing of bees in flowers; in *olfactory imagery,* we may reinstate in our "mind's nose" the odor of sweet peas, of boiling coffee, or the fumes of anesthetics; on our "mind's tongue," we may be able to call up a vivid *gustatory image* of the taste of chocolate, or of vinegar. And so on for each of the other avenues of sensory experience.

Children possess vivid images; grown-up individuals, while most of them still have rather strong images, are obliged to deal with a great amount of thought material which does not lend itself to concrete imagery in any of the sense modalities; consequently, most people pay relatively little attention to images of this sort, but rely greatly upon *subvocal images,* or *language symbols.* That is to say, most of us as we carry on our thought life find ourselves constantly engaging in a sort of "talking to ourselves." We tend to arouse our vocal muscles to a kind of inner speech, and while our lips do not actually move there is, when we stop to think of it, an incipient *subvocal* process running on as we study a lesson or reason out a course of action or cogitate upon this, that, or the other intellectual theme. Occasionally, it is true, most of us find visual or auditory or other concrete images coming into our minds, even as we cogitate. Such arousals of concrete images seem to lend richness and reality to much of our ideational experience.

The psychology textbooks of some years ago carried considerable discussion as to whether material to be learned was best learned through the eyes or through the ears. People were supposed to be either largely eye-minded or largely ear-minded. Research has seemed to indicate that, other things being equal, we learn about as well through one major sense as we do through another. Most people, in other words, are neither eye-minded nor ear-minded; they belong rather to what we may call a "mixed type," and are able both to learn and to recall through all the principal sensory avenues, one tending to supplement another.

This being the case, it is obvious that when one is engaged upon the study or the mastery of an assignment, she ought to see, to hear, to write and to speak. Merely seeing words is not enough; merely hearing lectures is not enough; the mechanical taking of notes is not enough; "talking lessons" are not enough. Good learning includes for most students a good deal of reading, a good deal of listening, a good deal of writing, a good deal of recitation, in order that eyes and ears and muscles may all be gotten into the game. Since, however, much of the material of learning is in language symbols, printed or oral, memory and recall of much of the ideational content of what one has learned is in large measure, as we have seen, in terms of subvocal speech. As one proceeds further and higher along the educational pathway, he finds concrete images playing less and less part and verbal or symbolic imagery becoming increasingly predominant in his learning and in his thought life generally.

Trial and Error and the Nurse. There is much that the nurse can learn only through trial and error procedure, even though she has the guidance of expert example or instruction always about her. In the development of sensorimotor skills in which dexterity and nimbleness or deftness of touch are the end to be acquired, the student nurse must be expected to pass through a somewhat bungling stage in which she is learning slowly to make the right coordinations and to eliminate the clumsy or inadept ones. Thus, in such situations as applying and adjusting bandages, making a bed, handling a patient, manipulating instruments, pouring liquids, bathing, and massaging, she will require practice before the random and irrelevant movements of her muscles give place to precision, deftness and smooth performance. The gaucheries and fumbling which characterize the motor responses of the untrained person are in striking contrast with the deft and nimble manipulative skill of those who, like nurses, have learned to perform smoothly and efficiently.

Ideational trial and error will also find place in the learning process of the student nurse. Whenever she is confronted with a new situation, particularly an emergency, she may find herself hesitating and deliberating between several procedures which she might follow.

What to do, for example, when a supposedly convalescing patient's respiration fails or his pulse grows feeble? What to do when a hemorrhage occurs? Or when a patient's groans disturb or frighten some other seriously ill person in the ward? Or when there is a sudden turn in the condition of a child, the doctor being not immediately available? In the very nature of the profession of nursing, there are certain to arise emergency situations in which the very young novice will be in doubt regarding the proper procedure or technique to be followed. At such times she may conceivably do the least desired thing; or she may even lose her head and do nothing constructive. At best, she will hastily think of several alternative solutions and will select as promptly as possible the one that appears most rational or germane. The sequel may show that her selection was wrong; in any event, she is learning by trial and error, and in the course of time her judgment will become much more sound and reliable. If it is a decision of some importance, she should check her response immediately with the head nurse or supervisor, whose broader experience will lessen the likelihood of error.

The Nurse as Learner. In the nursing profession, as in most others, the school relies upon three fundamental kinds of learning activities: mastery of theory, growth of appreciation and insight, and the development of skill. The first takes place in the routine classroom study and discussion of subject matter; the second results from courses in the professionalized subjects of psychology, sociology and mental hygiene; the third, the practice side of nursing education, is afforded in the actual performance, under careful observation and direction by experts, of the kind of duties which the mature nurse will be called upon to perform. The professional worker in any field needs both the theory and the practice, and the school of nursing is organized to afford both to the young novice. The nurse must know not only the various kinds of micro-organisms that are responsible for disease: she must know also how to handle patients whose bodies have been invaded by them; she must know not only the principles of dietetics: she must know how to serve food to the sick; she must know not only the principles of anatomy: she must know how to treat a patient with a fractured skull; she must know not only the proper body temperature: she must know how to use and care for the clinical thermometer; she must know not only the psychology of sick people: she must know how to adapt herself and her personality to her patients.

Epitomizing the viewpoint of the preceding paragraph, we may say that the nurse must have, on the one hand, *information*, and on the other, *skill*. The information which she must acquire is in part to be achieved through the use of books, through lectures and discussions. Getting promptly to work on her assignment, maintaining a favorable and interested mental attitude, looking always for the essential thought in all materials presented for study, making logical outlines and abstracts, putting forth constant effort to connect new material with old, and maintaining an active, analytic mental process —these are the *sine qua non* of all study, whether of the theory and art of nursing, or of engineering, medicine, or any other professionalized subject matter. A clear envisagement of goals to be achieved, an awareness of progress being made toward them, proper distribution of practice periods, employment of the whole method whenever feasible, learning for logical meanings rather than for words, realizing that mental fatigue is relatively nonexistent and therefore not something to be apprehensive about, making occasional but sparing use of artificial memory aids, carrying on persistent self-training in paying attention, using as many as possible of the sensory avenues of learning, and conducting continuous search for general principles that will carry over from one setting to another—these are equally important procedures to be observed by all students in all learning situations. Those who achieve most in ideational learning follow these principles consistently.

The skills which the nurse must master arise out of repeated drill in performing with the muscles. Such practice duties as bathing and massaging, bandaging; cleansing wounds, making beds, moving patients, handling dishes, clothing and instruments, depend almost exclusively upon repeated, day-by-day practice. Proficiency and good form in the performance of these acts are to be achieved by careful and attentive observation of demonstrated techniques, by clear understanding of whatever verbal instruction may be given by superiors, and then—principally—by months of actual drill and practice. Neuromuscular skills such as these depend, once the general informational pattern has been grasped, upon repeated performance. Ultimately, like all other habits, those centering about the physical care of the sick come to be "second nature" in those who serve faithful and long apprenticeship.

THOUGHT PROBLEMS FOR THE STUDENT

1. Suggest several recent learning situations in which you have made use of trial and error techniques. How do you recognize them as such?
2. What human learning situations might be cited as comparable in general setup with the problem box and maze-learning situations used in experimenting upon the learning process in animals?
3. Mention mnemonic devices other than those in the text that you have personally found helpful. Have you ever constructed a mnemonic of your own? If so, explain it. In what way or ways have you found devices of this nature helpful?
4. If it is impossible to train the memory, how can one who forgets easily what he learns ever hope to improve his condition?
5. Explain in your own words the meaning of "inner speech." To what extent do you find yourself using this kind of voco-motor imagery as you study or think?
6. Many scientific terms have been added to your vocabulary since you entered this school. What has been your method of mastering this extensive terminology? What suggestions have you received from this chapter which should prove helpful to you in developing an extensive and accurate acquaintance with medical terms?
7. Discuss the goals which you had set for yourself and achieved by the end of your preclinical period in the school of nursing.
8. Consider the following principle of nursing and match the statements with courses (other than Materia Medica) in which related learnings emerged.

LEARNING: SOME COMPARISONS AND PRINCIPLES

Such facts thought through in their proper relationships make for an adequate concept on the use of medicines in the care of the sick.

Principle: Effective administration of medicines is dependent upon mastering related knowledge. (Examples *a* and *b*.)

(*a*) Specific drugs are used in some diseases caused by micro-organisms .... Bacteriology
(*b*) Some drugs such as acids or alkali preparations produce definite changes in the blood................................ Chemistry
(*c*) Tonics are administered before meals.................................
(*d*) Drugs are used as antiseptics.......................................
(*e*) Drugs may produce local or general effects........................
(*f*) The discovery of certain drugs as effective medicines was accidental..
(*g*) Vaccines are used as preventive measures for typhoid fever.........
(*h*) The use of a skin disinfectant is essential for preoperative preparation..
(*i*) Antitoxins are used as curative agents..............................
(*j*) Drugs may produce stimulating or depressing effects on one or more systems of the body..
(*k*) Dosages vary according to age, size, and condition of the individual..
(*l*) Medications are administered only on a doctor's prescription........
(*m*) Careful record is kept of all medicine administered, of the amount, time, method and the effect produced..........................
(*n*) Doses prescribed must be measured accurately with equipment provided..
(*o*) Solutions of drugs used in treatment of disease vary in strength.......

9. Illustrate relationship of knowledge which you receive in different courses to make one unified whole, such as:

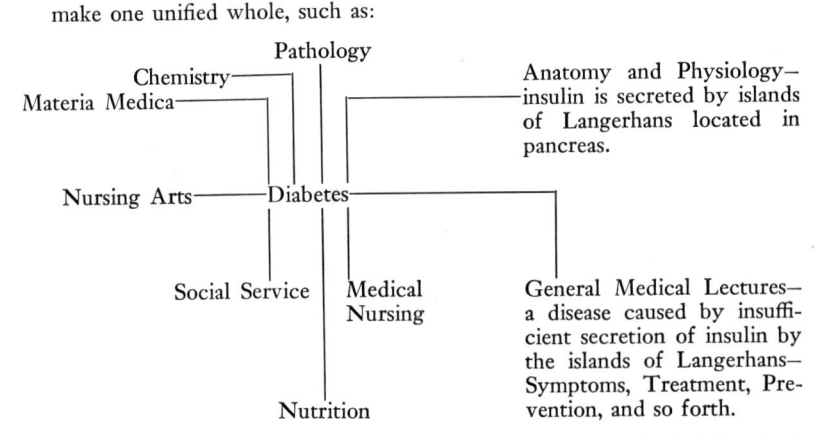

```
                    Pathology
        Chemistry──┐       ┌────────  Anatomy and Physiology—
Materia Medica─────┤       │          insulin is secreted by islands
                   │       │          of Langerhans located in
                   │       │          pancreas.
Nursing Arts───── Diabetes ────────────┐
                   │       │
                   │       │
        Social Service   Medical      General Medical Lectures—
                         Nursing      a disease caused by insuffi-
                                      cient secretion of insulin by
                                      the islands of Langerhans—
                                      Symptoms, Treatment, Pre-
                    Nutrition         vention, and so forth.
```

10. Does Exercise 6 carried through thoughtfully characterize logical learning? May rote learning to some degree be combined with logical learning? Discuss some rote learnings which you, because of long acceptance, still find difficult to reject, such as "All men are born free and equal."

11. After you learned how to make an unoccupied bed in this school, how was your behavior modified from previous times when you made beds at home? After

you had learned the names of the bones of the body, was your conduct or attitude in any way changed? On consideration of this, discuss what is really meant by "learning."
12. Compare your mental attitude in approaching a nursing procedure which you have done repeatedly with your attitude when you are asked to do a procedure for the first time.

SUGGESTED READINGS

1. Crow, L. D., Crow, A., and Skinner, C. E.: *Psychology in Nursing Practice.* New York, The Macmillan Co., 1954.
    Cf. especially the section on "The Learning Process."
2. Cruze, W. W.: *Psychology in Nursing.* New York, Blakiston Division, McGraw-Hill Book Co., 1955.
    Chapter 2, "The Psychology of Efficiency," will be found helpful.
3. Munn, N. L.: *The Evolution and Growth of Human Behavior.* Boston, Houghton Mifflin Co., 1955.
    Considerable material relevant to the contents of the present chapter will be found in Munn. Chapters 11 and 12, dealing with the development of symbolic processes and language, should be read.
4. Ruch, F. L.: *Psychology and Life.* 4th ed. Chicago, Scott, Foresman and Co., 1953.
    Pages 262–268 present an excellent discussion of conditioning. Cf. also, in the following pages of the same chapter (Chapter 11), the author's discussion of verbal learning, problem solving, trial and error, and insight.

Chapter 10

Beware when the great God lets loose a thinker on this planet!

RALPH WALDO EMERSON

THE INDIVIDUAL LEARNER

THE PROGRESSION OF LEARNING

Learning Represents Progression. We have referred repeatedly in the immediately preceding chapters to the learning *process*. Learning is not something which springs suddenly full-grown and complete into being: learning rather represents a progression, a growth over a period of time, the cumulative effects of many repetitions or of much experience. It does not matter whether one is learning to operate a typewriter, to handle a new language, or to use his mind efficiently in studying: in whatever learning task he engages, he will require time and the opportunity to practice.

Suppose one were to compare his present skill and facility in penmanship with his skill and facility when he was in the third grade in school; or his speed and accuracy in adding and subtracting, then and now; or the size of his vocabulary; or his conception of honesty, of democracy, of the expanding universe. He would discover that, in these and in other learning situations whose changing status he was to compare over a period of ten years, he has not been standing still, but rather he has been *progressing*. The standards and norms of achievement are progressively higher for each grade and for every subject included in the curriculum.

The Learning Curve

In experiments conducted in the laboratory under controlled conditions it has been interesting to keep exact records of the progress made by various subjects—human and animal—in learning a new skill or a new informational content. These records are usually embodied in what psychologists call the *learning curve*. By keeping constant the length of the daily practice period and noting the increasing amount of equivalent material that can be learned within the given time limit, or by keeping constant the amount of material and noting the diminishing time required for mastering it, one is enabled to construct curves to indicate graphically the amount of progress being made by the learner. The modern up-to-date school encourages the constructing of curves and graphs for purposes of motivating the pupil. In the day by day recording of his progress in learning arithmetic fundamentals, penmanship, spelling and historical information, for example, the young learner finds a strong incentive to greater effort in his learning, since he has before him constantly a graphic and evolving picture of the progress he is making.

Let us consider for a moment the following learning curves of two college students in a psychology class. A class of freshmen was taught by the instructor a new way of writing digits. Instead of the conventional 1, 2, 3, 4, the students were taught to write the digits in the form of the symbols shown in Figure 20.

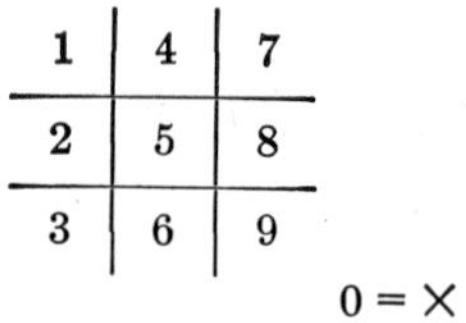

1	4	7
2	5	8
3	6	9

0 = ×

Fig. 20. Materials for a digit-symbol substitution experiment.

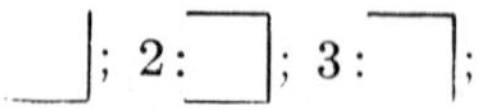

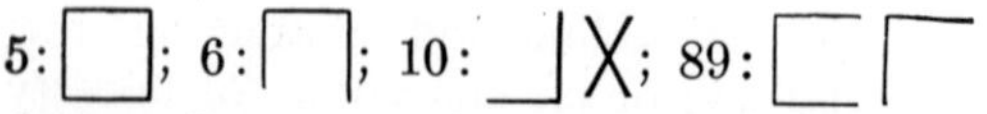

In this scheme of enumerating, 1 becomes ⌋; 2: ⌉; 3: ⌐; 5: ☐; 6: ⌈; 10: ⌋×; 89: ⌊⌐ The diagram as shown above was placed upon the blackboard and the students were permitted to go through it once with the instructor, after which it was erased and practice was begun. Each practice period was sixty seconds, and the experiment was continued twice daily for sixteen consecutive days on which the class met. The students were requested to do no practicing outside and to try to keep the entire experiment out of their minds except during the actual drill. Time was kept accurately with a stop-watch. At the beginning of each practice period, the instructor said: "Ready! Go!" At the end of sixty seconds, he called: "Stop! Fold over the paper! Ready again! Go!" Each time the subjects were to begin with the digit-symbol for 1 and go as far as possible in the sixty seconds allotted. They were not to look back and copy any symbols, but were instructed to think out each one as they proceeded. The learning curves represent the learning process of two students. They are fairly representative of such practice curves:

In this experiment L. started out with 22 symbols in the first practice period and achieved 81 symbols in the 32nd; W. started off with 18 and achieved 52 in the 32nd. When the learning curve of each subject has been constructed (Figs. 21 and 22), it shows

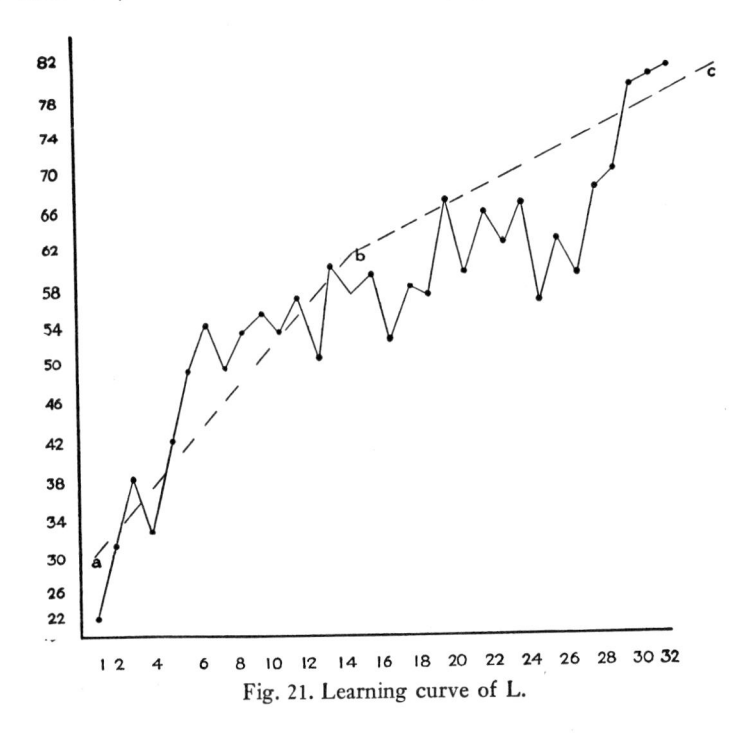

Fig. 21. Learning curve of L.

graphically and strikingly the picture of the progress made in learning the new skill. Some of the typical features of most learning curves are discussed in the following paragraphs.

Characteristics of Rising Learning Curves. The curves represented in Figures 21 and 22 are typical of most learning curves in which the acquisition of skill and dexterity is the principal goal. They would depict alike the process of learning to operate a typewriter, to send or receive telegraphic code, or to take shorthand.

1. *Initial Rapid Rise.* Curves of sensorimotor learning show typically a rapid initial rise, followed after a relatively small number of trials by a slower rise. In part this rapid initial rise is due to the novelty and to the strong motivation with which the learner starts

off on the acquisition of a new skill; in part also it is due to the relatively simple moves which can be quickly mastered at the outset. As the practice continues the novelty wears off and the moves become more complex, thus retarding progress. In the first 7 trials, for example, L. gained 32 symbols (from 22 to 54); in the remaining 25 trials, she gained only 27 additional. W. gained 19 in the first 3 trials (from 18 to 37), and only 15 additional in the remaining 29 trials. The lines *ab* and *bc* have been drawn in to indicate the general rise of the curve in each figure.

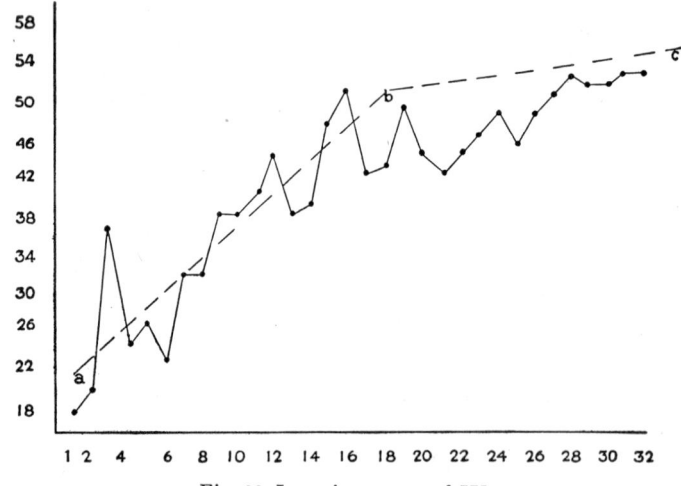

Fig. 22. Learning curve of W.

2. *Day-by-Day Variations.* Most human learning shows considerable fluctuation up and down over a period of time. *Learning is not an even, continuous progression;* it is rather a series of daily rises and falls, although the general direction is upward. These short-time variations are to be accounted for in terms of fluctuations of interest, attention, ambition; or in terms of varying physical condition, of health, wide-awakeness, readiness and cooperativeness. The student probably has noted in her own experience how much more apt and competent she is in studying or in learning on some occasions than she is on others. Sometimes the existence of a touch of indigestion, a preoccupation over some personal problem, the temporary dominance of an attitude of detachment, or even uncomfortable atmospheric conditions, will make the difference between disappointing performance and satisfying performance.

3. *The Plateau of Learning.* If the 32 practice periods had been

extended to 500 periods, another striking phenomenon of the learning curve would have appeared in the form of a *plateau.* That is to say, a line projected from *c* in the general direction of the progression of learning would have been substantially parallel to the base line of the graph, indicating that little or no improvement was taking place. The learner of any sensorimotor skill comes sooner or later to such a level place in his curve, to which the term *plateau* is applied. There are many reasons for the emergence of a plateau in the learning curve. Motivation has failed in the monotonous and long stretches of practice; fatigue and boredom have set in; effort which was at first keen has become weak and ambitionless; there has come a satisfaction with present achievement; or certain uneconomical habits have persisted that must be broken up, and there is either a failure to recognize them or a lack of desire to substitute more economical ones for them. These reasons, singly or together, may account for the emergence and the continuance of the plateau in learning. In some long-continued acts of skill we may, if there is motivation enough, rise from one plateau level to another, and perhaps to yet another, until at length we reach our *physiological limit,* a point of performance beyond which it is impossible for us to increase the rate of mental or muscular reaction.

Few people, however, ever reach their physiological limit in anything. We are inclined to be content to stay on a plateau far below our possible limits of achievement. We write well enough; we spell well enough; we typewrite well enough; we play tennis well enough; or we swim well enough. Only with persistent effort and with a strong and continuing ambition to excel are most people likely to exert themselves enough to rise above the lower plateaus. All of us perform at a much lower level of efficiency in most skills than we would be able to if we were willing to pay the price in terms of effort. Those who break records, or become "stars" or "champions" in any field do so because they will not rest content with mediocrity. The price of dexterity and efficiency in any art or skill is high, though hardly prohibitive, for everybody.

Various Types of Learning Curves. Curves of the sort we have been discussing continue to rise more and more slowly as practice continues beyond the initial period of rapid gain; each day's practice yields, in general, less in accomplishment than the previous day's. The law of diminishing returns is thus seen to operate, and the resulting curve is said to be *negatively accelerated.* Curves of negative acceleration are also *rising curves:* they start from a point at or near the base line and proceed irregularly upward to a point high above the base line. The amount of rise indicates graphically the amount of learning.

Other rising curves may show *positive acceleration*, in which the progression upward is accelerated with continued practice. The initial rise is ordinarily slow on such curves, increasing with each subsequent practice period. Such curves are concave in appearance, as Figure 23 illustrates. This type of curve is representative of the progress made by a learner in a situation in which the grasping of meanings and logical relationships or rules is of prime importance to progress. During the first year or two of foreign language study, for

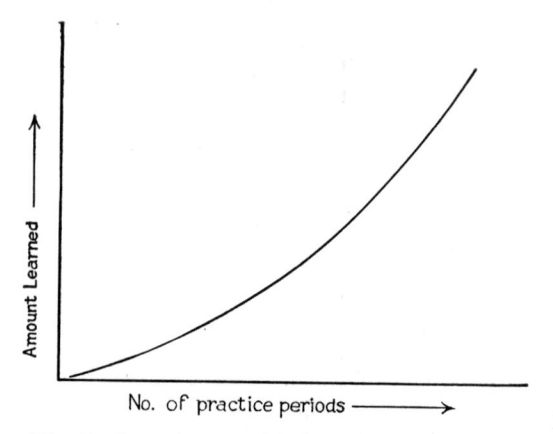

Fig. 23. A concave, positively accelerated curve.

example, the basal mastery of common rules, derivations and prefixes makes one progressively more competent to learn new words as the weeks pass.

Probably the ultimate curve of learning for ideational, informational or logical material, however, tends to be an *S-shaped curve*, as in Figure 24. The S-shaped curve shows somewhat slow initial progress, followed in the intermediate stages of practice by rapid progress, with a diminution setting in toward the end of practice.

Progression in learning may also be shown in *falling curves*, as Figure 25 indicates. If the amount of material is held constant, the curve will show the decrease in amount of time required in successive trials to perform the task. Figure 25 records the results of the first 10 trials of a card-sorting experiment in which the subject's task was to sort a pack of 500 cards into their proper compartments. The subject's time for the first sorting was fifty minutes; for the 10th sorting she required only twenty-five minutes.

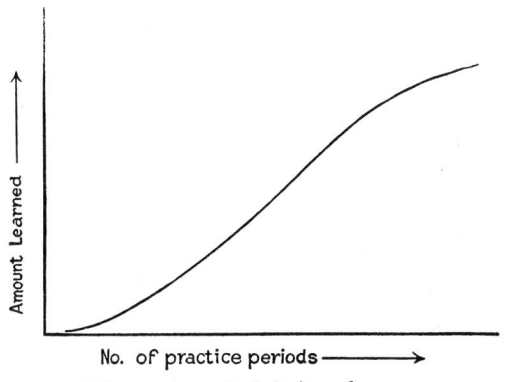

Fig. 24. A typical S-shaped curve.

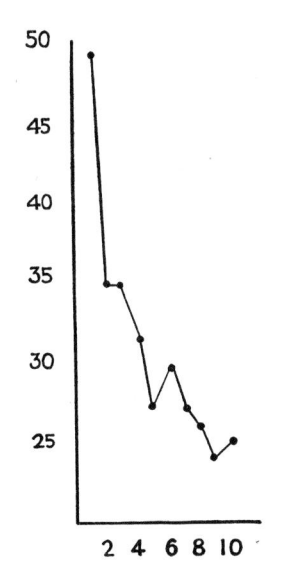

Fig. 25. A falling curve of learning.

Progression of Learning in the Nurse. Most of the learning of the student nurse may be expected to be positively accelerated. Her study of the theory and practice of nursing, of dietetics, of hygiene, of psychology and of mental hygiene will provide her with a fund of general principles that will enable her to make progress in comprehending the art and philosophy of nursing and the nature and behavior of human beings. She need but pause at almost any moment after she has been in the school of nursing for a few weeks and reflect upon the broadening horizons which have already opened out before her to realize that she is learning rapidly. Certainly during the first year of the course her curve of learning in the professional subjects will be positive in its acceleration.

During subsequent nursing education, the rate of rise in the learning curve of the student nurse will be somewhat reduced, and an S-shaped curve will ensue as she endeavors to consolidate and professionalize her fund of information and knowledge and make it flexible and workable in everyday performance. It would be impossible for her to continue to amass information at the rate at which the process proceeded during the earlier months of learning; efficiency and insight in nursing, as in all other professional occupations, depend in the first instance upon the original learning of a vast deal of relevant material, and, in the second instance, upon the actual and practical utilization of this knowledge. In consequence, the ultimate learning curve for professional workers tends to rise less rapidly after the earlier stages of informational absorption have passed. In manipulative skills, of course, such as typing notes, cleaning and tidying, bandaging, massaging and handling patients, the nurse's learning curve will, as in all other sensorimotor skills, tend to be negatively accelerated.

THE PLACE OF INTELLIGENCE IN LEARNING

Intellectual Differences among Learners. If we were to test the intelligence of a million people taken at random from the population, we would find that they would represent a continuous gradation from the idiot to the genius. It would be just as incorrect to say that all the people in the world are divided into geniuses and idiots as to say that they are divided into the bright and dull. There are all degrees of brightness and all degrees of dullness.

Psychologists have found that intelligence distributes itself among the people in the world in accordance with the mathematician's well known *curve of normal distribution*. That is to say, the greatest number of people fall within the "average" classification. Half the remainder group themselves in decreasing numbers from the average to the idiot, and the other half group themselves similarly in decreasing numbers from the average to the genius. Roughly, perhaps 55 per cent of people are "average"; 22½ per cent are "superior"; 22½ per cent are "inferior." Among the 55 per cent average, however, there are some who are "high average"; some who are "low average"; some who are "very high average"; and some who are "very low average." Similarly, among the 22½ per cent superior, some are "geniuses"; some are "very superior"; some "slightly superior"; some "barely above average"; and among the 22½ per cent inferior, some are "slightly inferior"; some are "very inferior"; some are "imbeciles"; some are "idiots."

Figure 26 represents the curve of normal distribution. The height of the curve above the base line at any point represents the number of people of that specific degree of intelligence as compared with the numbers of people of all other degrees of intelligence. Not only is intelligence distributed among the population according to the normal frequency surface (another term for the curve of normal distribution), but other traits—*e.g.*, height and weight—exist in the same ratios. Of course, it is necessary to study *unselected groups* if

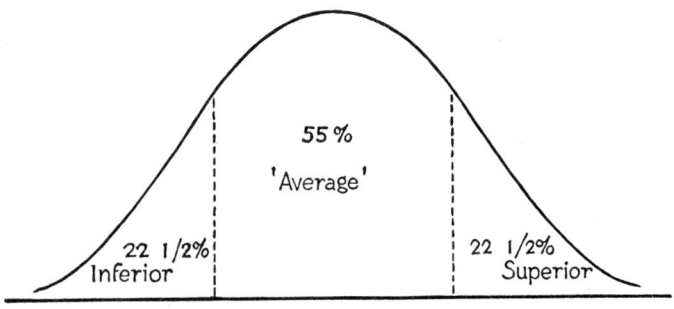

Fig. 26. The curve of normal distribution.

we are to find them classifying themselves in accordance with this curve. If we were to measure the intelligence of a million idiots or a million geniuses (if we could find them), or the weight of a million fat men or of a million lean men, our curves would be definitely *skewed* to the right or to the left. *Selected groups* of course yield a different sort of picture from that furnished by unselected groups.

The Mechanism of Heredity. All the above is tantamount to saying that some children are "born short" intellectually and that others are "born long." While the majority of children (some 55 per cent, as we have seen) are of substantially average intellectual endowment, almost a fourth of all children are inferior intellectually, while almost another fourth are definitely superior. Since one's intellectual endowment is not likely to be greatly influenced by his educational or social experiences as he grows up, it is a reasonably safe assumption that the adult population of any country is comprised of approximately these 1:2:1 ratios. Almost a fourth of the people in the world are inferior; more than half of them are average; something less than one fourth of them are superior. This would mean also that the capacity to learn is mediocre in half the population, poor in a quarter of it, and extremely good in the remainder. Thus, while we may stand upon the principles of good learning that we have been discussing in recent chapters in this book, we must recognize the fact that there are many people who can never be expected to learn satisfactorily for the simple reason that they are poorly endowed. Most of them drop by the educational wayside as they proceed through the lower schools; those who are high average or superior commonly go on to the higher schools and the professions.

The significance of this situation educationally may be seen in the circumstance that among our 31 million school children, 700,000 are mentally retarded to a degree that makes it impossible for them to profit from undifferentiated class work. While most of them must attend the regular schools, fortunately many communities now provide special or opportunity classes for backward pupils. It is estimated that this wise provision affords special education for approximately 15 per cent of the entire group of the retarded, thus leaving 85 per cent of them, however, or nearly 600,000, still enrolled in the conventional grades. Twenty-five children in every 1000 (2.5 per cent) will never reach a mental age greater than 12 years, even as adults, and while half of them are mentally retarded because of damage or accident to the brain and nervous system during the fetal period, at birth, or subsequently, the other half are definitely "born short" from the standpoint of heredity.

What is this strangely potent force that we call *heredity?* It would be beside the point of this book to attempt an answer to this question. The whole matter of heredity is a highly complex one, and we know little with certainty regarding the mechanism that controls it. It is sufficient for our purposes here to suggest that according to the accepted theories of genetics each parent contributes to the new offspring the determining elements of heredity, known as the *genes*. The moment fertilization of the ovum begins, these genes—many thousands in number—unite in the new individual to form all manner of new combinations of traits as well as to perpetuate certain of the old family traits. Some of the genes become determiners of eye color; some become determiners of stature; some, of hair texture; and some, of intelligence. Every trait which the new individual is ultimately to possess is believed to issue from some combination of the parental *genes*. Since these genes are so innumerable, since they come from two different lines of descent, and since they may combine and recombine in the new individual in diverse ways, geneticists find that, except for identical twins who are really the result of the split of a single fertilized ovum with therefore identical genetic background, no two people in the world, and no two children in the same family, are ever exactly alike.

Family Heredity. How often do we hear it remarked, "He's a chip off the old block," or, "Like father, like son." In the main, these homely old expressions reflect a fundamental truth. Scientific study of the nature of heredity demonstrates that children are likely to resemble their parents more than they do anybody else. Sir Francis Galton believed that a child inherits one half his traits from his parents, one quarter from his grandparents, one eight from his great-grandparents, and so forth. Modern research tends to throw some doubt upon the mathematical exactitude of such hereditary doctrine, but accepts the fact that the farther back into the family forebears one goes, the less important do the hereditary contributions appear to be. Indeed, strange as it might seem, statistical studies of family heredity have indicated that the children of two parents resemble one another somewhat more closely than they do the parents themselves. If, for example, we let 100 represent perfect similarity, then we may express the degree of resemblance of parent and child as 40, and the average degree of resemblance of the children to one another as 50. But even so, there remains a wide margin of non-resemblance between child and child, as well as between child and parent. About all one can safely conclude is that the children of a given family tend to cluster about the parental average, some of them being fairly close to it, others being strikingly different from it. There is no way of predicting how the genes will group themselves in any individual offspring. Hence we often note both striking similarities and equally striking differences among children of the same parents. We may be reasonably sure that children whose line of ancestry has for generations been superior will tend to be superior, while those of a long line of inferior forebears will tend to be inferior. Goddard's study of the Kallikak family, Dugdale's study of the Jukes family, and Winship's study of the Edwards family testify to the truth of this general principle.

Racial Heredity. Among our schoolmates there may have been American, English, French, German, Italian, Lithuanian, Swedish and Chinese children, or children from other racial or national extractions. Who of them were superior by virtue of their racial origin or nationalistic pattern? The results of scientific testing of various racial and geographical groups are not any more flattering to any one of them than to any other. When due allowance has been made for differences in language facility and in cultural or educational opportunities, the fact emerges that there are no striking national or racial superiorities or inferiorities. Mankind wherever it exists in the world on comparable levels of culture is endowed with substantially parallel intelligence.

Sex and Intelligence. Who are intellectually superior: males or females? Does the fact that most of the great people of history have been males indicate that men are superior intellectually to women? Does the modern rise of women in Western nations suggest that they are becoming superior to the males and will shortly supersede them in conducting the affairs of the world? While studies have indicated that girls are superior in English and language and that boys are superior in science and mathematics, carefully controlled experiments fail to show any significant differences in learning capacity between young men and young women students. Whatever differences in point of superiority either may have over the other are accountable for in terms of interest, ambition or physical potentialities, and not in terms of a generally "superior" or "inferior" sex.

The Relationship of Environment to Intelligence. It is idle to debate the question as to whether heredity or environment is the more important factor in stimulating the intellect to exert itself in learning. Both are important, and if the edge of the argument is slightly on the side of the hereditarians, that does not mean that the environmentalists have no powerful arguments. A boy "born short" by endowment may be placed in ever so perfect an environment: the world will in all probability hear little from him; a boy "born long" by endowment will ordinarily achieve far less in a sordid and unstimulating environment than he will if he is transplanted to a more stimulating one. Those social reformers who term themselves *euthenists* and whose philosophy is to improve the home surroundings, do away with the slums and provide normal opportunities for youth, cannot fail to change favorably the life outlook and ambitions of legions of people. As playgrounds multiply, as schools become more adequate to meet the needs of their patrons, and as the general economic level of a people is raised, there comes about a more enlightened mind and a better trained intelligence. This does not mean that the degree of intelligence in an individual or a group of individuals can be increased above that with which they are endowed by nature; it means rather that circumstances may be such as to encourage the cultivation of the amount of intelligence they actually have.

Thus, intelligence testing done among sequestered or isolated people has shown that the further they are removed from the outside world, the poorer they rank; that the older the children in such communities, the less their intelligence quotient, suggesting that isolation and nonstimulation may actually make for stagnation; and that, in general, the lower the cultural status the less the intelligence. Testing has further indicated that children removed from meager environments to good foster homes have gained more than 10 points in intelligence within a period of four years; that immigrant children in a favorable new environment come shortly to test higher than do children of the same or similar extraction who remain in the old environment; even that children of similar extraction but placed in better schools show a marked increase in intelligence over their fellows who remain in inferior schools. There is abundant evidence of a reliable nature to indicate that the real fundamental differences in intelligence and school achievement that exist among different groups or people, whether of the same race or of different races, are cultural and economic: that is to say, environmental. Good heredity is essential to intellectual growth; good environment provides the stimulus by which heredity may express itself. In the best environment, poor heredity will set a sharp limit to an individual's development. Good heredity will sometimes rise above a poor environment.

Intelligence Testing. Early in the present century, concerned because of the numbers of children in France who were not succeeding in the schools as well as was to be desired, the Minister of Public Instruction invited a noted French psychologist, Dr. Alfred Binet, to endeavor to devise some sort of intelligence test by which it might be discovered which children were mentally deficient and which ones were retarded for some other reason than native endowment. With an assistant. Dr. Théodor Simon, Binet set to work upon the task assigned him and produced, in 1905, the first elaborate scale ever devised for measuring intelligence. The Binet-Simon scale was revised in 1908 and again in 1911. Its validity recognized on every hand, the scale became a model for other investigators, among them Dr. Lewis M. Terman, of our own country. Dr. Terman and his associates at Stanford University adapted the Binet-Simon tests to American conditions and published, in 1916, what has since been known as the *Stanford Revision of the Binet Scale.* In 1937 a greatly extended revision of the scale, in two forms, was published. While other adaptations of the original Binet-Simon scale have been made, notably by Goddard and Kuhlman, the Stanford revision by virtue of its having been the earliest, has been most widely employed in measuring intelligence in this country.

The 1937 Revision of the Stanford-Binet Scale comprises 129 tests, and is adapted for use with persons ranging all the way from two years of age to superior adults. In general, the scale is arranged as follows:

Age	Number of tests	Worth of each in mental age, months
2	6	1
2½	6	1
3	6	1
3½	6	1
4	6	1
4½	6	1
5	6	1
6–14	6 for each year	2
Average adult	8	2
Superior adult I	6	4
Superior adult II	6	5
Superior adult III	6	6

The tests for the various age levels include questions or problems involving comprehension, word-naming, drawing designs, memory for digits, giving differences and similarities, defining abstract terms, etc. At the age of two and a half years, for example, the scale comprises the following six tests:

1. Tells use of the following miniature objects attached to a card: cup, shoe, penny, knife, automobile, flatiron.
2. Identifies parts of body, using picture of a doll: hair, mouth, ears, hands.
3. Names familiar objects in miniature: chair, automobile, box, key, fork.
4. Recognizes familiar objects in a picture: shoe, clock, chair, bed, scissors, house, table, etc.
5. Repeats two digits after the examiner.
6. Replaces three insets in a simple form-board: circle, square, triangle.

If the child can pass all six of the tests satisfactorily at this level, he is credited with six months of mental age; while if he can pass but five of these, he is credited with five months.

The I. Q., or *intelligence quotient*, of an individual is computed by dividing the total number of months of mental age (M. A.) earned in the test by the number of months of his chronological age at the time tested (C. A.). The resulting quotient is the I. Q. Note the procedure illustrated in the following sample. The child tested is 4 years and two months old.

Credit assumed for first 3 years		36 months of M. A.
Year 3½	5 tests passed	5 months of M. A.
Year 4	3 tests passed	3 months of M. A.
Year 4½	2 tests passed	2 months of M. A.
Year 5	2 tests passed	2 months of M. A.
Year 6	1 test passed	2 months of M. A.
		50 Total M. A. in months

$$M. A. = 50$$

$$I. Q. = \frac{M. A.}{C. A.} = \frac{50}{50} = 1., \text{ or } 100$$

Terman's original evaluation of the I. Q. in terms of mental normality or abnormality was as follows:

I. Q.	Interpretation
Above 140	Near genius, or genius
120–140	Very superior
110–120	Superior
90–110	Normal, or average
80–90	Dull
70–80	Borderline
Below 70	Feebleminded

Tests of the Stanford-Binet type are often referred to as *individual tests of intelligence*, since they may be given to but one subject at a time and must be administered by an experienced clinical examiner. They are in wide use in identifying children who need to be placed in special or opportunity classes, who should be sent to institutions for the feebleminded, or who should be accelerated because of superior ability. They are also widely used in establishing the mentality of criminals and delinquents, on the one hand, and on the other, of candidates for special educational or cultural preferment.

The Stanford Revision (1937) covers a wider range and is more accurately standardized than the 1916 edition. The fact that it comprises two equivalent scales makes it possible to retest the same individual or individuals at any time subsequently.

The Stanford-Binet type of intelligence test is also known as an *age scale*, since I. Q.'s are calculated from it in terms of age norms. The Stanford-Binet has been found to be less reliable for adults than it is for children, since it shows a decline in mental age for age ranges much above 20 years. Point scales, on the other hand, arrive at an individual's intelligence by indicating the number of items at any age answered correctly, and therefore the number of points earned. The *raw score* thus achieved is then converted into a mental age score by reference to a table of norms. Prominent among point scales of intelligence are Kuhlman's *Individual Tests of Mental Development* and the Wechsler-Bellevue *Intelligence Tests*. The former takes into consideration the speed at which the subject performs on the test; it also allows varying amounts of credit depending upon the quality of his performance. The latter test—the Wechsler-Bellevue—is an excellent test for post-childhood years, comprising as it does one scale for adolescents (10 to 16 years), and another for adults (16 to 60 years). Like the Kuhlman, it considers quality of the response made as one element in the calculating of an individual's intelligence.

Group tests of intelligence date back to the First World War, at which time it was found needful to examine the mentality of tens of thousands of conscripts in a short period of time. There are available today numerous group tests, adapted to all ages from the kindergarten to the college level. They may be given by an untrained examiner or by a teacher, and they may be administered simultaneously to as many individuals as can be seated within range of the examiner's voice. They are much less reliable than individual tests, but they do possess the strong advantage of enabling a teacher to select out of a group those who are the brighter and those who are the duller.

Some intelligence tests are *verbal*, while others are *performance*, or *nonverbal* tests. The former rely principally upon the use of language in answering questions; the latter test an individual's ability to use his hands in manipulating objects like a formboard, a picture puzzle or a maze. Verbal intelligence tests have been criticized on the ground of their seeming to put a premium upon linguistic, academic ability and dooming a person who may be clever in using his hands but who is slow and inadequate in his use of language to show up poorly. Psychological examiners are usually careful to give both types of tests to those whom they examine. It should be noted that Test 6 for year 2½ in the 1937 Stanford Revision, above, called for performance while the other five tests were verbal in nature. By utilizing verbal tests, nonverbal tests, individual tests and group tests it is now possible for school people to evaluate the abilities of the individual learner and to know in advance with reasonable reliability what his prospects are of acquitting himself creditably in the educational world. Verbal group tests are employed in the schools of this country today as a means of classifying and sectioning young pupils. The Stanford-Binet Test is of chief importance in diagnosing children. While it may be applied to older subjects, its use with adults, excepting those of inferior caliber, is less satisfactory.

THE INDIVIDUAL THINKER

What It Means to Think. Learning takes place, as we have pointed out heretofore, through the active, analytic use of the mind. In any learning situation, with the exception of those in which the subject memorizes *verbatim*, there is bound to be a great deal of *thinking*. From the early months of the child's life onward he is a thinker, in the sense that he brings to bear increasingly the results of past experiences upon the present situation in an effort to understand and analyze it. The four-year-old who asked to go out in the rain so that he might grow fast, or the five-year-old who dug up the kernels of corn his father had planted but an hour before so that he might see if they were growing, were both *thinking*. True, the background of experience and information in both instances was limited, and the evaluation of the present situation was correspondingly deficient, but both children were thinking, and their thinking was sound for little folks—possibly a bit more sound than is that of many a fifty-year-old who consults a palmist to predict his future. What we should like to guarantee in all thinking is that it shall be done clearly, logically and without bias.

We think in terms of concrete images and also in terms of language symbols. The possession of a language gives the human being an advantage over the animal in envisaging a new problem situation. Language symbols release us from the limiting scope of images and enable us to search for abstract meanings and establish general principles, to make inferences and form hypotheses; they set us free from the cramping particulars and put us down on the high road to universals; they enable us to proceed from generals to particulars (deductive reasoning), or from particulars to generals (inductive reasoning). The acme of the mental life and potentialities is reached in *man the thinker*. It is his power to think and reason that differentiates him most conspicuously from the animal; it is this same power and potentiality that enables him to understand his environment, to adjust to it, or to make it over. Civilization as we know it is the resultant of man's active thinking.

Earmarks of the Poor Thinker. But not all learners are good thinkers: some of them are disappointingly poor at using their minds thoughtfully. We noted in an earlier chapter that it is hard for most of us even to *see* an occurrence as it actually is and to report it as it actually happened. It is still harder for most people to think about a problem adequately and logically, whether it be a problem of personal import, or one of social or political or economic import, for the simple reason that we are dominated in such vast areas of our mental processes by prejudice and bias. The individual learner will find himself cutting a poor intellectual figure if in his wrestling with a thought problem he is activated by suspicion, "hunches," unsound attitudes or viewpoints, prejudices, bias, and the like.

Yet the thinking of an amazingly large number of people is distorted by these tendencies. One has but to converse for five minutes with almost any person to find that his thinking is a mixture of logic, superstition, misinformation, prejudice and the "will to believe." He is convinced, for example, that if one bottle of a certain patent remedy has virtue, six bottles will have six times the amount of potency; that the stars control our destinies; that doctors "don't know anything"; or that it is foolhardy to walk under a ladder.

It is surprising how quickly an incidental or isolated happening can become the basis for a firm belief in most of us. If we observe that one Oriental is dishonest, we jump to the conclusion that all Orientals are dishonest likewise, even though we may have had dealings with scores of others who never show the trait. If we note that the son of a poor man makes good, we are convinced that it is only the children of the poor who really amount to anything and that the children of luxury turn out to be idlers and wastrels. The circumstance that other poor men's sons may remain as wretched and as poor as their sires makes no difference. The will to believe is strong in us. We should prefer to believe, if we are poor, that only the poor make good; if we are conservatives, that liberals are villains.

Wishful Thinking. The term "wishful thinking" has been applied to the thinking of those people who interpret the universe and the events and affairs of the universe as they wish them to be. We wish to be good, so we think we are; we wish to think our children are dutiful, noble in character and of high ideals, and so our eyes are blinded to any evil or mundanity in them; we wish that "everything will work together for good to those who love the Lord," and so we continue to love the Lord and trust to a kind Providence that the evil in the world will be conquered without any help from us. Before any of us can become good learners, we shall have to learn the greatest lesson of all: namely, that good learning springs from openmindedness, freedom from prejudice and "hunch," and a determination to weigh all the evidence. *An important part of learning is learning to think straight.*

The Nurse as Thinker. Perhaps the most universal preoccupation with which people are obsessed is the question of the status of their physical health, their stamina and their likelihood of an extended longevity. By the very nature of her profession, the nurse will find a large sector of her thought life given to the topic of health, not alone as it relates to herself personally but as it relates to those with whom she comes in professional contact. Such being the case, it is necessary that she shall endeavor to think logically and sanely regarding the all-important subject of health and disease. She will be thrown in contact with all manner of inadequate, misinformed attitudes and beliefs with reference to these matters on the part of her patients. She will encounter superstitions, errors, wishful thinking, ignorance, apprehension, remorse, despair. In the face of these human foibles and weaknesses, it is of the utmost importance that she who ministers to bodies and minds diseased shall herself hold fast to what is rational, to the logic of cause and effect, to the essence of things-as-they-are. If she is stampeded by fears and indecisions and uncertainties, if she is inclined to trust to luck, to let her emotions control her reason, or to permit her ministrations to be influenced unfavorably by the moods, attitudes or behavior of her patients, she will hardly be an efficient worker and cannot be a satisfactory learner of her art.

The nurse, like everybody else, may school herself to think logically and sanely regarding her specialized vocational problems, however, and at the same time continue to be a slipshod thinker about the extracurricular or extraprofessional situations amid which she passes her life. She may do a lot of wish-thinking about her future; she may be prejudiced in her opinions of certain people, events or occurrences; she may be building up strong dislikes and intolerances which a few moments of clear thinking would show her to be utterly without basis; she may be an individual who jumps to conclusions. She may be superstitious, suspicious, given to "hunches," gullible. In the interest of character as well as of efficiency in her profession, it behooves her if she has not already formed the habit of logically controlled thinking, to begin at once to cultivate it. In a world in which there is altogether too little clear and sound thinking, it would be well for all of us—teachers, students and laymen alike—to rediscover this essential principle of waiting until the evidence is all in before drawing conclusions.

CERTAIN PHYSIOLOGICAL FACTORS DETERMINING LEARNING

1. **Age.** It has been established that mature people can learn more quickly than immature ones. Other things being equal, the younger the learner, the less his learning competence; and conversely, the older the learner, at least up to middle life, the more efficient he is. This is quite contrary to the older notion that childhood is a "golden age for learning"; it now appears that the golden age for learning comes in the twenties and thirties, and perhaps even a bit after that. Thorndike has demonstrated that older learners are superior learners, as soon as they can rid themselves of the notion that because they are older they are too old to learn, or as soon as they can revive long-unused study habits. The senior author has had in his classes many an older student, returning to college at forty, who within a few weeks' time was literally cutting educational circles around young adolescent collegians of no lower I. Q. The modern movement for adult education through extension, correspondence and matriculation in schools and colleges, is by no means a misapplication of psychological principles.

2. **Efficiently Functioning Sense Organs.** Inasmuch as most of the materials of formal education are to be apprehended through the eye and the ear, it follows that these organs must be in first-class condition

if the subject is to learn efficiently and economically. Upon the eyes falls a great deal of the responsibility of taking in the materials of education. As we know, considerable strain is placed upon the ciliary muscles by the act of reading; if those muscles are weak or if they do not function smoothly, the resulting strain may become so great as to be almost intolerable. Careful records of eye tests made in the schools of this country over the past quarter of a century indicate that approximately 25 per cent of the pupils present visual defects—principally myopia, hyperopia, astigmatism and strabismus. Myopia, or nearsightedness, is known to increase during the school years, no doubt directly as a result of the strain that school work places upon the muscles of the lens. Most educational communities now require periodic tests of the eyes and provide special sight-saving classes for those children whose vision is seriously impaired. While it cannot be proved that a child with poor eyes is a poor learner, it is certainly true that efficient learning is usually conditioned upon the possession of efficient eyes, and that those who have deficient ones are under a serious handicap in the schoolroom.

Defective hearing is hardly less important than defective vision. Probably not far from 15 per cent of the children in our schools have impaired hearing, and of this group one in every five or six is or will shortly become deaf. Most of the auditory deficiencies of children result from neglect of the common respiratory diseases of childhood. Unlike the eyes, the ears do not suffer from continued use, but like the eyes they cease to be powerful assets in a young learner if and when they can no longer function normally. The younger the child, the more seriously will deficiencies in the ears interfere with his normal educational evolution. If he cannot early in life hear sharply the patterns of speech, his own vocalization will tend to be metallic and toneless; if he cannot hear the discussions and instructions of the schoolroom, he cannot participate; if he cannot apprehend what his comrades and playmates are saying, he cannot join freely with them in their games and playground activities. For these reasons, the hard-of-hearing child comes early to feel himself "different" from the others, to hold himself aloof from them, and even to be ignored or actually bullied by them. The importance of early and competent ear-testing programs in the schools, of medical care for ailing ears, of special classes for those children whose infirmities are notable, and of a comprehensive program of aural hygiene becomes self-evident when one considers these circumstances.

3. **Normal Endocrines.** We have referred in a previous chapter (Chapter 7) to the importance of the endocrine glands in regulating human behavior. From the standpoint of efficient learning, it must

be obvious that if there is underactivity or overactivity or imbalance in the operation of these important body laboratories, the personality and the physique of the subject are almost invariably affected. He may, for example, be restless and excitable; he may be sluggish and inert; he may even be mentally deficient; he may be encumbered with an abnormally obese body; he may tire at a minimum of physical or mental expenditure; he may possess a low amount of energy; he may possess an undue amount; he may be emotionally intense and unstable; he may be psychoneurotic. The reliable, earnest and capable learner needs a full equipment of normally functioning endocrines, and while certain learners may continue to be satisfactory learners in spite of underlying glandular dysfunctioning, in the long run and for all learners, balanced and integrated activity among these tremendously important structures is almost certain to be associated with creditable and satisfactory learning.

4. Freedom from Deformities and Other Abnormalities. Every teacher knows how the psyche of the child may be influenced by a withered arm, a crippled leg, or a harelip. While some children compensate for physical deformities and defects by developing their intellectual or social or athletic side, many others fail to compensate and become morbid and introspective. They are apt to dislike to put themselves forward in a learning situation or in a social situation; hence various secondary or derived characteristics appear, notably seclusiveness, intellectual detachment, an assumption of mental inferiority commensurate with the physical, loss of self confidence, and the like. It is of importance that *correctable* physical defects and abnormalities, such as conspicuous birthmarks, impacted teeth, squint and bowleggedness, be looked after at the earliest possible time in order that resulting defects of character and personality may be avoided. It is equally important that all *preventable* physical defects be eliminated by a competently administered preschool and school health, nursing and medical service. There is a positive correlation between physical soundness and freedom from abnormality, on the one hand, and on the other a competence and a readiness to learn. Nothing interferes more with the normal exertion of the mind in the young learner than does the so-called "feeling of inferiority," which may take its rise in some physical deformity or deficiency.

5. Adequate Nutrition. School health records indicate that not far from 15 per cent of the children in our schools are improperly nourished, and this despite our school feeding programs, our school nursing and follow-up, and the general public enlightenment that exists in the world today. While serious errors have no doubt been made in the near past by school examiners who have based their judgment of nutritional status of children upon their height and weight as read from height-weight tables instead of upon careful anatomical examination of individuals, there is a great deal of serious malnutrition among school children. Classroom teachers recognize a closer correlation between malnutrition and poor learning potentiality than some of the studies have seemed to indicate as existing. In the more extreme cases of serious malnutrition the correlation is high. To be a good learner, the individual child needs to be properly fed: that is to say, he needs to have the maximum of physical and muscular development possible for his particular organism, in order that he may have an adequate physical foundation upon which to build scholastically.

EFFECTS OF CERTAIN EXTRANEOUS FACTORS UPON LEARNING

1. **Tobacco and Alcohol.** It is difficult for the investigator to get reliable scientific data regarding the effects of tobacco and alcohol, either upon the physical organism or upon learning efficiency. There is a tremendous amount of prejudice and bias in the thinking of most people about tobacco and alcohol. If one is an abstainer, these agents are anathema; if one is an indulger, they are claimed to be among man's greatest sources of comfort and satisfaction. Even in controlled laboratory experiments it is difficult to obtain reliable data, since the temporary effect of a drug may be wholly misleading and provide no adequate basis for predicting its long-time effects.

There is no doubt in anybody's mind that *excessive use either of tobacco or alcohol is bad both for the body and for the mental functions.* There is no doubt, either, about the unwisdom of addiction to either in the early years. Until the growth impulse has completely run its course, it is poor policy to introduce periodically even small amounts of poison into the human body. After one is fully grown, of course, whatever deleterious effects tobacco and alcohol may have will be limited to impairment of function of organs that have at least achieved their full and final growth.

The most carefully controlled experiments in the use of tobacco by young adult smokers and nonsmokers (those carried on by Dr. C. L. Hull) showed a heightened pulse, continuing for about forty minutes after smoking; a greater susceptibility of the heart to excitement; a tremor of the hands, which continued for twenty-three minutes; and a reduction in learning rate during the sixty minutes following smoking. On the other hand, Hull found no impairment of muscular efficiency, even a slight improvement in reaction time and in adding, and the suggestion of a reduction in fatigability. These experiments, like others conducted in the artificial atmosphere of the laboratory, leave unanswered the important question as to what may be the permanent effects of long continued and moderate use of tobacco.

A similarly carefully controlled experiment upon the effect of alcohol (that carried on by Dr. H. L. Hollingworth) indicated what medical men have come rather generally to feel: namely, that alcohol is not a stimulant but a depressant. Hollingworth demonstrated that the only bodily function which alcohol accelerates is pulse action; there was found to be a distinct loss in both mental and motor efficiency in every other function studied. Furthermore, his results indicated that the greater the dose of alcohol taken, the more deleterious its effects. While there is some evidence that, administered in a moderate dose after strenuous physical work, alcohol may promote relaxation, it is a significant fact that medical men today make little use of alcohol in their treatment of the sick. Alcohol is a tissue poison and is medically so recognized.

In most cases habitual use of alcohol is resorted to because of its profound effect upon the feelings and attitudes. By offering them escape from unpleasantness, misery, or a sense of failure or inadequacy, alcohol tempts most of its victims. Maladjustment thus leads to the alcoholic habit probably much more often than alcohol leads to maladjustment. The well adjusted man or woman has no desire to escape from himself or herself. Dr. W. R. Miles* has expressed the subtle necromancy of alcohol as well as its dangers in the following quotation:

> "The peculiar charm of alcohol lies in the sense of careless well-being and bodily and mental comfort which it creates. It unburdens the individual of his cares and his fears; relieves him of his feelings of inferiority and weakness. . . . The fundamental animal drives of the organism have free rein; the intellectual self-critic makes no strong pull to the right, for he is dozing. Under such conditions it is easy to laugh or to weep, to love or to hate, not wisely but too well. Warmth of friendship may be expressed in ways seemingly appropriate but actually absurd. . . . Alcohol has a particularly weakening effect on the control of sex impulses in women . . . and it positively increases the urgency of these impulses. . . ."

2. **Caffeine.** Our knowledge of the long-time effect of caffeine upon physical and mental functions is imperfect, for no long-time scientific studies of it have been made. From careful laboratory experiments continued over short periods, however, it appears that small doses have no significant effects physically, but that large doses may interfere with motor control and efficiency. The mental effects, even of large amounts of caffeine, appear from these experiments to be

* Miles, W. R.: Psychological Effects of Alcohol in Man, in H. Emerson (Ed.): Alcohol and Man. New York, The Macmillan Co., 1934, pages 263–264. By permission.

slight. Four grains of caffeine were found not to affect the sleep of the subjects, but when the dose was increased to 6 grains there was an interference with the sleep of most of them. Regarding caffeine, as regarding also tobacco and alcohol, there is a vast amount of bias, some coffee users insisting that the blacker the coffee, the greater the number of cups, and the nearer the bedtime hour they are drunk, the better they sleep. Others find even small amounts to interfere with sleep or to produce headaches. It must not be forgotten, however, that certain geographic groups are perennial coffee drinkers from their earliest years, and seem to have been so with impunity.

So far as learning efficiency is concerned, except as it may be adversely influenced by headache, insomnia or other derived effects, it is probable that caffeine is of little significance. It should, of course, be understood that caffeine is the active principle not only in coffee but also in tea and some soda-fountain drinks.

3. **Distractions.** Everybody has experienced interference with mental efficiency when unnecessary noise, excitement or other sources of distraction occur about him. There are always, of course, a certain number of distracting stimuli in the environment, and we find it ordinarily possible to thrust out competing stimuli unless and until they become too strong. Irrelevant ideas continually bombard us as we write, read, think or study, but in the main we learn to sidetrack most of them and to hold our line of thought clear and unobstructed. External stimuli are less easy to disregard, for they may become at any moment so intense as to interfere seriously with our best mental resolves. It is probable that we actually need a certain minimum amount of nonfocal stimulation; a moderate degree of it acts as a sort of challenge to the mind to keep it to its task. But when such stimulation passes an optimum and minimum point, it becomes impossible to concentrate effectively. We may put forth much greater effort and we may resolve heroically to permit nothing to interfere with our mental processes, but we shall be able to hold to our resolve but partially, at best, and then only at considerable and costly expense to the nervous system.

In the laboratory it has been demonstrated that mature subjects can hold themselves to a task against considerable distraction if their motivation is sufficiently strong. A subject may say to himself, for example, "I shall keep at this task whatever may be the surrounding circumstances, if for no other reason than to prove that I can focus my mind as I will!" This attitude will help greatly. In the schoolroom, however, and in most nonschool tasks which we may be called upon to perform, we shall be activated ordinarily by no such grim determination. It follows therefore that we should strive to control the surrounding environment in such a way as to reduce distraction to the minimum. We cannot eliminate it entirely, and indeed it would probably not be desirable to do so if we could; but we can control it to some degree. After we have convinced ourselves that the surroundings are as favorable as they can be reasonably made, or as we personally can make them, we must learn to discipline our attention and to perform our tasks efficiently and without grumbling. One major form of distraction is provided for the dissatisfied individual who persists in lamenting the nature and the numbers of the distractions around him. The efficient learner controls his environment as well as he can, and then proceeds to control himself.

4. Physical Surroundings. What has been said about self discipline in the face of distracting influences might well be said about self discipline in adjusting to one's physical surroundings in general. Ideally, we should like to keep the *temperature* at approximately 68° or 70° F., under all conditions, for the most efficient mental work; we should like to keep the *relative humidity* at approximately 50 per cent; we should like to be sure that the *air-conditioning system* is providing us with a continuous flow of air to which moisture and heat may have been added as needed, or from which excessive moisture or heat may have been removed; we should like to have the *lighting* of home, workroom, office, schoolroom or ward adequate for comfortable and prolonged use of the eyes, without strain. All these and other environmental conditions known to be optimum for comfort and efficiency in the learner are greatly to be desired.

Rarely, however, shall we find our physical surroundings as ideal as all this. Few private homes are constructed or maintained on this high plane of physical comfort; few schools meet such standards; few public buildings, few office buildings, few hospitals meet them. This being the situation, it is reassuring to know that carefully controlled experiments have indicated that unless the physical influences surrounding his work are decidedly unwholesome, strong motivation fortifies the learner with a power to concentrate and to achieve under various unfavorable conditions. Granted that the rooms in which we live and the environment in which we work are reasonably well protected, it appears that efficiency in the individual worker is principally a matter of his own determination and industry. The efficient learner can perform creditably with the temperature at 65° or at 75°; in stagnant air or in moving air; in dim light or in strong light; it is all largely a question of habit and mental attitude. This should not be taken as condoning those physical surroundings which are definitely uncomfortable or needlessly straining to the organism.

5. Time of Day. Can one study best in the morning or in the evening? At 7 A. M. or 7 P. M.? In midmorning or in midafternoon? Many students discover, or fancy that they have discovered, that they have especially favorable times when they can concentrate best and when they can learn most readily. There are large individual variations in this matter. Experiments conducted in the laboratory and in the school seem to indicate that, in general, one's efficiency in intellectual tasks increases throughout the forenoon hours, reaching its peak shortly before noon; in the afternoon, there is found to be a drop during the first hour, followed by a rise by midafternoon but probably to a peak somewhat lower than the forenoon peak, and by a tapering off toward the end of the day.

Under certain laboratory conditions of strong motivation, some experiments have indicated that there is a continued maintenance of one's abilities throughout the day, without periods of diminution or loss. Under normal conditions of work and study, however, it is probable that the diurnal variation in the efficiency of one's mental performance is somewhat as we have indicated. This suggests that one should plan to do his most taxing intellectual tasks in the forenoon and get all his hardest work out of the way before lunch. The curricula of most of our schools follow this policy in more or less detail, the "hard" subjects coming in the morning and the "easy" ones in the afternoon.

For the older student and the professional worker, we have no adequate data. The probabilities are that one time is about as good as another in which to do intellectual work, with the possible exception of the half-hour or so immediately before and after mealtime. If one gets into the habit of applying himself optimistically to his task whenever he has time available, whether it is at one hour or at some other, he will find himself accomplishing to his satisfaction the work which he has to do.

THOUGHT PROBLEMS FOR THE STUDENT

1. Contrast the effectiveness of your own learning facility on different days and under different conditions of interest, physical health, readiness, and the like.
2. Make a list of the various skills which you yourself have developed that appear to be now upon a plateau level. Try to account for the lack of present progress in each instance.
3. Explain in your own words why it is incorrect to classify people in general into two opposite types. Suggest additional popular contrasting types, like, for example, the "fat" and the "lean," the "wise" and the "foolish," and indicate the terminology that should properly be used.
4. List your own more obvious and fundamental physical and mental traits and attempt to determine from which parent, if either, each has been inherited.

Do you find traits that are quite dissimilar to the parental? To the grandparental? How do you account for such departures from the family pattern? Are you and your sisters and brothers more alike than any of you are like your parents? Explain.
5. Make a list of the various kinds of intelligence tests available. If the nursing school has a collection of such tests, select one of each kind for a careful examination. Report in class upon the results of your inspection.
6. Give several examples of good and of poor thinking selected from your own reactions or from those of people whom you know, or from both. What factors seem to underlie poor thinking? Good thinking?
7. List a half dozen common superstitions about which you know. How do superstitions originate in the first place? Evaluate those listed in the light of intelligence and of logical thinking.
8. What "wishful thinking" have you ever done? Are you inclined still to be a wishful thinker?
9. Cite cases known to you in which a learner has been handicapped seriously by physical deficiencies or abnormalities. How might the situation be adjusted?
10. Contact five or more adult persons for whom you have respect and query them regarding their personal attitudes toward: (1) tobacco; (2) alcohol; (3) coffee; (4) dope. Try to determine to what extent their several viewpoints represent clear, sound thinking and to what extent they represent prejudice. Report your results in class.
11. In your care of patients what disorders have you observed which have had as their basis poor nutrition during growing periods? What defects have you observed which may be the result of improperly fitted clothes? Of inadequate clothing and shelter?
12. Are you still improving on your technique of bathing a bed patient? What standards, according to your Nursing Arts instruction, would be the basis for scoring the performance of this procedure? For the coming week make an honest effort to rise above this plateau level; score yourself on this procedure at the end of the week and report results in class.
13. List the factors, other than intelligence, which contribute to success in life. Carefully consider the nurses with whom you have worked. Select the two who seem to you the best. In so far as you can judge, would you consider them the most intelligent? Do they possess those attributes or qualities which you have listed?
14. Give two illustrations of "slipshod" thinking" which you were guilty of before you became a student in the school of nursing but which you have now corrected.
15. Select the true statements from the following list and give illustrations from your personal observation and experience proving their correctness:
    (a) Successful nurses have formed habits of emotional balance to meet various kinds of situations.
    (b) All patients have overlearned such reflex habits as winking and swallowing.
    (c) Learning how to improvise for the comfort of each individual patient is insured by experience.
    (d) Reasoning in nursing situations is secondary in importance to doing what you have been taught to do.
    (e) Patients differ as to intelligence in degree only.
    (f) In selecting mental diversion for a patient, one should consider his mental age.

(g) All children who have reached the age of ten have the same intelligence quotients.

(h) A nurse learns that patients may vary in the degree to which they compensate for their illnesses.

16. Summarize the effects you have experienced from the use of products containing caffeine; the observations you have made as to the responsiveness of patients who have received endocrine preparations.

SUGGESTED READINGS

1. Anastasi, A.: *Psychological Testing.* New York, The Macmillan Co., 1954.
    Part V, "Measurement and Evaluation," is particularly good.
2. Garrison, K. C., and Gray, J. S.: *Educational Psychology.* New York, Appleton-Century-Crofts, Inc., 1955.
    Chapter 5, "The Nature and Measurement of Intelligence," and Chapter 11, "The General Nature of Learning," will provide excellent supplementary reading for this chapter.
3. Ruch, F. L.: *Psychology and Life.* 4th ed. Chicago, Scott, Foresman and Co., 1953.
    Cf. especially the following pages: for heredity, 49–56; for intelligence testing and cultural factors, 85. It will be helpful for the student also to track down in the index the references on individual differences, learning ability, alcoholism as escape, thinking.
4. Thorndike, R. L., and Hagen, E.: *Measurement and Evaluation in Psychology and Education.* New York, John Wiley and Sons, 1955.
    A good general reference on the objectives of testing.
5. Thorpe, L. P.: *Child Psychology and Development.* 2nd ed. New York, Ronald Press, 1955.
    Contains excellent material on intelligence, nature-nurture, and the learning process. Consult the index for page references.
6. Travers, R. M.: *Educational Measurement.* New York, The Macmillan Co., 1955.
    General reference, emphasizing the understanding and critical appraisal of educational tests.

Unit 5

The Process of Growing Up

Chapter
11

> While childhood, and while dreams, producing childhood, shall be left, imagination shall not have spread her holy wings totally to fly the earth.
>
> CHARLES LAMB

PSYCHOLOGY OF CHILDHOOD AND ADOLESCENCE

PHYSICAL GROWTH OF THE CHILD

The Meaning of Growth. The chief business of the baby is to grow. Physically helpless and tiny at birth, he must in a few years achieve the fulness of adult stature and control. Nature has implanted within the cells that comprise his anatomy the impulse of growth, and for two decades this impulse will take precedence over everything else. Only a few inches long at birth, the human individual will within two decades and less rear his head 5 or 6 feet into the vertical plane; weighing but a few pounds, he will in the same period multiply his weight 20 or more times. Aimless in movements and helpless in control, he will achieve a precision and a deftness of muscle that are little short of a miracle; indeed, it is a miracle: the miracle of growth and maturation.

By the lay observer, growth is understood to be increase in size, the adult individual being presumed to be the child grown big. While it is of course true that the gross size of the organism does increase throughout the period of growth, to interpret growth as *mere* accretion of height and weight and bulk is to commit a blunder. Growth is not an even, harmonious process which causes the organism to fill out in all directions and uniformly, after the fashion of a rubber ball as air is forced into it; growth is irregular and uneven. Each separate organ in the body has its own peculiar rate of growth, its periods of rapid increase and of subsequent rest or slow accretion. When the organ or part is growing rapidly, adjacent or remote organs or parts may be growing very slowly if at all.

Interesting evidence of this unevenness of growth is to be observed in the original disproportion of body parts in the infant when compared with adult ratios. Thus, the head of the newborn baby (see Fig. 27) is approximately as broad from side to side as the shoulders are, and if it should continue to grow uniformly with them the resulting adult individual would present at twenty years of age a monstrosity that would find place in the circus. Similarly, the legs

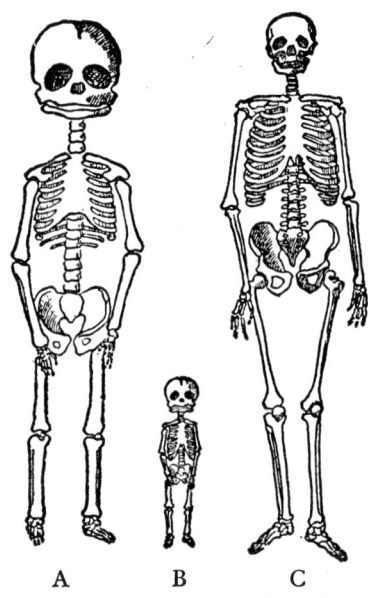

A B C

Fig. 27. This plate is specially designed to show how much the proportions of the newborn child differ from those of the adult. To make this difference more striking, the skeleton of a newborn child (A) and that of an adult (C) are here represented drawn on different scales. (B) represents the newborn child drawn on the same scale as (C). (From a photograph by Professor Sanford, in S. Hall: Adolescence, Vol. I. D. Appleton-Century Company.)

and arms of the baby are relatively shorter than the trunk to which they are attached, and they must accordingly grow faster than the trunk if normal adult proportions are to be achieved. The growth of muscles also is a good illustration of this principle of disharmonious development: at seven years of age, a child's muscles comprise only about one fourth of his total body weight; by the end of the growing years, they constitute approximately one half of his body weight.

So, too, with the disproportionate growth of heart and arteries. At birth the ratio of heart to arteries is as 5 is to 4; at twenty years it is approximately as 5 is to 1. The hygienic significance of this last fact alone is tremendous when one stops to realize that in childhood a relatively pigmy heart is charged with pumping blood through relatively giant arteries, thus providing low blood pressure and becoming easily damaged by overstrain; in adulthood, on the other hand, a relatively large heart inundates the relatively small arteries with blood and puts it under much higher pressure, thus providing resources for the strenuousness and the endurance of the mature individual. From these and numerous other instances of irregularity of growth, it should be apparent that the true concept of growth is quite different from what it is popularly interpreted to be. Growth means maturation of organs and functions at varied rates; it means proportional development today, or in this organ, disproportionate development tomorrow, or in that organ. And yet withal, it means an integrated process, for despite its unevenness it yields ultimately a physically perfect and well coordinated machine which can adapt itself to a tremendous range and variety of reactions.

Sex Differences in Growth Rate. Significant also are the growth differences between boys and girls. At birth the girl is smaller and lighter than the boy, the latter maintaining the lead up to approximately the age of ten years. Sometime after the tenth birthday, however, the girl succeeds in outstripping the boy both in height and in weight, continuing superior to him in these two categories until about fifteen, at which time the boy again forges into the lead, normally retaining it in both height and weight thereafter consistently. Girls begin to grow fast from one to two years younger than boys do, the general period of rapid growth starting in the former at about the age of ten or eleven, and being delayed in the latter until about the age of twelve. Thus the girl gets a running start over her brother which enables her to keep ahead of him physically for several years just at the end of childhood and at the beginning of pubescence.

Misuse of Height-weight Tables. In this connection a word needs to be said in warning against the use of height-weight tables in determining whether a child is "underweight" or "overweight" for his age and height. For a number of years teachers and nurses have commonly made use of the height-weight tables to read off the "proper" weight for a given individual child, and according to this rating they have been accustomed to classify him as "satisfactory" or as "unsatisfactory" in weight, and therefore in nutrition. It is easy to misuse tables of this sort and to cause needless worry to parents of children who show up poorly on them. Height-weight tables, it must be remembered, represent statistical averages of large numbers of children of the same age. They express what the *average* child weighs. They ignore factors of racial and family heredity, *natural* heaviness or lightness of bony structures, and stockiness or slightness of musculature. Modern methods employed by the physician and the physical examiner to determine the nutritional condition and the general satisfactoriness or unsatisfactoriness of growth in a child do not include comparing him with the mythical average. The expert examiner is interested in condition of muscular tissue, of the subcutaneous fatty deposits, in the size and condition of the bones, the appetite and general vegetative tone. In the words of the White House Conference, we may say that "each person has his own normal weight, irrespective of tables, which takes account of his build, type, inheritance, age, endurance, and resistance to fatigue and infection."

MOTOR DEVELOPMENT AND CONTROL

1. **In Early Childhood.** One of the most striking characteristics of the infant is his incoordination of muscle. He cannot at first focus his eyes; he cannot reach or point with precision; he cannot move his body except in the mass; he cannot grasp, hold or throw either with gracefulness or towardness; he cannot speak, stand, sit, walk, raise his head. His muscles are flabby, undeveloped, uncoordinated. All his activity is random and uncertain. There is, to be sure, a considerable range of individual differences in degree of helplessness and incoordination, some infants being considerably more facile than others. Thus, Irwin found one infant in his investigations whom he rated as 290 times more active than another infant studied. But even the most active infant is lacking in coordination and control of his muscles. Precision and dexterousness are foreign to all infants.

Note, however, in the following catalogue of achievements (selected from the researches of Dr. Arnold Gesell*) the gradual replacement of the infantile mass incoordination with a growing power and control over the neuromuscular system in the first two years of life:

At 6 months—Sits alone momentarily when placed in a favorable position.
At 7 months—Stands firmly, with help.
At 10 months—Pulls self to standing position.
At 12 months—Walks when led.
At 15 months—Walks alone.
At 18 months—Climbs stairs.
At 21 months—Walks backward.
At 24 months—Runs.

2. **In Later Childhood.** During the preschool years subsequent to the two years of infancy, the child develops his motor skills and

* Cf. Gesell, A.: Infancy and Human Growth. New York, The Macmillan Company, 1928, pp. 128ff. By permission.

coordinations amazingly. No one who watches the six-year-old as he plays about the yard or the house can fail to note the progress he has made since the random and uncertain days of babyhood when his actions were still undifferentiated from the mass. He can now propel himself with speed and good coordination; his hand is steady and he can use it with a good deal of strength and dexterousness; he can now aim accurately, throw with force and some precision, climb, use

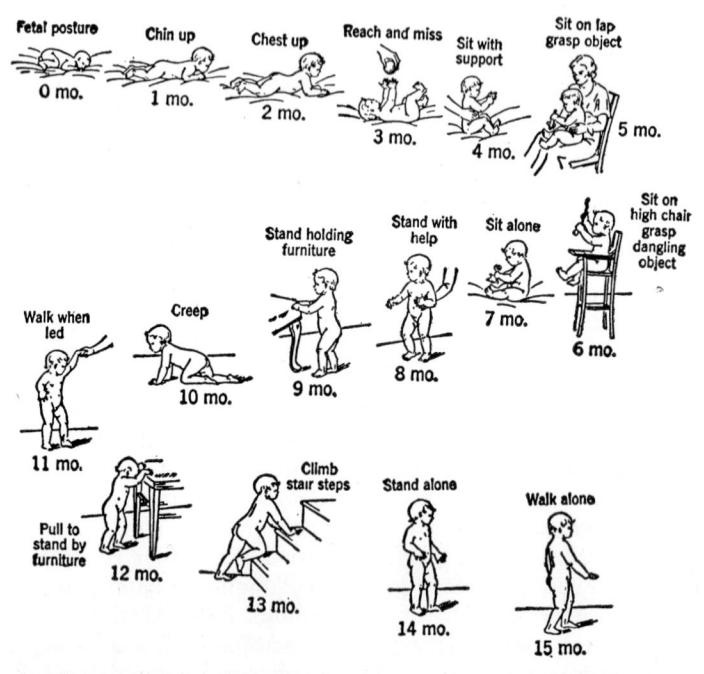

Fig. 28. The general development of motor sequence. Some of the outstanding items in the behavior of the infants are represented in their order of emergence. The ages given are only approximate; the items are not equally spaced in time, and different infants differ considerably in the general rate of development, though not in the order of the items. (Dashiell, from Shirley: The First Two Years. University of Minnesota Press, 1933.)

his vocal apparatus to produce well articulated speech, balance himself in any position or plane. The world of objects and forces is almost literally his for the taking, and he can express his will and purpose physically with exactitude and with power.

The later years of childhood up to the dawn of puberty will but add to and extend and refine the motor skills and controls which have been already founded before the school years begin. The years of the elementary school will supply the child with opportunities unlimited for developing skills and grace and power through play, games, gymnastics, competitive sports, and through the performance of the home tasks, chores and simple work which fall to the lot of children to carry on. By the arrival of adolescence the infant of yesterday will be a robust, strong, skilled and almost tireless user of his muscles, a master of his body and withal a physically accomplished and clever actor.

MENTAL AND EMOTIONAL GROWTH; HABITS

Mental Growth of the Preschool Child. The newborn child is as helpless mentally as he is physically. We can imagine what life must be like to a tiny individual who is thrust suddenly into an environment which is strange to him and which offers no immediate points of contact or of leverage. People and objects move across the horizon meaninglessly and vaguely at first. There is no awareness of the self or of other selves, no differentiation between the personal and the impersonal. The sense organs are dull and uncoordinated: only the more intense stimuli have the power to arrest the attention and even then the nature of the stimulus is unintelligible; tables, chairs, blankets, faces of people, sunlight patches on the wall, conversations, all blend into a meaningless riddle.

Little by little, however, meanings begin to emerge from this heterogeneous mass of stimuli surrounding the baby. The mother's face, the breast, the bottle, preparations for feeding, the dog that trots across the nursery floor, the bright-colored ball, the bath, the fingers and toes, the bed, the covers—all shortly come to be associated with meanings and familiar events in the actively seeking mind of the tiny, wide-eyed observer. As the baby adds week upon week, these meanings come to be greatly extended. He is carried from one room to another; he is carried or wheeled out onto the porch or along the sidewalk; he sees the trees and flowers and houses and automobiles and animals and people; he begins to recognize and to remember and to anticipate; he learns to manipulate small objects, awkwardly at first but with increasing coordination; he gleans certain simple meanings from the conversation going on about him; he develops an elementary sense of his own identity as distinct from other individuals or objects. Later still, when he can toddle about by himself, he can explore his surroundings more satisfactorily, and he proceeds to add new laurels of knowledge and of conquest to his achievements. He carries on an elementary language of grimace, of gesture, of mass vocalization, and finally of "baby talk," until by the age of approximately seventeen or eighteen months he is able to put speech three or four words together in a simple sentence to express desire or purpose.

After the age of two, the toddler grows apace in his mental evolution. Increasing mastery of words provides him a medium for expressing himself freely and spontaneously; increasing maturation of muscle and body makes it possible for him to extend greatly his peregrinations, and so brings him into contact with things-over-there as distinct from the contiguous objects to which he was earlier limited. So begins for him and for adult observers of his behavior a most interesting drama. Periods of intense explorational or interpretative activity, in which the young investigator carries on a running conversation with himself and with the animistic world around him, alternate with other equally intense manipulative periods in which he falls into silence and devotes all his motor energies to the task at hand. He passes now through an aloof, observational era; now through an active stage of the "kiddy kar" and the cart and the wheelbarrow and the sand pile; now through a slide and swing and paper-cutting era; now through a running and jumping and climbing era; now through a fairy tale and Mother Goose and story period; now through an exploring and a taking-apart-and-putting-together-again period; and at length he arrives at the age of school entrance possessed of a considerable range of information about common objects and relationships and of a keen mental curiosity.

Emotional Growth of the Young Child. As we know, the emotional attitudes and reactions that are established in early childhood are of tremendous future importance in orienting the personality healthfully and hygienically. Strongest of all emotional needs of the child, perhaps, is his need of a feeling of security and of being wanted and loved. Few things affect the juvenile personality so disastrously as does the discovery that his home is insecure, or that his parents tolerate rather than love him. It is easy for the child's house of cards to be demolished in such an atmosphere and for him to become at first miserable, and later on perhaps even delinquent, in order to secure that feeling of importance and of success that ought to have been his through an acknowledged and secure place in the family setting.

Anxiety. One of the more serious results of lack of stability in the environment is a persistent, haunting feeling of anxiety which dogs the footsteps of not a few children in middle childhood and beyond. Most typically, perhaps, it is a vague and ill-defined apprehensiveness which may arise from the disconcerting nature of the external surroundings, or from a dim, unconscious sense of incompetence or inadequacy to project oneself acceptably and satisfyingly upon the environment. By no means limited always to childhood, this feeling of anxiety is apt to be peculiarly keen in the earliest years of life.

So far as it derives from an insecure or unstable environment, we may presume that anxiety proceeds from either (or both) of two principal situations—a shaky home setting or an ill-adapted and unsatisfying school experience. We shall consider at some length in Chapter 15 the first of these sources of juvenile maladjustment and anxiety. It is sufficient here to anticipate the later discussion by insisting that every child has one inalienable right, preeminent above all others—the right to be born and reared in a home in which unfailing marital harmony and affection reside. In such a secure family background there is never the slightest fear that his home is in danger of disintegrating. For the child, as for the adolescent that comes after him, a home should be a haven of security, founded upon the rock of love, sympathy and faith. Let once the awareness be sown in the fertile mind of a child that all is not well between his father and his mother, and the seed will grow. A home that is perceived to be but a house of cards which is apt to collapse at any moment of crisis is bound to be a continuous source of anxiety to its juvenile members. Deriving from this uncomfortable fear—more or less articulate—of impending doom, all manner of anxieties may obsess childhood. So characteristically does a basal anxiety spread across other areas of experience that from a nameless, half-understood dread of a collapsing home, the apprehensive child will be likely to feel a bewildering sense of inadequacy and insecurity in everything, and a dread of the tasks and the demands of tomorrow.

Anxiety which derives from a disturbing school experience can be but little less disconcerting to a child who is sensitive. Failure to do creditable classroom work, whether from limited mental capacity or from some other cause; dislike or actual fear of teachers; dread of examinations and report cards; boredom and lack of interest; uneasiness over censure or thinly veiled sarcasm from teachers; non-acceptance by other children; resentments and jealousies at the better performances of others—these are among the school sources of anxiety in a child. While most normal children either do not experience it or else are able to throw it off without damage to their personalities and their outlooks, some children suffer intensely from anxiety and apprehensiveness. Often the feeling is ill-defined and unfocalized; its existence is, however, real and upsetting.

Mastery of anxiety, whatever its source (and besides family and school origins, anxiety may of course spring from any other area of juvenile experience), depends upon either the removal of the exciting causes or else acceptance of them as inevitable and the making of a suitable adjustment to them. Homes that are in danger of disintegration through such preventable causes as marital conflict and disharmony ought to be salvaged and revamped by intelligent and sympathetic reorientation. Schools and teachers that inspire resentments, jealousies, failures, worries, ought likewise to be recast in molds that will make it easy for children to experience success and be nurtured in the fine arts of confidence, appreciation and serenity. The goal of the childhood of a nation ought to be happiness and security rather than apprehensiveness and fear. Happiness and security spring from schools and teachers that are understanding, and from homes that are sound in their organization and solicitous in their zeal to help their children develop emotionally so that they may face life undismayed.

After all, too, life itself is an uncertain adventure to us all in a changing age such as the present. Undoubtedly no small amount of the vague and disconcerting anxiety that many children experience is but an expression of their uncertainties and presentiments regarding it. Natural enough to anybody—young or old—this anxiety is intensified in those younger persons whose immediate background is itself insecure.

Dangers in Oversolicitousness. On the other hand, too much babying, oversolicitousness and spoiling may work much havoc in the child personality, especially as it develops into later childhood, for there is bound to emerge the deep desire to be independent, to be one's own master, to rule one's own conduct. While a naturally retiring or seclusive child may capitulate and permit himself to be dominated and spoiled by parental solicitude, the child of spirit and aggressiveness is likely to chafe against such domination and to seek ways to evade or counteract it. If he does not resort to delinquency because of too great repression or domination, as a means of proving himself, he is likely to grow up with a false sense of values and with poor adjustment to an adult society in which will be found little place and small comfort for the baby, or for the tyrant, or for the nonconformist.

Other Unfortunate Emotional Attitudes. The correction of other undesirable emotional attitudes should not be neglected. For example, it is of importance that the child learn to appreciate and respect the rights of others and not to resent interference with his own selfish wishes. It is important, too, that he control envy and jealousy; that he learn the pleasurableness of sharing, of helping, of working, rather than fall into the habit of moody selfishness and sulky idleness. Pleasurableness and an awareness of well-being should be associated with assigned tasks, with the performance of acts of courtesy, with cooperating with others. It is easy for a young person to fall into the habit of feeling annoyed and cramped by the work he is assigned to do, or by the social participations which are expected of him. If the proper attitudes in these and other matters are established in the early years of life, it will be easy and natural for them to persist into the life of later childhood and so on up through adolescence to the years of adulthood. Parents, teachers, nurses and others whose work brings them into intimate control of children should feel a deep responsibility for laying the groundwork of wise and beneficient emotional attitudes in the growing individual.

Identification. We shall discuss at some length the tendency—strong among many children who are unable to adjust themselves to their situation—to seek through phantasy a vicarious sort of satisfaction. (See Chapter 13.) Defeat and failure are harsh outcomes for a child to face in any area of juvenile experience, and he naturally strives to compensate. The immaturity of childhood's estate is in itself a distinct limitation to the full and unhampered expression of the personality; hence, for this if for no other reason, it is understandable why a young child tends to identify himself at first with his father, or with some other adult in his environment who represents to him the embodiment of power and success. Thus, he experiences vicariously a thrill of pride in the person who stands for strength and dominance, and—vicariously, too—a feeling of superiority. "My daddy is the greatest man on earth." "My daddy drove clear to Chicago and back last week." "My daddy has lots of men working for him." These are examples of the boastful assertions small people are often heard to make regarding those grown-ups with whom they identify themselves and through whose powers they themselves share a reflected superiority.

This tendency to temper one's own inferiorities and failures by relating oneself to somebody else who has not failed is by no means limited to identification with the parent. When the sense of defeat or futility in a child is strong, he may also compensate by gloating over his material possessions. Identifying himself with his belongings yields him a certain sense of security and feeling of achievement which is flattering. He may also identify himself with his playmates, play group, gang, team, school, class, or club, and so find reassuring evidence of his own worth and importance. Juvenile identification occurs likewise with any strong or appealing individual, notably with somebody possessed of power or striking personality, or who enjoys popular acclaim; included in such categories are "Big League" baseball players, football heroes, aviators, actors and actresses, military heroes. Identification may also occur with characters of fiction or comic strips, the juvenile compensator losing himself at least temporarily in following the deeds and fortunes of his hero until his own personality is pretty well submerged in the former's. Such identification of a child who feels inferior or thwarted with somebody who is successful and acclaimed may, of course, work either one of two ways: it may confirm the juvenile in his insecurity and make him feel still more sharply, by contrast, his own shortcomings and defects; or it may serve to inspire him with fresh courage to attack his problems and achieve success, like his hero.

Importance of Habit in Childhood. What we have just been saying about emotional attitudes is equally applicable to the whole range of physical and mental habits. Our habits come about typically as a result of repetition. Tying a knot, holding one's body in good posture, showing deference to age or dignity are all examples of repeated response to the same recurring situation. So are profanity, ungrammatical speech, poor posture, slipshod performance, careless dress and untidiness.

Mere repetition, however, is not enough to insure that a habit will be established. If it were, parents would have only to repeat instructions about brushing teeth, combing hair, hanging up clothing, closing doors, and the like. Along with the practicing or the repetition of a response there must go also a conviction on the part of the learner of the need or wisdom of the habit which is being demanded of him, coupled with a feeling of respect for the imposer of it. When a child is continually reminded to brush his teeth by a parent who herself possesses no toothbrush and whose mouth is unsightly and foul in consequence of neglect, we may well be surprised if the habit is ever strongly established. Habits are powerful forces in the economy of life; they require, however, much more than simple repetition of admonition if they are to be established positively. They depend upon a deep inner conviction either of their essentialness or of the wisdom and consistency of their promoters, or of both.

THE PROBLEM CHILD

Some years ago a circular published by the National Committee for Mental Hygiene carried on the cover a highly significant illustration. In the background of the picture was a building bearing the sign: Child Guidance Clinic. In the doorway stood the director. On the walk leading up to the door from the street were two people: a mother and a little girl of five. The mother was dragging the child by the hand; the child was struggling to escape. Under the picture was the following:

MOTHER: "Well, you see, doctor, I've *brought* her!"
DOCTOR: "So I see, madam. I am inclined to think, however, that *she* should have brought *you!*"

The implication in this dialogue is clear. Problem children are frequently the products of problem parents who themselves stand in need of clinical attention and reeducation. Very commonly back of the disobedient child are parents who do not demand obedience or who are not consistent in demanding it; back of the tantrum-indulging child is the parent who has been overindulgent or who is perhaps herself a practitioner of the art of tantrum-throwing in order to get her own way; back of the deceitful child is the parent who is dishonest in the family or community or in common social relationships; back of the incorrigible child is the incorrigible parent; back of the thumb-sucking, nail-biting, bed-wetting child is the nervous, unstable or neurotic parent who has failed to surround the offspring with orderliness and calm. Of course the parent is not always the only guilty party, and not always guilty at all. Responsibility for producing the problem child must be shared in many cases by the parents and/or the teachers, the community, the gang, perhaps even the church.

In general, we may say that whatever makes for insecurity, for irregularity of regimen, for overstimulation, for uncontrolled emotional outbursts, for inner conflict, or for a feeling of futility may be responsible for the descent of children into waywardness and delinquency. We are extremely prone to blame wrong behavior in children upon the viciousness or the depravity of men; as often as not it is fostered by the less spectacular causatives of faulty discipline, parental incompetence and general home and family inadequacy. We shall return in later chapters to consider further problem children and their reeducation and readjustment.

THE ONSET OF PUBERTY

The Pubescent Change. A rough though fairly satisfactory division of the life span assigns to the period of childhood the first dozen years and to adolescence the second dozen years of life. Strictly speaking, this arbitrary division is somewhat inaccurate, for various reasons. In the first place, girls ordinarily enter pubescence at least a year younger than boys, the former becoming pubescent at about the age of thirteen, while the latter do not enter the period until about the age of fourteen. Secondly, individuals vary rather widely in age of maturing, anywhere between the ages of eleven and fifteen being deemed within the normal range; some investigations show a range as wide as from ten to sixteen years of age. Hollingworth, in a study of

3500 girls, found variations in the first menstrual period as great as eighteen years, the youngest having matured at eight and the oldest not until she was twenty-six. Still, despite these individual variations in the time of onset of pubescence, we may assume in general that it occurs for the greatest number of people somewhere in the neighborhood of the thirteenth birthday.

What is the "pubescent change," and what is its significance? The changes which take place in the organism with the coming of pubescence are such as to fit it to carry on the mature functions of adulthood, including most typically procreation and childbearing. Previous to the early teens, the individual has been concerned principally with growth and the evolution of the juvenile characteristics. With the coming of pubescence, however, he casts off the restrictions of childhood and launches himself upon the road to maturity and the exercise of his full adult powers. In the girl, the pubescent changes include a striking development of the womanly contours, notably a broadening of the pelvis and a filling out of the breasts, and the establishment of the menses typically somewhere in the fourteenth year. In the boy, the advent of pubescence is heralded by a growth of hair in the armpits and the loins and in the appearance of a beard. A striking indication of the arrival of pubescence in the boy is likewise to be observed in a deepening of the voice, due to the change in structure of the throat and the vocal apparatus.

Other Factors Determining the Onset of Puberty. The sex and the individual peculiarity of the person are not the only determiners of the time of onset of pubescence. The *previous condition of health* is an important factor. Maturing is delayed in those children who are sick a good deal during middle or later childhood. Good health throughout those years favors the early maturation of the organism. The *economic condition of the home* is also of importance in determining when the pubescent changes begin. It is generally true that underprivileged children and those coming from poor homes remain in childhood somewhat longer than do those who come from the more fortunate and comfortable homes. Inferior nutrition and defective hygiene retard maturing; on the other hand, good nutrition and the observance of the better principles of child and family health promote and hasten it. Somewhat analogous to the economic condition of the family, *freedom from excessive work or care* during childhood should also be mentioned as fostering early maturing. Children who are caught in their tender years in the economic machine and compelled to spend in toil long hours which ought to be spent in sport and on the playground are likely to be dwarfed in their physiological development and to continue in childhood longer than do those children who have freedom to play and romp and grow as nature intended they should do. There are doubtless still other conditions which have a bearing upon the time of the pubescent changes, among them being *climate, racial stock, temperament, the endocrine complex* and *heredity*.

PUBESCENT AND ADOLESCENT GROWTH

Sudden and Gradual Development Patterns. While it has its ups and downs, as we have seen, growth during the first twelve years of life is fairly uniform. A boy of seven is just a bit taller and heavier than he was when he was six; a girl of eight is just a bit taller and heavier than she was at seven. Each childhood year adds a fairly constant and even amount to the bulk and the height of the body. This tolerable evenness of growth renders it possible for the child to exercise a growing and continuous control over his muscles. There are no sudden sharp increases in the length of a bone here or in the size of a muscle there to interfere with the increasing skill with which bones and muscles can be moved. Each day's practice is cumulative, and by the end of twelve years the child possesses an amazing degree of motor control and skill.

When pubescence comes, however, all this is sometimes changed abruptly and profoundly. Probably more than half of all children enter a period of rapid growth somewhere near the thirteenth year. Many cases have been recorded in which a single bone, the femur, has grown more than 2 inches in length within a twelvemonth, thus causing the body almost literally to "shoot up overnight," and interfering seriously with the motor control of the individual. Of 105 case studies made by the senior author, 64 individuals grew rapidly in height somewhere between the ages of nine and fourteen years, while the 41 others continued to grow slowly and evenly throughout adolescence, as they had done throughout childhood. We have, of course, no way of predicting what child will grow jerkily and what one will grow evenly. Perhaps all that can be said at present is that some children who grow slowly throughout childhood will continue to grow similarly throughout youth; that some other slow growers in childhood will grow rapidly in adolescence; and that most of those who grow rapidly in childhood will slow up considerably in adolescent growth.

The late G. Stanley Hall held that at pubescence there is a sudden augmentation in all bodily and psychic traits and capacities. Later investigators, using exact measurements of large numbers of individuals have tended to discredit Hall. In their delight at finding this great master in error, some of them have gone to the other extreme of asserting that there is no sudden spurt at adolescence. The truth of the matter is about as we have stated above: slightly more than half do unquestionably "shoot up" suddenly; slightly less than half continue to grow slowly and evenly. We can therefore accept neither Hall's theory nor a "gradual development" theory championed by other investigators. Maturation is so largely an individual matter, dependent upon so many factors, that it is impossible to explain it under any single theory.

Growth in Early Adolescence. For most pubescents, growth throughout the organism goes on typically at a heightened tempo, notably of course in the case of those individuals who follow the "shooting up" pattern. *Bones and muscles* develop greater bulk and mass. The trunk bones lengthen, the pelvic arches broaden, the facial bones lengthen and thicken, cartilaginous parts ossify, and the entire skeleton is knitted more firmly together. This sudden and abrupt increase in size of bones and muscles introduces new ratios and is responsible for much of the awkwardness and ungainliness commonly observed among those youths who grow rapidly. As we have noted above, the child is able to develop increasing control over his muscles and is ordinarily by the end of childhood a clever and competent master of them. Then comes pubescence, to upset all of his fine controls. A leg that has grown abruptly longer thrusts farther outward when one steps and comes disconcertingly in contact with the leg of a table or a chair. An arm that has similarly lengthened has a longer reach, and the same amount of leverage that yesterday brought the hand in contact with the muffin or the marmalade today thrusts it into the butter or the soup. There is fumbling, *gaucherie*, dropping, upsetting, breaking and colliding. It is all in all a rather trying time both for the innocent offender and for the uncomprehending parent who inclines to scold for carelessness rather than to ascribe the difficulty to natural occurrences taking place within the young person's organism. It has been well said that at this awkward age nobody loves a boy except his mother.

Circulatory changes in the growing adolescent include an enormous increase in the volume of the heart and a consequent stepping up of blood pressure. These conditions make for far greater capacity for physical expenditure in play and muscular activity and for a tremendous increase in endurance. *Respiratory changes* include a greatly increased lung capacity, a slowing up in the respiration rate and an increase in the volume of the tidal air. *Changes in the brain and nervous system* include a maturing of the brain cells and an elaborate interconnecting among them, especially in the vast associative areas of the cortex where the increasingly rich mental experience is recorded and organized.

The interaction of all these rapidly maturing organs and functions of the body in early adolescence is most interesting. Larger bones and stronger muscles require more blood to nurture them; more blood must have more oxygen to aerate it; more blood and oxygen necessitate a larger heart and more powerful lungs; the resulting availability of greater energy in the body requires better mental organization to direct and control it; better mental organization means elaboration of brain and nervous system to underlie it. Thus do all the parts of the biological organism work together to promote the harmonious development of the individual. Small wonder, considering his increasing capacity for physical prowess, for endurance and for self direction, that the young adolescent is so profoundly interested in sports, in games, in dancing and in the innumerable other outlets for energy which the social scene makes available. The only unfortunate thing about it all is that some of the outlets, as we shall see shortly, are not all that might be desired from the standpoint of the physical and moral health and safety of the individual.

Regardless of whether the young adolescent grows in sudden spurts or whether he continues to grow at a moderate pace, the accumulating years find him in process of becoming a hardy physical specimen, enjoying on the whole good health and stamina, and equipped to run fast and far the race that is set before him. True, there are likely to be certain circulatory disturbances and some digestive and nervous irregularities in early adolescence, but these are usually only functional and incidental to the inharmonious growth in various supplementary organs and functions. <u>Fewer deaths occur between the ages of five and fourteen</u> than in any other equal age group. Puberty used to be thought a critical time and one in which certain safeguards, especially for girls, must be meticulously observed. Nowadays physicians and psychologists incline to the belief that normal activity and the maintenance of the ordinary routine represent the best preparation for pubescence and the most rational passage through it that can be afforded. Obviously the girl will need to be taught certain precautions to be observed during the menstrual periods, but these should not be such as to interfere with the living of a happy and physically active life.

ADOLESCENT INTERESTS

It would require a catalogue to mention all the things in which youth is interested. The childhood years were filled with amassing sensory and perceptual information, with developing motor skills and physical prowess, with rough and tumble play and the beginning of socialized games, with gang pursuits. The adolescent's sphere of interest is enormously extended to include everything tangible or knowable in the universe.

Personal Appearance. Perhaps nothing has been traditionally more striking in the varied assortment of adolescent interests than youth's concern over personal appearance. Childhood, and boyhood in particular, takes small note of personal appearance. While on occasion some boys may enjoy dressing up and parading about, in the main they are callous to these matters. They are not concerned over holes in their stockings, or in the seat of their trousers; they waste no time in lamenting dirty shirts or faces; they are not intrigued by the attractiveness of clean ears and neck and fingernails; they would rather go without a necktie than bother to find and adjust one; they affect disreputable caps or hats, old trousers, shapeless sweaters; their hair is free to lie down or stand up as it may choose. Those boys who know no better than to "dress up" are promptly set upon, teased, or given fitting nicknames. Boy values do not include dress, neatness or finery.

But when adolescence arrives a change comes in most cases slowly but surely into evidence. There is a new interest in personal appearance, notably in the girl. What a scene is enacted in every home where there is a young adolescent daughter when a party or dance approaches! New frocks, new dancing shoes, new evening wraps, new this, new that. And what attention is given to coiffure and complexion! Beauty salons reap golden harvests not alone from the woman who has stepped a bit over the meridan and who desires to have the facts discounted: her daughter is quite as good a customer. There must be "permanents," "waves," and "facials" until nature's original handiwork is all but transformed. And when the young lady walks out, she is quite as conscious of the strong impression her charm is making upon others as she is of her own flattering self-satisfaction and complacency.

The adolescent boy may or may not respond in kind to the urge to "dress up." Many a young fellow passes through adolescence without ever developing a strong consciousness for dress and personal appearance. Many another one, however, feels the strength of the urge and while he cannot devote himself to these matters as persistently as his sister does, he responds none the less positively. Many mothers can testify to the fact that their young sons frequently get out the family ironing-board and press their suits and overcoats and ties so that their ensemble may appear as neat as possible. Clean shirts and collars, harmonizing ties and socks, trousers of just the right flare and style, these items become of importance to the young fellow who as a boy three or four years before could scarcely be got by any persuasiveness that his mother could summon to take the slightest interest in personal appearance.

Within the past two decades, however, a drab uniformity has made its appearance in the garb of adolescents of both sexes. Stemming no doubt from the wartime shortages of materials and the rise in costs of clothing, dungarees, "pedal-pushers" and "shorts" in cheaper cottons and corduroys have become almost universally popular as the garb of youth, not only for play but for work, school and party. This contagion appears to be almost endemic for all classes and economic levels on both sides of the tracks, about the only differentiating feature between the wardrobes of the two sexes being the omnipresent sweat shirt of the male and the very casually untucked-in boy's dress shirt worn by the female. This trend has persisted too long to be considered a fad; it represents in all probability a permanent shift in clothing values among adolescents—as well as, incidentally, among large numbers of their mothers and fathers!

Sports. In an age in which so much attention is being devoted by the adult generation to out-of-door activities, tours and week-end trips, it is obvious that the younger generation will be also intrigued by opportunities for activities in the open. In an age, too, in which there is little demand or need in most homes for the "chores" and family tasks which supplied the needs of an earlier generation for physical activity and exercise, it is fortunate that there has arisen so universal an interest in wholesome recreational activities as obtains today among the adolescent group. Baseball, football, basketball, volley ball, tennis, golf and similar sports of a more or less competitive nature challenge and receive the interest of youth everywhere. In connection with their high school athletics and gymnastics a vast amount of interest and enthusiasm is whipped up. When classes or schools compete in field day activities or track meets, the juvenile population is swept off its feet in zestful participation. School colors wave from every automobile; school bands blare; school songs rise to heaven; school yells punctuate spectacular plays or runs; automobile horns honk raucously; everybody is excited. There are few more wholesome influences in the present age upon youth than that exerted by sports and athletics. Fortunately every season offers its peculiar types of such activities; during three hundred and sixty-five days of the year there is something always intriguing in sports.

Gang Interests. While the nature of the social urge changes somewhat in adolescence, the crude games of later childhood being now somewhat outgrown, its strength is if anything still greater. There is likely to be a holdover into early adolescence of the childhood gang, and there is much interest in hangouts, shacks, and other secret places of rendezvous where the members of the group may hold their meetings and indulge in their favorite recreations. Some of these meeting places of the inner circle are fearfully and wonderfully made. Some of them are equipped with all sorts of athletic paraphernalia; some with reading tables, books, magazines, and the like; some, with tools and workshop furnishings; some, with stage and wings and dramatic setting. Many gangs enjoy all-day hikes, with the attendant "weenie roast" and foraging; many enjoy the purely tribal activities of camping, cooking over an open fire; many prefer organized athletics and sports; some have no particular aims for existence but enjoy the sheer secrecy and charm of clandestine meetings, passwords, "business" discussions, and the like. The thrall of gang life is likely to extend well into the teens, after which it tends among normally evolving youth to yield place to more conventional group activities connected with school, club, church and community in general.

School Interests. The school interests of the adolescent cover a wide range of wholesome activities. In addition to the athletic, these include dawning fascination with some specific branch of study, with the attendant reading, investigating and discussing; the appeal which is made by membership in clubs and by participation in extra-curricular activities, such as music, dramatics, science and language organizations; editing the school paper; managing or directing teams or clubs; and planning programs. Prominent also among the interests centering in the school life of the adolescent is that aroused in autograph books, memory books and similar non-literary mementos of school life and its associations. There is also keen interest in the school and class dances, plays, musicales and exhibitions of talent. Wearing animated raincoats, caps, berets, ankle-socks, hieroglyphic decorations, shoulder ornaments, sport and "turtle-neck" sweaters; going hatless, tieless, or stockingless; affecting smart expressions and foreign accents; painting lips and cheeks and nails; wearing sweaters backward or inside-out; arranging hair in the same style, *e.g.*, a long shoulder-bob with curled ends or done in pony tails and horse tails; wearing ornamental "bobby-pins," fancy woven belts, rings on the forefinger, earrings in the lapel, "bangs," and so forth are a few of the epidemic interests which are observed to sweep through a high school or a junior high school. There is no limit to the originality of youth, and once one of its number conceives or adopts some new fad it is but a matter of hours before the entire group falls into line.

Movies, Actors and Actresses. Strong interest attaches to the movies and to actors and actresses of the screen. Adolescent patronage of the cinema is practically universal, as is apparent to anyone who will "listen in" for five minutes to the conversation going on in any group of young people. Sooner or later the conversation will turn upon this popular theme. Almost every youth has his or her favorite actor or actress. The feeling which young people have often falls little short of adoration. They read everything that they can find about their favorites in the screen and trade magazines; they write them "fan" mail; they adorn the walls of their rooms with their photographs; they ape their style of dress, of coiffure, of conversation; they familiarize themselves with the details of their lives, and talk familiarly about them. They are frequent and regular attendants at the movies and at informal get-to-gethers of young people often terminating in a wind-up trip to movieland.

Home Interests. During the relatively few hours which adolescents find free to spend indoors in their own homes, radio and TV offer a prominent source of enjoyment and interest. Even home study is likely to be carried forward to the tune of some ditty from the loud-speaker. Jazz, dance music, songs, musical comedy, thrillers, mystery dramas, "give-away" and "quiz" programs—all have their devotees among the juvenile audience. Since television necessitates using the eyes as well as the ears, it is inevitable that reading and studying of books, which seems to be possible to a degree when only the loud-speaker is operating, is coming to be seriously interfered with in many a home where televised programs are available to children and youth.

Reading appeals to hosts of young people in every age. In the earlier teens, mystery and adventure stories find favor, and are likely to continue popular up through adolescence and into adult life, as witness the prevalent popularity of detective and "murder" stories among all groups. Scouting stories begin to lose interest for most boys by the time they are fourteen; girl scout books interest girls not much longer. Interestingly enough, there is a parallel and timeless interest in certain of the classic tales of childhood, notably such stories as "Little Women," "Treasure Island" and "Heidi." Supplementing the adventure stories, there grows up among young people of the senior high school age an interest in romance and love stories, biography, "movie" magazines, "true story" and "confession" types, and in the always popular home magazines. Other interests available in homes that still maintain concern for wholesome leisure time opportunities for their children and young people include, for girls, cooking, housekeeping, knitting sweaters or dresses, and for boys, gadget making, washing and polishing the family car, and bench and workshop activities.

Dancing and Sociability. Always popular, dancing probably intrigues a larger number of the adolescent generation today than ever before. Even the school or class "play," or the musical club performance cannot hope to get the crowd out unless the ticket carries the magical and enticing appeal: "Dancing afterward in the gymnasium until one." Even a visit to the restaurant after the show is made more appealing by the opportunity offered to dance between snacks. Dancing is able, through the rhythm of the music, the raucousness of certain modern orchestral arrangements, the gaiety of lights and gowns and decorations, the close association of others who are like-minded, the contagiousness of youthful spirits, the intimate swing upon the arm of one's partner, or through all of these things combined, to tap the social springs of youth and cause them to gush forth cheerfully.

Food and Gastronomic Interests. Mealtime is and should be for most young people a time of comfort and enjoyment. In youth, one can eat anything, any time, anywhere; at least, it almost so appears. It is nothing short of a pleasure to watch a hungry young fellow clean off his plate and look over his shoulder for more.

Still, with all the splendid appetite and heartiness of the adolescent, there appear many pronounced idiosyncrasies and whims connected with the dietary. A favorite dish may be partaken of so liberally, if nobody remonstrates, that there will be no room left for anything else. Such things especially as pies, cakes, desserts, sweets, pickles and highly seasoned foods may be relished most. Individual aversions may be strong and decided to such foods as spinach, greens, butter, eggs, milk or fish. Months later, however, so unstable and inconsistent is adolescent appetite, that a dish which was detested formerly may become a favorite. The craving is likely to be strong among adolescents for candies, gum, carbonated beverages, ices and other offerings of the confectionist and the soda dispenser. Girls who are told that sweets mean pounds in weight may deny themselves indulgence in candies and toothsome desserts in order to keep their bodies conventionally slim and lithe. Boys, too, if they get a notion that pimples on face or neck are due to too much sweet, may renounce it permanently or at least until the pimples have cleared up.

ADOLESCENT DELINQUENCY AND MISDEMEANORS

Sociologists and welfare workers are dismayed at the current tendency for the type age of the criminal to be constantly lowering. A generation ago the average law breaker was a middle-aged person;

today, he is an adolescent; there is a strong incidence of crime extending downward into the early teens, and even into childhood. The middle-aged crook cannot hope to succeed in his nefarious career today, with rapid-fire guns, police teletype, short-wave and swift automobiles for pursuit. There is demanded in the modern criminal, on the contrary, a coldblooded daring, a quickness of reaction time, a control and a precision of muscle which only the younger criminal can exhibit. Hundreds of boys and girls hardly yet in their teens are entering today upon criminal careers. Psychologists, social workers and police officials are eager to discover the cause or causes back of this situation and to check the downward penetration of criminal behavior into the ranks of youth.

Delinquency in the United States. Between the years 1948–1951, there was an increase of 17 per cent in juvenile crime in this country; by 1955, it had increased almost 30 per cent, and in some courts as much as 50 per cent, over a five year period. In 1954, approximately 1,000,000 young persons were arrested; 385,000 of them—2 per cent of all 10- to 17-year-olds in the nation—appeared before juvenile courts. This shady army of child and adolescent lawbreakers is recruited from every stratum of society, from every economic level, and commits almost every conceivable type of crime and misdemeanor. Reaching a peak at the 18-year level, at which age more crime is now committed by boys and girls of America than at any other life age, lawbreaking tapers down in the one direction into the 8 to 10 year level, and, in the other, upward into adulthood. While, as the U. S. Children's Bureau points out, there exists a far vaster army of 18,000,000 other boys and girls between 10 and 17 who are not picked up for crime and who conduct themselves creditably in their communities, the existence of the other shady army tends by the monstrousness of its conduct to focus upon itself wide adult attention and to overshadow in the adult mind the creditable behavior of the great mass of children and young people. It is this latter conforming group of youth that we have been discussing in the preceding pages of this chapter. These may be presumed to be safely on the road to well adjusted and normal adulthood, after the turbulence and stress of adolescence are over. In the present section, we pause to consider briefly the delinquent sector of the adolescent generation.

A Disconcerting Situation. The misdemeanors committed by wayward children and youth are extremely varied in type. In Chicago, vandalism on public school property amounts to some $400,000 damage in a year's time. In Baltimore, more than 22,000 school windows were smashed in a twelvemonth. In Detroit, juveniles broke into a public library branch, smashed glass cases, ripped books apart, strewed the floors with index cards, poured glue over them, and then made off with valuable movie equipment. In a California community, youngsters ran an automobile over a cliff into the Pacific, "to see it splash," as they reported. In New Bedford, 5 boys—all of them under 14—slashed $15,000 worth of store windows with glass cutters, set fire to a church, a drugstore and an automobile. Four Brooklyn juvenile members of a homicide gang feloniously assaulted and killed two men, battered several others, and horsewhipped two girls, all in one night's orgy. A King's County (N. Y.) judge deposes that roaming the New York streets are hordes of juvenile sadists and young sex criminals, committing serious crimes. More than 300,000 runaways from home—of whom between 40,000 and 100,000 are estimated to be girls—are thumbing and hitch-hiking and jumping their way from state to state and from section to section of the nation. This formidable number of migrant children has posed a formidable problem for every community into and through which they pass. In many Pennsylvania counties, for example, authorities have no other alternative than to use the jails to house them. California, which receives some 2000 runaways every month, is compelled to charter a number of eastbound "deportation trains" every year in order to return migrant children and youth to their own states.

And so the drab picture of delinquency and waywardness unfolds. Everywhere mounting concern over the urgency of the situation is in evidence. The Secretary of the Department of Health, Education and Welfare brands juvenile delinquency "one of the most complex social ills facing our nation today." A Senate Judiciary Subcommittee spends a number of months probing the matter. In the summer of 1954, a conference of 460 specialists is held in Washington to study the problem. New York City's associations of high school teachers and principals cite the "appalling increase of insolence and acts of violence in the schools," deplores the misdeeds of "an undisciplined, selfish and lawless minority" of youth, and calls upon the Mayor to appoint a special commission to report in three months' time "some definite plans for safeguarding the educational system." New York's City College opens courses for truant officers in the fields of child psychology, personality, discipline, etc., better to prepare attendance officers for their herculean tasks. The Director of the National Institute of Mental Health deplores the fact that, while previous to 1945 only 2000 narcotic addicts were admitted to federal treatment hospitals, between 1950 and 1955 more than 4000 have been admitted each year. The increase of admission of minors has been even more notable. At the National Health Center in Bethesda, Md., a searching study is being conducted into the causes of extreme aggressive and destructive tendencies in children. Finally, federal authorities predict that there will be a 50 per cent increase in juvenile crime between 1950 and 1960.

Prevention and Control. In order to set backfires to this disturbing conflagration of juvenile excesses, various means of control and correction have been proposed or actually undertaken. One Long Island community would fine and/or send parents of delinquent children to jail themselves, as is the common practice in Great Britain, as being jointly responsible with their errant children for acts of waywardness, and would impose a 9:30 p.m. curfew for all children under 16 years of age in order to keep them off the streets and away from nocturnal temptations and adventures. A sheriff in another community in the same state recommends that police officers be directed to use their night sticks on delinquent children and that their parents be advised to restore the "slipper and woodshed" practice of yesterday in controlling them. Recalling perhaps that Jacob A. Riis, a half century ago, explained New York's Lower East Side gangs as representing "a distemper of the slums," scores of our American cities are carrying forward slum clearance projects and opening new and more attractive housing units to replace them. Notable among these cities is Norfolk, Va., where more than 193 acres (about a third of the city's entire area) are being cleared away and rebuilt at a cost approaching fifty million dollars.

Factors Associated with Delinquency. There is no single cause back of this unfortunate trend; there are many associated factors. Most of all, broken or inadequate homes are breeders of delinquency. When the steadying influence of a good home and of loving parents is not to be had, and the young person loses the feeling of loyalty and the sense of security which he covets, he is extremely likely to seek some sort of exciting adventure that will supply a substitute experience for the emotional satisfactions which his family environment cannot afford him. The road to crime is for young delinquents a road into which many flee in order to drown their unhappiness and seek a substitute happiness and security. Drab and cheerless homes, where there is much harshness and bitterness with life and what it is bringing, likewise are frequently responsible for driving young people to find the happiness and gaiety which are denied them in their own family circle, in "fast" company, in unwholesome gangs, in the light and thrill and excitement of the white way, whence it is often but a short and easy step over into waywardness and crime.

Youth's passion for the limelight is fired by the spectacular accounts of crime which are heralded in black type in the newspapers and tabloids. Hero worshipping and publicizing the culprit as we so often do today have the unwholesome effect of making the way of the lawbreaker appear attractive to many a youth who has not yet learned perspective. The appeal of easy wealth, the necessity for possessing plenty of ready spending money, the adult example so often set of seeking to get something for nothing, the leadership and example of bad associates, bad community recreational influences, the boredom of idleness which often weighs heavily upon active-bodied and active-minded young people in an age in which there is little work to be done at home, the exaggeration of the sex urge which is played up on every hand, the drabness of industrial employment and the increasingly long free time after hours, the false ideals and impossible standards purveyed by movies, comics, salacious literature and morally loose grownups—all these influences play upon young people in our communities today, and it is hardly to be expected that they can all escape contamination by them.

CHURCH AND RELIGIOUS INTERESTS

Many adult critics of youth make the mistake of inferring that, because they observe youth to be pleasure-bent and often only sporadic in their attendance at church and Sunday school, young people today are irreligious. Nothing could be farther removed from actuality. Modern youth is liberal rather than conservative in things religious, as in other human relationships, and hence finds it not impossible both to love the Lord and to love a good time, even to love the Lord and go to church irregularly or rarely. Young people conceive faith to be an inner thing of the spirit, and not dependent upon external forms of expression. They are unwilling to subscribe to narrow and restricting creeds and denominationalisms; they are interested to strip away the theological and ecclesiastical trappings with which churchmen and religionists have invested faith, and to worship in spirit and in truth. They are at considerable loss to understand why it is that two thousand years of the Christian religion, not to mention a still greater period of the existence of other religions, have failed to teach the human race the elementary lessons of peace and good will among the nations. They understand that men have never really tried the religious way. They have no interest in disputation, credos and pretense as touching religious matters. They regard religion as positive, dynamic, releasing, not as inhibitory, negative and repressing.

Most people experience religious skepticism sometime in adolescence. Because inadequate foundations for faith have been laid by well intentioned but inadequate Sunday school teachers, and because of the subsequent disturbing influences of the study of science, of certain schools of naturalistic philosophy and of mechanistic psychology which postulate a degree of materialism, a youth is apt to enter upon a period of religious doubt before proceeding very far in his high school and college studies. If only a broadly secure foundation could have been laid in childhood, and if the created order of the universe could have been presented to the unfolding mind of the child as the manifestation of a mighty evolving plan that is not yet completed, the young person would never be called upon to make bitter readjustment later on from the limited God of the Sunday school to the limitless God of starry universes.

As it is, some adolescents are unable to make the adjustment, and they remain indifferent or actually hostile to things religious for the remainder of their lives. Most of them, it is to be hoped, succeed in reshaping their faith and making it broad enough and high enough to endure. For these latter, faith should become increasingly strong with the increase of intellectual understanding of the great underlying scheme of life and of the universe. The Deity should become infinitely grander and nobler than the Deity of the Sunday school; religion should become more vast and consuming than was the religion of childhood; worship should become more than a one-day-a-week garment: it should become instead a transforming and infusing power which has no limit.

The modern, up-to-date church has learned that in order to attract and hold young people it must offer them social opportunities and inducements that the churches of a generation and more ago did not deem necessary. Formerly there was much less opportunity in the community life for social good times, and the church met little competition. Now, with the elaborate modern community organization, there is more to intrigue youth outside the church, and the church has found it essential to make a stronger appeal on the social side in order to survive in a competitive social atmosphere. Some young people, of course, are attracted to the church by the religious element of worship; others are attracted in part at least by the social opportunities which affiliation with it affords. Socials, young people's societies, plays, entertainments, conferences, church suppers, choir practice, athletics, class participation and class parties, combine the spiritual with the social in a most effective and gratifying manner, and hordes of young people are held under the benign aegis of the church by these most excellent and challenging activities.

COMMUNITY INFLUENCES NEEDFUL FOR YOUTH

Thus far, about all that our communities have done publicly to provide an adequate and satisfying environment for young people to grow up in has been to provide reasonably good schools and fairly numerous playgrounds. Private and semi-private agencies have supplied amusement places, clubs, camps and church programs. Before we can rest satisfied, however, these opportunities must be extended and supplemented. Our American communities are still lacking in opportunity for young people to indulge in positive and creative endeavor. Among the things which will some day be included in the general setup of the community for the promotion of adolescent welfare will doubtless be the following: (1) some reliable and consistent means for guaranteeing to every family an adequate income so that there may be economic security and vocational hopefulness among the children; (2) the elimination of political corruption, so that young people may not be cheated out of their social birthright; (3) the enforcement of law, so that they may escape exploitation at the hands of the unprincipled; (4) the maintenance of ever better schools for the training of the *whole* child, not merely of the mind; (5) the provision of a program of educational and vocational guidance, so that they may be aided intelligently to find themselves in the work of the school and in the subsequent work of the world; (6) the making available of clinical facilities, so that those who are maladjusted or abnormal may be helped to develop their personalities wisely and constructively; (7) the extension of literary facilities to include school and community libraries stocked with interesting and suitably adapted reading material that will be available seven days a week; (8) the provision of camps, huts and cabins outside the city where, under proper leadership, young people may experience all the social joys of "roughing it" and the charm of common habitation; and (9) last but not least, the setting up of a program of training leaders in numerous non-school fields, so that young people may have opportunities to indulge their intellectual, mechanical, artistic and dramatic bents in healthful and developmental ways. In this last connection, there will be found to be need for a wide extension of the present limited community center facilities where juvenile clubs and non-school activities may be focused. When these things have been done by the community, we may look forward to a golden age for youth in which effective backfires will be set to the disconcerting moral conflagration which, if unchecked, will, it is to be feared, sear the spirit and the soul of the rising generation, along with those of its elders.

Viewed against this wider concept of the community of tomorrow, many of our towns and cities of today are quite inadequate as stimulating environments for the wise and hygienic rearing of children. Even clearance of slums, now proceeding vigorously in every major city in America, and the ensuing mass replacement overnight with standardized and sanitized new communities, may, while squalor and overcrowding evils are happily eliminated, fail to provide transplanted youth with any neighborhood challenge and inspiration beyond those offered by a filling station and a supermarket. A community that aspires to promote many-sided growth and development of children will be found sooner or later to be vastly more than a mere aggregation of identical dwellings projected like mushrooms in a new city basis.

RELATIONSHIP OF NURSING TO CHILDHOOD

Throughout her professional life the nurse will commonly find among her patients sick or ailing children. It makes no difference whether she is a nurse in a hospital or whether she is a public health nurse; she will be concerned with the health of the young. Whether she serves in the general ward, in the children's ward, or the maternity ward; whether she is employed publicly as a district nurse, as a visiting nurse, or as a school nurse; whether she is employed privately as an industrial nurse, as a physician's nurse, or as a dental nurse—in these and in most other nursing situations, she will be called upon to administer to children or to advise with their parents concerning their care and training. Some of her work in this connection will be curative or corrective; most of it will probably be preventive or educative.

The position of the nurse in the economy of childhood is coming to be better appreciated and more secure with every decade. Whereas a generation or two ago medical and nursing service was limited principally to the handling of those who were ill, today there is no such limitation. Indeed, the clarion note of modern health programs is *prevention*. Society has learned the lesson that the health and well-being of its members, both adult and juvenile, is something to be safeguarded and promoted systematically and continuously. Most strikingly, perhaps, one observes this new emphasis upon preventive hygiene in the increased attention people are giving to control of some of the great modern scourges like diphtheria, poliomyelitis, tuberculosis and cancer, through propaganda, free clinical service and widespread information in the schools. But these efforts to eliminate the dread diseases we have mentioned, while they loom large upon the health horizon, are perhaps not the most important and promising controls of disease and suffering that man is exercising. He has learned to go much deeper into the problem of guaranteeing health and efficiency to the generations.

Modern Health Programs for Childhood. Modern health programs start long before the child is born. The expectant mother is taught by physician and nurse to maintain her physical health on such a level of excellence that her own life and that of her child may be protected during the months of pregnancy and so that both individuals may emerge from the ordeal of birth with prospects of future physical soundness and the expectation of health and happiness. After the baby arrives the mother is afforded professional advice and counsel in feeding, in caring for him, and in training him throughout the preschool period. Nursing service is now furnished for workers and their families by employers, by the community or by the state, so that children's chances of health and robustness are enhanced over what they were a quarter of a century and more ago. Baby clinics, guidance clinics, habit clinics, demonstration clinics, welfare centers, feeding centers, milk stations, summer roundups, vaccination and inoculation programs—all these add to the opportunities which modern parents have at their very doors to aid them in bringing their children safely through infancy and early childhood.

Moreover, when the toddler ventures forth from the protection and care of his home to the nursery school, and later to the kindergarten and the grade school, the solicitude of society for his good health and happiness is not then relaxed.

Almost every school community today maintains some kind of program of health inspection and follow-up, in charge of physicians, clinicians and nurses. State laws or local regulations require in most instances methodical and regular examination of school children to detect incipient defects and to prevent their occurrence or to correct them if they have already made their appearance. Clinics, staffed by professional practitioners and nurses, afford opportunities for parents to have physical abnormalities or defects in their children remedied promptly. Full-time inspection is maintained, usually under the direction of a school physician, but under the immediate supervision of school nurses. Home visitation for the purpose of familiarizing parents with the objectives of the school health program and of enlisting their cooperation in guaranteeing the benefits from it is ordinarily in the hands of the nurse, and in her professional contacts with parents she has opportunity to spread her evangel of health and good adjustment.

In all of these efforts to make available the benefits of modern medical science to the masses, the nurse plays a major role. And most particularly in relationship to the health of childhood the nurse today dominates the picture. The medical man is primarily a diagnostician, a prescriber of treatment, a healer of the sick. The nurse, on the other hand, is primarily, and especially in her school relationships, a teacher of parents, of teachers and of children themselves. She stands for the popularization of scientific knowledge, for the disseminating of helpful information that the layman and the child can understand and respect, and she affords a point of intimate contact between the medical specialist and the layman. At her best, she is a sympathetic adviser in the home; an effective, reassuring professional worker in the clinic, the doctor's office, the hospital, the community center, and wherever else mothers and children in need of her ministrations may be found. This being the case, every nurse should be familiar with the fundamental psychology of childhood and adolescence.

Nursing the Sick Child. One of the important lessons a nurse can learn is the necessity of entering into the sick child's interests with him in order that the hours of illness and convalescence may be made to pass more agreeably. The understanding nurse should make herself familiar with the spontaneous activities of children of different age levels, so that she can utilize them in caring for her young charges. Not only may many irksome days of sickness and of succeeding convalescence be easier to bear for the little patient, but he will react much more favorably and cooperatively to the nurse's wishes and suggestions if he feels her understanding interest in him and his activities.

Encouraging the sick child to do things for himself, in so far as his condition warrants, is likewise of the utmost importance if the nurse wishes to hasten improvement. It is therapeutic for any ill person to keep his thoughts as much as possible away from himself and his ailments. This is doubly desirable in the junior patient. If it becomes necessary to take a child to another room for treatment, he should be encouraged to take along what he is working on to show the doctor. If he frets because many days or weeks must be spent in a wheel chair, one may tempt him to bear the inconvenience and discomfort by dubbing the chair a chariot for His Royal Highness and allowing him a brief period every day when he may receive attention and confer honors. If a little girl ill with measles chafes against the long isolation, she may be kept happy with a little jingle taught her by the nurse while she is being bathed:

> Brown-eyed girl, tucked in her bed—
> All because her face is red:
> Caught the measles on the run;
> Now comes rest and, later, fun!

For a convalescent child on isolation, easily constructed jigsaw puzzles are entertaining. Such puzzles may be made by the nurse from attractive magazine covers pasted on cardboard, shellacked and cut with a sharp knife into various shapes and sizes determined by the age and ability of the child. Bedfast convalescent children may be kept pleasantly occupied for hours making picture letters. All that is necessary is a supply of illustrated magazines, paste, blunt scissors and plain paper. Scrapbooks may also be made, as well as paper doll families, paper animals, barnyard groups, and the like.

In all nursing situations it is important for the nurse to realize that children must never be intimidated in order to insure obedience or cooperation. One should speak gently but firmly to the sick child, never sharply and abruptly. A comforting feeling of security, so essential to normal progress toward recovery, accompanies nursing care that is methodical, unemotional and unconfused. Preceding the sleeping time, especially, it is desirable that there shall be calm and quiet surrounding the little patient. It is impossible for him to escape entirely the anxiety and apprehension that obtain in the hospital atmosphere; consequently, redoubled efforts need to be made to give him something pleasant to think about while he is drifting off to sleep. Most children receive assurance by a light handclasp or touch from the nurse when she tucks them in for the night. (A poor substitute for mother, but it often helps.)

Some children are accustomed to take to bed with them a favorite doll or teddy. When illness comes suddenly, the child is often rushed off to the hospital and Teddy remains at home. At sleeping-time, a little girl may thus find herself not only in a strange bed but also without Teddy, who has always slept beside her. This is likely to be a bit bewildering, not to say terrifying. A stuffed laparotomy stocking in the dark looks and feels somewhat like Teddy, and if a little hand can rest upon such a pseudo-Teddy so that the frightened little girl can fall asleep, such a substitute should be provided. Habits that may be otherwise negative but which encourage sleep and security should be fostered, not broken, during a child's illness.

THOUGHT PROBLEMS FOR THE STUDENT

1. What specific experience have you personally had in the care or handling of children? Has this experience been on the whole agreeable or distasteful to you? Do you get on well with children? Do children seem to like you?
2. Make a list of all the agencies and activities you know about which are concerned with the safeguarding or promotion of the health (1) of the expectant mother, (2) of the infant and preschool child, (3) of the school child, (4) of the family.
3. If possible, spend an hour or two in a family where there is a small child of

four or five years. Note especially striking evidences of his curiosity as indicated in "why" questions; by manipulative or investigative activities, etc. Report your results in writing.
4. Find in the researches of Gesell, Irwin, *et al.*, other examples than those cited in the text of the increasing power and control over the neuromuscular system which the young child develops during the first two or three years of life.
5. Cite all the examples you can of the mental evolution of the infant and the very young child as he proceeds to make order out of the "great booming, buzzing confusion" into which he is born.
6. What "problem children" have you known? Specifically what were some of the problems involved? What factors may have caused them to appear? Were all of the problems solved? What specific ones, if any, were never solved? With what ultimate personal or social consequences?
7. At what age did you become pubescent? Do you know whether any of your friends matured either considerably earlier or considerably later than you did? Can you account for any of the instances of retarded or precocious maturation?
8. Did you grow rapidly or slowly in early adolescence? Would you say that your curve of growth has proceeded in the main evenly, or irregularly, over the past ten or twelve years? If the latter, at what time has it risen rapidly? Compare notes with some of your classmates in this matter.
9. Make a list of the principal interests that you personally had during the earlier and middle teens. How do they compare with those mentioned in the text? Which of them still persist with considerable tenaciousness?
10. Have you observed some of the juvenile "epidemic interests" or fads that sometimes sweep through juvenile groups? If so, what are they? Have they been transient or persistent?
11. What instances of juvenile waywardness, crime or delinquency have you known about? Can you distinguish any of the possible inciting causes that led to this asocial behavior? In what way or ways might the unfortunate events have been prevented?
12. Would you consider the adolescent period a fortunate or an unfortunate time in which to direct the individual's attention to literature that tends to idealize matrimonial qualities in a mate? Give reasons for your answer.
13. (*a*) Plan occupational therapy for a girl of fifteen who has been ordered by the doctor to have bed rest for six months as a tuberculosis suspect. Make a list of the books you would recommend to your patient, and tell why you choose the particular ones you do. (*b*) Plan occupational therapy for the boy of sixteen who emerged from the last football game with a compound fracture of the femur. Make a reading list for him and indicate the reasons for your selections.
14. Suppose your cousin, now entering high school, tells you that she has her heart set on studying nursing; what advice and guidance can you give her relative to the following:
    (*a*) Subjects she should include in her high school course? In her college program?
    (*b*) Several non-technical books that would give her pertinent and authentic information about the nursing profession?
    (*c*) Procedure in choosing the school of nursing to which she should apply for entrance?
    (*d*) Hints as to the development of personality traits and habits of behavior?

SUGGESTED READINGS

1. Aldrich, C. A., and Aldrich, M. M.: *Babies Are Human Beings.* 2nd ed. New York, The Macmillan Co., 1954.
    An excellent guide book on how to bring up happy and healthy children. "A nationally famous book."
2. Blair, G. M., Jones, R. S., and Simpson, R. H.: *Educational Psychology.* New York, The Macmillan Co., 1954.
    A valuable coverage of the areas of child growth and development.
3. Carmichael, L. (editor): *Manual of Child Psychology.* 2nd ed. New York, John Wiley and Sons, 1954.
    An advanced text, masterful in its content and a storehouse of materials in the field.
4. Cole, L.: *Psychology of Adolescence.* 4th ed. New York, Rinehart and Co., 1954.
    Presents a clear picture of all phases of adolescent growth, with evaluation of each study and abundant illustrative material.
5. Jenkins, G. G., Shacter, H., and Bauer, W. M.: *These Are Your Children.* New, expanded ed. Chicago, Scott, Foresman and Co., 1953.
    An intimate and able discussion of problems in guidance of children's physical, mental, social and emotional development, at home, in school and at play.
6. Jersild, A. T.: *Child Psychology.* 4th ed. New York, Prentice-Hall, Inc., 1954.
    Readable and comprehensive, this book provides a systematic treatment of child development.
7. Munn, N. L.: *Psychology.* 2nd ed. Boston, Houghton Mifflin Co., 1954.
    Presents authoritative discussion of various phases of development at the child and adolescent level. Refer to the excellent index for specific topics.
8. Thorpe, L. P.: *Child Psychology and Development.* New York, Ronald Press, 1955.
    Cf. especially sections on "Physical Growth and Health," "Children's Play and Interests," and "Personality and Character Formation of the Child."

Chapter 12

*It is not growing like a tree
In bulk, doth make men better be!*

BEN JOHNSON

ACHIEVING ADULTHOOD

The Coming of Adulthood. In civilized society, we take it for granted that the coming of biological maturity brings with it the achievement of those emotional and intellectual attitudes and viewpoints that we associate with people who have "grown up." By virtue of the years spent in the schoolroom and of the training received in his home, his church and his community, it is assumed that by the time a person reaches his later teens he has matured in his personality and character and emotions as certainly as he has in his height and weight and girth.

The student nurse has chosen to prepare herself for one of the important modern professions, that of ministering to the sick. It is a profession that will challenge the finest qualities within her, and merit her thoughtful service. Work such as that which she is to perform for her fellowmen is not the work of a child; it is essentially the work of an adult who has left childhood's estate behind. It will be well at this juncture of our study of psychology to try to determine what it is that makes an adult individual. All about us we see so many people who have never grown up in the fullest sense that it behooves us to pause to inquire: What does it mean to be an *adult*?

The Adult Individual Has Been Psychologically Weaned. There comes a time in the early life of all mammals when it becomes necessary to wean them from the natural sustenance of the mother's milk and substitute for it a new dietary. This process of weaning involves a biological readjustment and the emergence of a new freedom and independence from the physical body of the parent. A familiar example is the interesting process of weaning a kitten. The mother cat begins to discourage her offspring from its incessant nursing, and may even emphasize her growing averseness to the kitten's advances by cuffing it whenever it begins its nursing exploration. In a few days the kitten has learned to seek its food elsewhere: it has been "weaned."

This process of weaning, which takes place with the human baby as well as with the animal offspring, is a necessary prelude to the achievement of self direction and self management. As long as the offspring must depend upon the physical body of the parent, it remains necessarily infantile and helpless. When it can exist apart from the maternal breast, it is well on the way to growing up and becoming independent. The release of the offspring from dependence upon the mammalian mother is termed *biological* weaning. Along with it, there comes of course also an increased independence in all other physical relationships. The young animal's movements and excursions grow less circumscribed; it learns soon to forage for its own food, to seek its own comfort, to provide its own protection and to sleep away from the sheltering body of the mother upon which it was earlier so completely dependent. The period of dependence is run through swiftly, and the complete physical maturity of the animal is achieved within a few months, or at most a very few years.

But the achievement of adulthood in a human being is something far more than the mere biological maturation of the body. The mere circumstance that a young woman has lived to be eighteen or twenty years old and finds herself in possession of a body that is physically mature is no sure evidence that she is an adult in the fullest psychological sense. Nor is it any guarantee of actual maturity that she finds herself equipped with a normal adult mental capacity and the ability to use her mind in studying a lesson or in other intellectual endeavors. Both biological and intellectual maturity we take more or less for granted in every normal young person by the end of the teen years.

Biological weaning and the coming of adult physical and mental age are of certainly no more consequence than is the achievement by an individual of the *emotional* age of an adult. *Psychological* weaning is, in other words, quite as essential for the maturity of an individual as is biological weaning. Some people brood and sulk over slights and inferiorities, just as children do; they go off in a "huff" when they are criticized or censured; they wither when they are compelled to leave the shelter of the family; they fly into temper tantrums when they cannot have their own way. All in all, they act just about as they did when they were wearing rompers and could make the world —or their little corner of it—dance to their music.

We have all met many such grown-up infants as these. We have known more than one person who had to be babied and indulged and pacified if she was to be kept in good humor; whose wishes and preferences had to be consulted before any plans involving her could be made; or who had to be given the easiest task or the lightest load or the most prominent role, or the most sheltered nook. We have known persons who have failed in their work because they could not get along with their associates; could not hold themselves to a line of attack; could not control their tears or their temper; could not adjust to new tasks and new goals; could not take suggestion or direction from their superiors. All such individuals are but grown-up children. They are still infantile in their fundamental reactions, being separated from the nursery stage of their development only by the calendar. They have never been able, emotionally speaking, to stand alone and walk. They are psychologically unweaned from the estate of childhood. In a grown-up world, they flit about as children, unable and unwilling to assume their proper and responsible role as adult individuals.

In order to be psychologically weaned the young woman must have reached the point in the evolution of her personality where she can realize and accept the fact that she is no longer to be sheltered and defended from the give and take of life, as she has been in childhood and earlier youth. She must learn to stand on her own feet, without the aid and support of others. She must be reconciled to the fact that this business of preparing for a vocation can be successfully and happily carried through only by those who are ready to leave behind them the restricting and hampering habits and attitudes of childhood and to cultivate aggressively those qualities of character and personality which are commonly associated with mature and responsible people.

If a student has these qualities, then we may suppose that she has been psychologically weaned from childhood's estate and is ready, like any other adult, to enlist her powers in working toward her goal.

Being psychologically weaned should not, of course, be interpreted as in the slightest degree minimizing the priceless boon of a happy and secure childhood home, and of the overshadowing love and solicitude of two parents. Perhaps no force or influence in one's whole life will ever quite equal the guiding and fostering love of her own home in directing her ideals and conduct. One way in which she may express her gratitude and appreciation of the parental devotion and sacrifice is by assuming willingly the stature her parents have cherished and envisioned for her: that of a true adult.

The Adult Individual Is Self Reliant. It is not sufficient, however, merely to have undergone psychological weaning and to have been set adrift upon the world. Having cast off the physical and emotional moorings which have held one fast to her childhood environment, one must thereafter straightway set about the cultivation of self reliance, with the aid of which she may hope to win her way in the new adult environment in which she finds herself. In the modern world of achievement and work, one must learn largely to "paddle her own canoe."

The young adult must accept her place in the social scene as an individual who will be compelled to establish herself principally by her own efforts. Her home environment has given her shelter and protection and has championed her cause throughout the tumultuous years of childhood and early adolescence; her experience in the elementary and high school has equipped her with usable knowledge and tool skills which are fundamental to her future evolution; nature has herself carried forward the development of and has presided over the maturation of her body and mind. The products of the sheltered environment in which one is nurtured through the years of growth and development embody in a sense the stock in trade with which the young adult in her late teens fares forth to conquer. With this capital, she must create her place in society by herself and by her own efforts.

The adult individual does not look about her for "pulls" or "connections" or "drags" by which to secure placement or advantage or preferment. That philosophy which preaches the indispensability of "influence" as basal to a young person's getting a foothold is not the philosophy of maturity; it is rather one of a large number of defeatist axioms which keeps the race immature and holds back its members. While influence and "pull" sometimes play roles in the complex world of today, the really mature individual is intelligent enough to realize that for the most part a person passes for what she is worth, and if she has in her the stuff of which success is made, she is more likely to amount to something than are those who are catapulted by "pull" or "connection" into some sheltered niche in the work of the world. To this end, she looks askance upon any schemes for her advancement which do not originate in her own initiative. She resists actively the preachment that the world owes her or anybody else a living, and subscribes whole-heartedly to the thesis that she owes it to herself to make something out of her life, and that if she fails it will be her own fault.

A person who has really grown up learns to take time out for personal reflection and evaluation. She does not close her eyes to her shortcomings; rather, she calculates as accurately as she can her chances of achievement, and she does not hesitate to pronounce solemn judgment against the more glaring of the negative traits or attributes that are holding her back. She does not wait for somebody else to point out to her needful habits that should be formed or unfortunate ones that should be broken; she assumes full control of her life and sets out resolutely to reach her goals. She cultivates a philosophy of her own and guides herself in its light; she is not stampeded by the opinions or practices of others; she avoids the stereotyped and creates her own personality; she conforms to the social group, yet she is not slavish and monotonous; she is socially minded and socially conscious, yet she respects her own individuality and her own personal slant and ambition.

The Adult Individual Has an Objective. Life is largely lacking in inspiration and interest for one who is motivated by no strong and persistent purpose. Unlike the immature individual, the adult who has achieved true maturation is activated by the desire to better herself. She cannot be content to drift aimlessly; she is impelled rather to strike out into the currents and battle her way upstream. She is intrigued by the idea of achieving an objective that seems to her to be worth striving toward. The pages of history are filled with the deeds of those who have enlisted themselves under the banners of achievement and have not been satisfied until they have won out. One thinks of a Moses, a Washington, a Lincoln, a Stanley, an Edison, a Curie. It makes no difference where we look, whether in the realm of politics, of conquest, of reform, of art, of social service, or in any other field of human endeavor: the leaders and trail-blazers appear to have been men and women who were activated by strong and definite purpose.

Perhaps this domination by the will to achieve is the thing that most characteristically distinguishes human beings from the animals. The latter, in so far as they have any demonstrable goals, are content with the mere acquisition of physical satiety and safety for themselves and their offspring. Their values are immediate and transparent. Human beings, however, are not limited to the merely physical, nor to the merely immediate and contiguous. They have won the right to stand at the head of the created order of the universe because they are dissatisfied with the past and turn their faces to the future with the determination to hew out a new life and a new day for themselves. Animal society is static, fixed, unchanging over a millennium; human society persistently moves forward, always seeking, trying out, experimenting, achieving.

The student of nursing has resolved to make her personal contribution toward the great forward movement of the race in the field of ministration to the sick. Having heard the call to serve, she has responded, and stands now at the threshold of preparation for her chosen profession. The objective which she has before her is an adult objective; it cannot be reached without persistent and serious endeavor; its attainment is only for those who have grown up enough to be willing to throw real effort into the conquest. The alleviating of pain and the bringing of cheer and hope, or at least of resignation, to those who are ill is a task that she will find sufficiently challenging to merit the identification of her entire personality in her work. As in most other professions, there are in nursing many types and varieties of practitioners, ranging all the way from those who make of it the dominant and absorbing task of their lives to those who feel in it no personal commitment, regarding it as a humdrum job that has to be followed because one has to do something, and nursing is no worse than anything else.

The student has set up as her immediate personal objective the winning of a nurse's diploma. She has, by entering a school of nursing, given expression to her determination to better herself, and at the same time to equip herself to serve her fellows. The steadfastness with which she drives toward her professional goal will be an accurate index of her emotional and intellectual maturity. The less mature an individual is, the fewer her wishes and the simpler her objectives; conversely, the more mature she is, the more she tends to envisage goals for herself that will be worth striving toward. Our goals and purposes are what make life intriguing. Worthy objectives somehow have a way of creating within us motivating force to achieve them. The very awareness that one has set up some remote or not immediately achievable objective serves to help her through many hard and discouraging situations and over many obstacles that intervene between the conception of a goal and its realization. The adult individual does not go to pieces emotionally over the difficulties that lie between her starting point and her objective; she steels herself to withstand the disagreeable and the difficult, and compels herself to make actual headway.

There is no royal road to the nurse's diploma. In the nursing vocation, as in all others, the way is not always easy and smooth. The student will be called upon during the months and years of training to do many things that may appear to her to be distasteful; she will be compelled to adapt herself to a variety of personalities; she will be obliged to experience emotional situations which may be trying to her; she will be expected to face problems of human relationships and adjustments that will challenge all her tact and all her best judgment; she will of necessity be thrown into intimate contact with broken bodies, despairing minds, and sometimes perhaps rebellious souls. In these situations and relationships she will find that the acid test of her effectiveness will be the poise and the directness with which she does the things assigned her.

Experiences such as these the student must expect to encounter in nursing practice; fortunately, she will meet other more agreeable situations: service, for example, among the helpful and the happy, who are grateful for the return of strength and health; association with other personalities that are winsome and inspiring. But regardless of the occasional unpleasantness and days of trying which she will have to face, she must remember that she is an adult, and that grown-up people do not allow themselves to be turned aside from the pursuit of their purposes by the obstacles that lie across their pathway.

The Adult Individual Possesses Healthy Mental Attitudes. The individual who has left childhood's estate behind her has developed normal and healthful mental attitudes toward the problems and circumstances that surround people. Many persons, in spite of the fact that they are physically mature, still nourish unhealthy and abnormal mental attitudes. Instead of behaving like other grown-up individuals, they conduct themselves much like children in the ordinary situations of life by which they are confronted. All of us have met such emotionally immature persons although we may not have paused to diagnose and label their oddities. There are maladjusted people all about us who, for example, are of the opinion that the world is fast moving toward destruction, and that society and culture are disintegrating; who insist that the rising generation is hopeless; who are suspicious and intolerant of any political party, religious faith or geographical locality outside their own; who can see neither honor nor virtue in those who have wealth; or who feel themselves superior to those who are impoverished.

These unfortunate types include among others those who are envious, suspicious or distrustful of everybody, their friends and associates not excepted; those who resent the supervision of their superiors or who are disdainful of their inferiors; those who rail at the man of science; those who despise everybody who is not of their own sacred nationality or race; those who defy convention and insist upon being "advanced" and "different"; those who resist change or progress that goes on about them; those who idle and loaf at their jobs, being interested only in closing time and pay envelopes; those who are preoccupied with themselves and their own immediate problems; those who in situations requiring control and resolution become panicky or squeamish or indecisive. All these people are maladjusted. They are infantile. They are in the grip of unfortunate mental attitudes that may reduce their present or potential social usefulness and may spoil their chances of future success and happiness.

Our attitudes are bound to stamp themselves in our personalities, and there is no way of eradicating them. Quite obviously, the man who is a chronic pessimist and faultfinder, and who believes that there is no hope of salvaging civilization from the shipwreck in which he sees it to be already half engulfed, is a cynic whose thinking is distorted and whose potential social worth and usefulness must be dubious. Similarly, the man who is hypercritical of his neighbor, observing in him and in his family the opposite of everything good and desirable, and expecting of him and it the worst possible behavior and conduct, is not a desirable man to live either with or near. Neither is the man who is shiftless and lazy and who regards the daily toil as hateful and as something to be escaped from by any means that he can conjure up; nor the woman who looks upon her children and her home duties and responsibilities as disagreeably inhibiting to the achievement of her personal and social ambitions; nor the social worker whose sympathies are not with the poor or unfortunate among whom she works, but who is compelled to tolerate what she terms the "filth and stupidity" of the slums in order to earn her living.

There are so many people in the world who react childishly, bitterly, unsympathetically, intolerantly, or casually to their common life experiences that one does not have to seek far to find them. Nursing is a profession in which the worker who is possessed of such unfortunate mental attitudes as these may be peculiarly sure to be unhappy and unsuccessful. Those who deal with the sick need to be possessed of the essentially grown-up attitudes of cheerfulness in the face of unpleasantness, sympathy in the presence of worry or suffering or apprehension, and faithfulness, reliability and optimism everywhere and all the time. Unless we have had it called definitely to our attention, we may have failed to realize how important a role our mental attitudes play in making us interesting personalities and efficient and satisfactory workers in the field of our vocational or professional choice. To be grown up is in no small measure to be activated by the mental attitudes and viewpoints that characterize mature and responsible individuals.

The Adult Individual Is Governed by Intelligence, Not Emotion. No trait is perhaps more universal among children, as we have seen, than is their proneness to be ruled by feeling and emotion. One is not surprised to find them making their decisions and choices in accordance with what their feelings dictate; they may be counted upon to do those things that will bring them pleasurableness and to shun those things that do not appear enticing to them; they seek the joys of the moment and are lackadaisical when it comes to tasks that are less intriguing; they follow caprice and fancy and find it hard to resist whatever is most appealing at the moment.

Children will often be observed to neglect the assigned and the expected task and to play hookey or otherwise seek to escape from it; they will postpone the distasteful or the difficult until the agreeable or the easy has been discharged; they will remain oblivious of the comfort and peace of mind of their elders, while indulging their flair for play and fun; they will monopolize the conversation in their thirst to be in the limelight; they will spring practical jokes that often have embarrassing or serious consequences, carry on minor predatory activities that may be extremely annoying to their victims, indulge in pranks and horse-play that may appear clownish and boorish in the extreme to grown-ups who have perhaps forgotten what it means to be young, and lead the happy-go-lucky lives of irresponsibleness that seem to belie any possible future achievement of seriousness and maturity.

Children will do and be all these things because they are still children and still look out at the world through the eyes of childhood. We expect them to pass through a somewhat long period of immaturity of this sort; they would hardly be real children if they did not wear their hearts on their sleeves and conduct themselves in a manner suggestive of emotion and feeling rather than of reason and intellect. Little by little, however, we expect them to learn to solve their problems by the use of thoughtful judgment and to rely less and less upon their natural passions and ecstasies. As the rule of emotion recedes, we assume that it will be replaced by the rule of reason and intelligence in every individual who aspires to the full stature of an adult.

There are, however, grown-up individuals who have remained infantile in their emotional evolution. They comprise those persons who seek thrills and "kicks" through indulgences and excesses; who leap first and look afterward; who are governed by their "hunches" or their prejudices; who trust in premonitions, in luck, in seances and in soothsayers; who marry in haste and repent at leisure; who measure their patriotism by the volume of their yells and cheers and flag-waving; who seek pleasure and the joys of the moment, without regard to the long-time consequences; who seek the blaring and the raucous; who devote themselves to speed, adventure and the bright lights.

We do not argue here for a world freed entirely from emotionalism and excitement. After all, life would be dull and insipid if we did not have the warmth and glow that our emotions provide. A society in which cold and unemotional intellectualists predominated would be as unattractive as one in which the most irresponsible emotionalists filled the scene. What we do argue for, however, is for men and women who have left behind them the yeasty and impetuous ideals of childhood and who have embraced the more substantial and satisfying ideals of serious and thoughtful human beings.

Those who are to join the ranks of the nursing profession stand in peculiar need of developing a rational and reflective mind, and of keeping their emotions under effective control. Many a student nurse has failed simply because she could not seem to learn to be the master of her feelings, and many a graduate nurse has been only moderately successful because in situations that called for calm and judicious thought she was emotionally infantile. In the practical experience during her student days, and in the service which she is to render subsequently, she will find it important to cultivate the habit of contemplating with a controlled mind the problems and the daily tasks that confront her. There is no place among the sick and the apprehensive and the peevish for nurses who are themselves little better than children in their emotional organization.

The Adult Individual Faces Reality. Many human beings refuse to face reality just as unintelligently and improvidently as the proverbial ostrich which buries its head in the sand when confronted by danger. Psychiatrists tell us that a common indication of the onset of mental disease is to be noted in the tendency of the individual to withdraw from reality and to build up a world of fancy within in which things are what he would wish them to be outside. If one has been for some time underprivileged, slighted, kicked about, despised or tyrannized, he may at length withdraw within himself and achieve through introversion the satisfaction and fame and honor which are denied him in the grim world of reality. Our mental hospitals are filled with victims of their own delusions. Witness, for example, the sizable numbers of Julius Caesars, the Columbuses and Washingtons, the Queen Annes and the Queen Marys that follow their mummery through the wards and corridors of the asylums for the mentally ill. Compensating for a harsh and unfriendly reality, they achieve a delusion of happiness and success that resists stubbornly attempts at breaking down.

One does not have to go to the mental hospital, however, to find those who will not face reality. We find them in those who postpone attention to organic malfunctioning because they will not admit to themselves that any abnormality exists; in those who will not admit the possibility of there being anything reprehensible in their offspring or their relatives or friends, even in the face of damaging evidence to the contrary; in those who will not face up to the limitations of their own personalities or capacities, even though they are misfits and bunglers in their calling; in those who refuse to recognize the shortcomings of their community, even though they are destructive to good citizenship. Such people turn their backs upon the actualities of the present situation, especially if it has in it anything that savors of an emergency or that requires some serious self analysis, and seek to dismiss it from mind. In the pathological group, these people include certain of the insane, the tramps and globe trotters, and many of the delinquents; among the nonpathological, they include the opportunists, the silly optimists, the evaders and the procrastinators, the visionaries and the get-rich-quick legions. Instead of facing reality, these types concern themselves with a false and unreal world in which they themselves are at much less disadvantage than they are in the stern world of actuality.

Practitioners of the nursing profession, of all vocations in the world, are in strategic position to recognize the importance of facing things as they are. Serving as they do at the frontiers of disease and suffering, they realize that evasions and refusal to face facts are frequently responsible for illness or disability. Many a patient would never have grown seriously sick in the first place if he had been willing to admit to himself the fact that some parts of his organism were not functioning normally and had sought medical advice promptly. Instead, he refused to entertain the idea that something was wrong and permitted the condition to run on unchecked until it finally compelled his attention; long illness, needless suffering and expense, and perhaps permanent organic impairment or destruction, were the price he was obliged to pay. Often it is only through some such bitter disaster as this that the individual is brought face to face with reality.

Taking her cue from this, if from no other teaching, the student nurse should feel strongly the desirability of forming the habit of confronting facts and conditions as they are, not as she might wish or hope them to be. Not merely with reference to her physical health, of course, but in all other relationships, she should make this a rule of her life. Recognition and acknowledgment of one's limitations, one's weaknesses and shortcomings, one's inconsistencies and besetting sins; frank evaluation of one's personality, one's aptitudes, one's chances of success; clear and uncompromising envisagement of one's problems, one's inner goals and longings—persistent cultivation of these attitudes is indispensable to the individual who is to be really grown up and willing to assume the full role of an adult.

The Adult Individual Is Socially Adjusted. Any one who has had any prolonged or intimate association with younger children has been impressed with the fact that they are only moderately well adjusted to one another and to the juvenile social group of which they

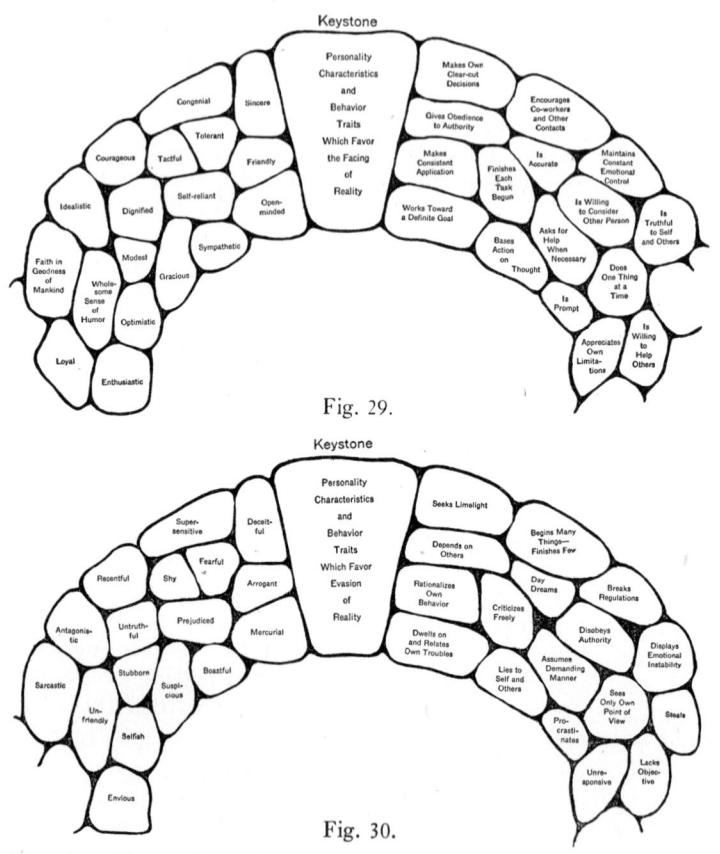

Fig. 29.

Fig. 30.

Figs. 29 and 30. Two different Arches of Personality, each held up by its keystone. Which suggests *your* life pattern?

are a part. Each one tends to be an individualist and often finds it impossible to get on harmoniously with other personalities for any great length of time. On the playground, in particular, one may observe most strikingly these social inadequacies and maladjustments. The children fall periodically into violent disputes and disagreements; they make no efforts to conceal their jealousies of one another; they feel individually a strong urge for the limelight and resent having its rays cast for long upon somebody else; they shirk and evade their responsibilities and are gratified if and when they can "get out from under"; they pay scant attention to rule and precept and rarely hesitate to play unfairly in order to win; they are bitingly critical and sarcastic of one another's efforts; they hold each other up to ridicule; they are often selfish, thoughtless and opinionated; they argue loudly, denounce roundly and wreak vengeance summarily.

It is a long road from the poorly adjusted estate of childhood to the good judgment which characterizes adult individuals at their best. It is, however, a road over which every person who aspires really to be grown up must travel. Let us note some of the common earmarks of the grown-up individual from the standpoint of the adequacy of her social adjustment.

The person who is socially adjusted is able to get on with other people about her, in the home, the community and the place of business. While she may find herself in disagreement with others, she has cultivated tact and self control, and actual friction between herself and them is non-existent or at least non-apparent. She has learned to respect the judgment and opinion of others, even when she is herself at variance with them. She does not feel called upon at the slightest provocation to trot out her personal views and opinions and set them against the convictions of somebody else. She does not antagonize and irritate those about her. She has no infantile craving for the limelight but finds it easy to encourage and inspire others to put forward their best efforts while she slips into the background. She is tactful and socially intelligent.

The socially adjusted adult individual assumes her full responsibility in the group or groups in which she moves. Unlike the immature person, she does not cast about for ways of escaping or avoiding the tasks and duties which face her. As a citizen of the community, she abides by its laws and regulations and conducts herself according to its accepted standards and mores; as a neighbor, she finds it possible to live at peace and in cordial relationship with others about her; as a member of the church, the club, the society, the guild, she bears her share of the burdens which membership imposes.

In all these relationships, she recognizes the worth and genuineness of other individuals and other personalities; she is not blinded to the virtues and merits of others by constant preoccupation with her own integrity or self righteousness. She inclines to accept society as it is, though aware of its shortcomings and imperfections, and she has faith in the ultimate goodness and salvation of human kind. She does not magnify human weaknesses, neither does she ignore or condone them. Up to the limit of her ability, she strives to throw the weight of her influence on the side of virtue. She is tolerant, unprejudiced, generous; she is not a dispenser of gloom and cynicism; she is not testy, grouchy or opinionated; she is fair-minded and socially minded.

The Adult Individual Acts Her Age. Having arrived at the age of maturity, the adult individual has presumably learned to put away childish things and to look out upon life and its problems as a grown-up individual ought. "Be your age!" is a popular warning for those who tend to carry their nursery outlook with them. There is something pathetically abnormal about any woman who departs radically in her behavior from those who belong in her age group. We are apt to feel rather sorry for the child who has been pushed too rapidly through the normal childhood experience and made prematurely adult before she is hardly out of rompers; we are sorry, too, for anybody who has been held back in her social and emotional evolution so that she presents at twenty a poor picture of a one-sided young adult who still bears in her personality the earmarks of the child. So, too, on the other hand, we do not care to associate with people who act the part of the senile while they are yet in the prime of life, nor yet with seniles who ape adolescents in their manner of living, dressing and thinking.

The adult individual acts her age. Having left behind childhood's estate, she strives to order her life and her general conduct and behavior as an intelligent and mature individual. It should not be necessary for her friends and associates to handle her with gloves, nor to tease, or flatter, or cajole, or bribe her to do the things desired or expected of her, as must be done in handling children. Her interests and attitudes and sense of values and fitness should be those of an adult; while never forgetting entirely how to romp and play on occasion as children do, her characteristic, day-by-day adjustment should be such as to allow her to view life and work as serious and important, and make her willing and eager to give of her best in order to achieve her goals. She should have the resolution and character to pursue with determination the line of activity which her ambition has projected for her.

The adult individual plays the game for the adventure and the abiding satisfaction of it, not that she may win out over somebody else; children and those who are immature in their social evolution do the latter. The adult is inclined to sacrifice the present or immediate gratification of her impulses and urges for a future and greater satisfaction which she may one day earn and enjoy. No adult can ever be or act her age who must be bribed or tempted by rewards and sugar-plums to stick to her task. The real adult cultivates the manner and the voice and presence of other adults; she has left behind her the excitability and the unreliability of the adolescent. She is not boisterous, loud and restless for the limelight of attention and flattery. She is not overcredulous, easily imposed upon, easily disconcerted. She does not affect an innocence or naïveté that are unbecoming in all those who have reached the years of responsibility and understanding. She is not infantile, not senile. She is *an adult,* and she *acts her age.*

The Adult Individual Is Vocationally Adjusted. The writer knows a man, now well into middle life, who is often heard to make this rather wistful remark: "If I had my life to live over again, I would never engage in this line of work, which I have followed for nearly thirty years!" There is tragedy in such a situation as this. To have worked at one's trade for half a lifetime, yet to have been rebellious and unhappy all the while, is a sad commentary upon the character of the man, or else upon the combination of circumstances which compelled him originally to enter his vocation or to remain in it for thirty years.

Yet there are hosts of people in the world who are vocationally maladjusted; they are square pegs in round holes. The day will come in the future when, through more adequate prevocational guidance and vocational exploration and testing at the junior high school level, young people will be more happily and aptly adjusted to their vocations even before they formally enter upon them. In the meantime, one must deplore the number of vocational misfits and the multiplicity of blind alley jobs everywhere in our complex industrial society, and strive by all means to choose wisely what his life work is to be. The vocationally adjusted individual respects his job, devotes himself earnestly to it and derives substantial satisfaction from its pursuit. He has neither the time nor the inclination to regret his choice, but expends in his daily tasks his best energy and interest.

Good vocational adjustment is particularly to be desired in the nursing profession. The intimate and personal relationships which the nurse must maintain with her patients demand on her part a devotion and earnestness of purpose which can leave no room for regretting one's original choice of profession, nor for lamenting one's way of life. The vocationally well adjusted individual is the happy and contented individual, whereas the vocational misfit is irritable, self-pitying and unhappy. No person who is ill cares to have the ministrations of a nurse who rebels, though ever so guardedly, against the nature of her work and who indicates by her behavior and her general attitude that she is a square peg in a round hole. The nurse's function, in addition to healing, is a spiritual one; it is a ministry of patience, sympathy, cheerfulness and silent efficiency; such a ministry can spring only out of a sincerity of purpose and a wholeheartedness of conviction that are characteristic of the individual who regards her life work as a calling worthy of her best devotion.

THOUGHT PROBLEMS FOR THE STUDENT

1. Recall to mind somebody whom you know who has never been psychologically weaned. What are some of the evidences of his infantilism? What factors have contributed to the continuance of the condition? In what ways might it have been prevented?
2. Do you consider yourself to be a reasonably self-reliant individual? If you do, cite evidences from your recent past experience to substantiate your opinion. If you do not so consider yourself, suggest several practical ways in which you hope to improve in this trait.
3. What external influences or personal motives have operated to set up for you the nursing profession as an objective? How long have you had this ambition? What obstacles, if any, have you thus far found in your way? What obstacles to the completion of your training do you foresee?
4. Study carefully the characteristics presented in the two diagrams, Figures 29 and 30; which qualities should predominate for good social adjustment? For good vocational adjustment? Give reasons for your answers. In a similar diagram illustrate your own personality characteristics and behavior traits. Underscore those you are endeavoring to change.
5. How do people who follow the rule of intelligence in ordering their lives differ from those whose behavior is influenced primarily by their emotions and their feelings? Contrast two individuals whom you know, one of whom tends to be guided in general by his intelligence, the other by his emotions.
6. List in two parallel columns as many healthful and as many unhealthful mental attitudes as you recall having observed in your friends and acquaintances. Arrange the healthful ones in descending order of their desirability and the unhealthy ones in descending order of their seriousness.
7. In the following dialogues you will find illustrations of different degrees of maturity; list those statements which you consider indicative of mature, well adjusted nurses, and those you consider suggestive of immature nurses. Give your reasons for identifying each one as you do. Suggest what should have been done in those situations which you feel were not well met:

   (a) PATIENT: Please, nurse, I wish you would loosen the covers at the bottom of the bed, they make my feet ache.

   MISS A.: I am sorry, but I have to tuck in the top covers snugly; the Supervisor will scold me if your bed does not look neat.

   (b) HEAD NURSE: But, Miss B., why did you not tell me when you found you would not be able to get Mr. Barr's eight and ten o'clock throat irrigations done? And why after giving him one at nine o'clock did you check off both eight and ten in the treatment book?

   MISS B.: Well, you were making rounds with the doctors at eight, and by the time I gave Mr. Barr a long irrigation at nine, I realized that I could not possibly get another one given, besides the rest of my assignments, before going to class at ten. I did not wish to leave ten o'clock treatments for the nurse relieving me.

(c) PATIENT: Nurse, bring me a drink right away.
MISS T.: A drink you shall have just as soon as the Doctor says you may, but right now, I am going to help you use a mouth wash and make your mouth feel clean and fresh in that way.

(d) PRECLINICAL STUDENT: I am shaking all over, I am so scared; whatever am I going to do if Miss Cary calls on me?
SECOND PRECLINICAL STUDENT: Just keep your chin up and do the best you can. Miss Cary will be sympathetic if your procedure shows that you have really done some studying of the assignment she gave us.

(e) MISS D. (*to her classmate*): I am through! That head nurse has picked on me ever since I came to this floor. Now she tells me I cannot be depended upon because I have failed to check one measly little order! I am going to my room and pack my bags this very minute. Mother will be glad to have me at home again, I know.

(f) JUNIOR NURSE (*to her head nurse*): Dr. Dick has just ordered a colonic irrigation for Mrs. McCabe; may I do it now under your supervision? I have studied the procedure; I think I know how to do it properly. Then I shall be able to relieve Miss G. on her off duty time. Mrs. McCabe is her patient this week.

(g) MISS K.: Just two more weeks before I shall be able to wear a white uniform. I hope to do General Duty for about six months, and eventually to become Night Supervisor either here or in some other hospital. What are you going to do?
MISS Z.: Oh, I suppose I shall be doing General Duty right here until John finishes Medical School; then we expect to marry and that will finish my nursing career, I hope.

(h) SUPERVISOR: Miss G., why did you not report it at once when you discovered that you had given the wrong dose of medicine?
MISS G.: I remembered that we learned in our course in Materia Medica that the adult dose may vary between $1/8$ and $1/4$ grain so I did not think that it really made such difference whether the patient received the $1/8$ grain which the Doctor ordered, or the $1/4$ grain which I gave.

(i) MISS J.: I am scared to death! I just cannot take care of that patient who has syphilis. I might get it from him.
MISS M.: Of course you can take care of him. We can review every step of our "precautions technique," and you can carry it out exactly as you did it when Miss S. supervised you, and you will be as safe as I am taking care of Mrs. Judd, who has scarlet fever.

(j) SUPERVISOR: I wonder if Miss T. who came to the ward today cuts too many corners when she thinks she is not being observed? Do you think her assignment for today was too heavy?
HEAD NURSE: No, Miss L., who was new yesterday, had practically the same assignment; she did thorough, finished work in the same time. The Head Nurse on Ward 20, where Miss T. has been on duty, suggested that Miss T. might need frequent checking of her work.

SUGGESTED READINGS

1. Bullis, H. E., and Kelly, C. W.: *Human Relations in Action.* New York, G. P. Putnam's Sons, 1954.
A simple but challenging discussion of what constitutes good human rela-

tions and how they may be achieved by individuals in all kinds of group situations.
2. Garrison, K. C., and Gray, J. S.: *Educational Psychology*. New York, Appleton-Century-Crofts, Inc., 1955.

   The student is referred particularly to Chapter 10, "Personality Adjustment and Mental Hygiene," for a good discussion of various aspects of achieving maturity in our human behavior.
3. Karn, H. W., and Weitz, J.: *An Introduction to Psychology*. New York, John Wiley & Sons, Inc., 1955.

   Good accounts of personal adjustment, including problems like feelings of inferiority, control of sex urges, and emotional maturation.
4. Munn, N.: *The Evolution and Growth of Human Behavior*. Boston, Houghton Mifflin Co., 1955.

   Chapter 15, "Development of Social Behavior," and Chapter 17, "Changes in Personality from Adolescence," are helpful sources of understanding better some of the problems of growing up discussed in the present chapter.
5. Ruch, F. L.: *Psychology and Life*. 4th ed. Chicago, Scott, Foresman and Co., 1953.

   Cf. especially pp. 132 ff.: "Emotions and Health"; pp. 151 ff.: "Frustration in Everyday Life"; pp. 327 ff.: "Problems of Marriage"; and pp. 339 ff.: "Problems of the Group."

Unit 6

Conflict and Tensions

Chapter 13

> *To be or not to be: that is the question!*
> *Whether 'tis nobler in the mind to suffer*
> *The slings and arrows of outrageous fortune,*
> *Or to take arms against a sea of troubles,*
> *And by opposing, end them!*
>
> HAMLET'S SOLILOQUY

CONFLICT, TENSION, AND FRUSTRATION

MENTAL CONFLICT

The Meaning of Conflict. Hamlet's soliloquy, which we recall from our high school study of Shakespeare, is a masterful portrayal of inner conflict and turmoil. Hamlet is torn by two opposing impulses; the one, to suffer in silence the bitterness which he feels over the murder of his father and the realization that the murderer is now king and husband to Hamlet's mother; the other, to still forever the mad fires within his soul by ending it all in suicide. Only Shakespeare, the master playwright-psychologist, could have portrayed mental conflict in a character so superbly as has been done in Hamlet.

Conflict does not exist alone, however, in the characters and personalities of literature. Conflict occurs in every human being who finds himself harboring two mutually incompatible desires or impulses. Just as Hamlet cannot achieve serenity by continuing to live and yet cannot bring himself to achieve serenity by taking his own life, so a harassed business man may see no way to retain his old standards of honesty and fair dealing and at the same time conduct a prosperous business against cut-throat competitors. His consciousness becomes, therefore, like Hamlet's, a sort of battleground between the desire to be true to his best impulses, on the one hand, and, on the other, the desire to make a success of his enterprise. Similarly politicians and men in positions of responsibility and influence often find themselves confronted with the necessity of choosing whether to do the honest thing or the expedient thing, the thing which will redound morally to their credit or the thing which will make their purse longer and stouter. "Ye cannot serve God and mammon." In attempting to choose between the two alternatives, one experiences mental conflict, the degree of which depends upon the power of the two opposed drives.

Conflict in Childhood. As a matter of fact, life for all of us is filled with conflicts of one sort or another. They begin almost as soon as we become aware of our surroundings in babyhood, and they continue until the last breath of life. In childhood, the desire to play and the repeated admonition to work cause mental conflict; so do the parental preachment to tell the truth and the selfish wish to escape punishment, the desire for praise and that to indulge a selfish impulse.

At the school level, the lust to enjoy freedom comes early into conflict with the duty to pore over books, and the attractiveness of "skipping school" with the duty of being faithful to school. At a still deeper level of the young personality there may be all manner of conflict and apprehension due to insecurity in the home, fear of sarcasm or failure, brooding over inferiorities, deformities and defects, and the growing battle between the dawning ideas of honor and morality, on the one hand, and the increasing attractiveness of unwholesome and wrong behavior, on the other.

Conflict in Youth. Conflict in youth is still stronger. With important habits and controls yet to be established and with the counter pull of "the world, the flesh and the devil," it is small wonder that young people often have a difficult time of it to establish their personalities. Ideals oppose appetites; the approved and expected conflict with the desired and intriguing; what is right stands eternally in opposition to what is wrong; the voice of conscience raises itself against the inroads of sin. Besides, Providence may have been unkind and given one straight and stringy hair or a sallow complexion; in the human struggle after acceptance and position among one's mates, the young person afflicted with liabilities in physical make-up can hardly hope to escape from annoying inner conflict. Similarly, the young student who possesses no more than mediocre ability at her books, or who never seems quite able to acquire the social graces and polish that come so easily and naturally to others, may suffer anguish in silence as she observes her own intellectual or social maladroitness in contrast with the finesse and polish of her friends.

Adult Conflict. Mental conflict in adult men and women is found on every hand. One experiences it in attempting to judge between two possible but opposed lines of action, in determining what is the honorable course to pursue in a dilemma, in effecting conjugal relationships and family adjustments, in facing moral issues, in deciding what is duty and what is privilege, in interpreting laws written and unwritten, in justifying and applying religious principles and beliefs, in solving political and social questions of the day, and in the expenditure of one's talents and money. Discord and dissension are rife in the world, and there are few people grown to maturity who are not compelled by force of circumstance to pass much of their time and energy in evaluating their own doubts and uncertainties and in arriving at some sort of livable and justifiable decision. Added to these social sources of conflict are the personal dilemmas arising out of dissatisfaction with our present lot or outlook and our concern for the future, the suspicions and hostilities which we experience frequently with regard to those with whom we are thrown in contact, and the frictions and tensions that we occasionally experience toward the personalities of our own friends and relaltives.

Lewin's Topological Concept. An interesting and helpful point of view with reference to conflict is embodied in the so-called *topological* theory of Kurt Lewin. According to Lewin's conception, some objects and situations possess a *positive valence;* that is to say, they tend to attract or draw us toward them. Others are said to possess *negative valence,* and hence tend to repel us. Borrowing from an

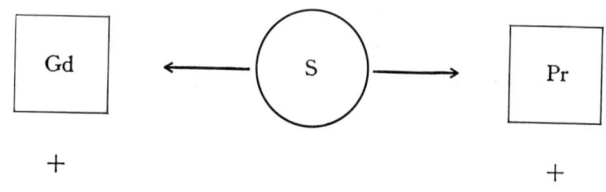

Fig. 31. Two positive valences.

electrochemical analogy, Lewin conceives every area or "field" of experience to comprise objects, conditions and circumstances exerting varying kinds and degrees of pull or valence. Our behavior becomes, from this point of view, the resultant adjustment to these "field forces" outside the organism. To illustrate valence, let us suppose that a student nurse is offered, at the close of her basic course, a scholarship to continue graduate study; as an alternative she has, of course, the opportunity to enter at once upon the practice of her profession. Either alternative is attractive. Figure 31 illustrates diagrammatically the pulling power of these two possible "field forces": S represents the nurse in question; Gd is the "go-to-graduate-school" alternative; Pr, the "begin-to-practice-nursing" alternative. The two arrows (vectors) show the pulling power of each "field." S will obviously undergo a considerable degree of conflict during the process of arriving at a decision as to which course she shall follow.

Two negative valences may also cause conflict in an individual, as Figure 32 will indicate:

Let S represent a student nurse who enjoys everything in the nursing curriculum except chemistry: that subject she finds difficult. If she fails in it, however, she cannot be graduated. Sc (study of chemistry) represents a negative force that repels S. The idea of failure and of flunking out (F) is also a negative force which likewise repels. The "to-study-chemistry" alternative and the "to-flunk-out" alternative both harass the student. The resulting conflict can be relieved only if and when stronger forces from somewhere overcome the repelling force of Sc and/or F.

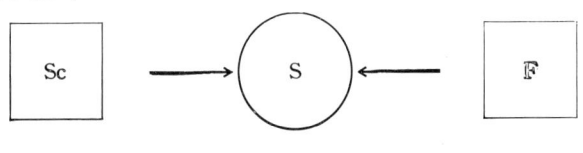

Fig. 32. Two negative valences.

Fortunately, it frequently happens that a positive and a negative valence operate simultaneously upon an individual, producing an inevitable and clear decision without conflict. Figure 33 will illustrate such a situation.

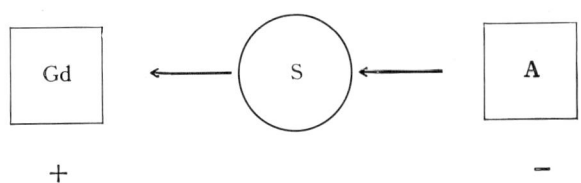

Fig. 33. A positive and a negative valence.

A student nurse (S) may be attracted toward Gd (going on to graduate school for a higher degree), and be repelled by the idea (A) of returning to her family after completing her basic course, to be nursemaid to a wealthy but exacting aunt. Here there is, at least on the face of affairs, no conflict. The "take-care-of-aunt" situation is repellent; the "go-on-for-further-study" idea is attractive. Other factors being inconsequential, the solution is simple.

Our Unattained Objectives. Conflict is, in general, healthful. The mere fact that a person is struggling to overcome her handicaps, to mend her personality, to learn to live harmoniously with others around her, or to choose the wisest among the alternative courses of action or behavior that confront her, is indicative of her good mental health. The person who does not struggle, but who chooses the easier or the simpler among her alternatives, suffers frequently from poor mental health. At its best, life is a continuous struggle for anybody who is possessed of ideals or standards and who is eager to attain to better things for herself and to improve the lot of others. Most men and women who achieve do so because they put forth determination and effort, either to conquer their own baser natures or to master the objective, material world about them.

But not every individual succeeds in obtaining her objectives, as we have noted in a preceding chapter. Some are beyond her reach; some elude her grasp just when she would close her fingers upon them. Sometimes obstacles which she cannot surmount lie across her pathway; sometimes she is lacking in the determination and perseverance necessary to drive her toward her goals; sometimes she loses courage, or else, from a consciousness of defects or limitations within her own character, she ceases struggling to achieve and settles back into defeat—now accepting her failure philosophically, now dejectedly or bitterly. Besides, of course, there are many people whom everybody knows who are turned aside by the first minor obstacle that presents itself; they decide that the rough road of achievement —whether of character or of material rewards—is too difficult, and they are content to give up without a struggle. Such individuals may indeed become economic problems, but they will hardly become psychological or psychiatric ones. Their failure neither discourages nor arouses them. They follow the line of least resistance and get on serenely, with themselves and with everybody else. They may, like the Arkansas fiddler, fail to take either themselves or their lacks and hardships seriously, being content merely to fiddle away in the cabin door.

Many of us, however, have our objectives and spend the major amount of our natural lifetime striving to achieve them. Young people set off in life in the main hopeful, eager and ambitious. At their best, they are impassioned with zeal to reform society or to impress their virile young personalities constructively and redemptively upon the world about them. Witness, for example, the lofty sentiments expressed in thousands of class mottoes and poems and prophecies that are recited and applauded in thousands of high schools every June, when the year's crop of adventurers into life is turned forth into the world beyond the school.

ADJUSTMENT AND MALADJUSTMENT

The Meaning of Adjustment. Unfortunately, failure to reach their objectives is likely to be the lot of many people as they pass out of youth into maturity and on into middle life. Thwarted in the realization of their desires and goals, they may or may not adjust hygienically to the thwartings. The following incident will illustrate clearly the undesirable effects of thwarting in a person who could not accept her misfortune rationally and healthfully.

A devoted young mother lost her only child, a small boy of five, in an automobile accident. On the afternoon of the tragedy, shortly before it happened, the little chap had been playing about the dining room with a ball of twine. In his play he had crawled under the table and had woven the twine in and out among the table legs. When the call came to go for a ride in the automobile, he ran off and left the web of twine fastened about the legs of the table. The child was killed within the next hour. That evening, the distracted mother discovered the twine. Hysterically, she wept over it and hugged the table legs in her arms. For months afterwards, she trembled on the verge of insanity and gibbered over the twine for hours at a time every day, permitting nobody to untie or remove it. For several years she remained inconsolable, clinging desperately to this grim reminder of the little boy whom she had lost.

Here is a pathetic case of a mother who, thwarted in the realization of that goal of parenthood and love of children which is so precious to all normal women, chose an unhealthful way of adjusting to her deprivation. Any one of a dozen other possible types of reconciliation that she might have effected would have been more rational and salutary than this. Instead, however, of adjusting to her thwarting by accepting the circumstance, griefstricken and heartbroken though she was, and by throwing herself into some kind of child welfare work, into social or community service, or into some new interest like music or art or club work in order to occupy her mind and perchance after a time turn the edge of her grief, she adjusted morbidly, and so, ineffectually. The degree of conflict in her own personality continued unabated and undiminished. For years her personality was dominated by conflict and bitterness.

One can hardly start too early in life to learn the lesson that when she is thwarted in achieving her purposes or goals, it is the part of wisdom to substitute for the things she would have liked, but which prove to be unobtainable, other desirable things which lie within her reach and the possession of which will ease the sting of failure and shortly perhaps yield her quite as great satisfaction as she might have experienced had she not met with thwarting in the first instance. The achievement of compensatory adjustment is essential for two reasons: first, in the interest of continued peace of mind, which must be attained if one is to live with herself; and second, in the interest of continued effort and achievement, without which one's mental health suffers. To brood over the thwarting, as did the mother referred to above, to lament one's fate, to admit defeat and stop trying, or to indulge in any of the forms of introversion which we shall presently discuss, is not worthy of any individual who possesses a personality that is adequate to rational and normal living.

Positive Ways of Adjusting to Thwarting. What are, then, the various ways, desirable or undesirable, by which one may adjust to the thwarting of her drives or purposes? We may say in general that there are two desirable or positive ways of adjusting and a considerably larger number of undesirable or negative ways. The remainder of this chapter will be devoted principally to a discussion of both types.

1. *Adjustment by Attack.* For many a person who fails in arriving at her desired goal, all that is necessary is to revise her methods of procedure, to make a different approach, or to reassemble her forces and attack again. In other words, the mere fact that one's efforts have failed in the initial drive must not be interpreted as indicating that the end sought is unachievable. She who gives up and withdraws from the field after the initial skirmish is a foolish person, not a wise one. Granted that her objective is one worthy of obtaining, she can ill afford to refrain from throwing all her resources into the fray and admit herself defeated before she has fairly started the fight. There is sound mental hygiene in the homely old admonition: "If at first you don't succeed, try, try again."

To adjust to initial thwarting by renewed attack implies that the individual is willing to face reality squarely. If she deludes herself regarding the size of the task; if she discounts the seriousness of the obstacles that lie in her way; if she overestimates her own strength; if she closes her eyes to her personal shortcomings and deficiencies; or if, in other words, she envisages either herself or her task in any other than the clear light of actuality, without self deception and without prejudice, she will be likely to suffer defeat and humiliation. The method of direct attack upon the problems which baffle us and which we fail in the earlier attempts to solve necessitates that we be honest with ourselves and face the whole situation in all its parts and from all the angles that bear upon it.

Adjustment by attack implies also that the goal upon which we are set shall be one that is within the possibilities of our achievement. To continue to thrust one's head, as it were, against a stone wall is more likely to be the part of folly than it is the part of wisdom. There are many individuals in the world who try to write literature, or compose music, or learn to speak a foreign tongue, who have neither the specialized capacities essential for successful practice in these arts nor the general intelligence needed as basal equipment. There are numbers more who are striving to go through college with a fifth-rate mind, or who are vocationally set down in occupations for which they are by temperament, training or mental equipment unsuited; and there are other individuals who continue to plod out weary days in a vain and hopeless endeavor to win out over impossible obstructions in their economic, social or professional pathways. By force of habit, they continue in the ruts in which they have fallen, having neither the courage nor the ability to climb out and start off in a new direction.

On the assumption that the obstacles are actually insuperable, to turn about and strike out on a different tangent is the only hygienically sane and healthful thing to do. Adjustment by attack is a virtue only so long as one has confidence that she is progressing, although the fact should not be lost sight of that sometimes merely to hold a line may be the part of wisdom and maturity. It becomes in such cases a question of whether the line is worth holding, or whether by yielding it and taking up a new position one will not be fortifying her personality and improving her mental health and adjustment.

2. *Adjustment by Substitution.* If one is inadequately endowed, if her obstacles are unsurmountable, or if the line is not worth the holding, then there still remains a psychologically sound alternative for the thwarted individual. It will not do to abandon the struggle and admit defeat, for acknowledgment of defeat is likely to undermine our personalities and discourage us from making new attacks upon new tasks. It becomes necessary to substitute for an unobtainable objective some other that will yield compensatory satisfaction. We are compelled to learn that everybody finds her happiness in this world in the confidence and hope with which she drives toward a limited number of worthwhile goals and in the complacent resignation with which she can turn aside from the pursuit of others that are beyond her reach, substituting for them some that are potentially achievable. In this balance between abandoned objectives and compensating successes most people find their happiness and serenity. Let us note a few examples of substituted goals.

A high school lad who turns out to be a poor scholar and is thus thwarted in the desire to impress his ego scholastically upon his fellows discovers that he has a bent for mechanical drawing. Convinced that he can never be a satisfactory student in the academic sense, he transfers to a technical school and has the joy of finding himself vocationally. A junior high school girl who has dragged along close to the ragged edge of failure through the lower school learns to her delight that she can visualize a dress and make a pattern that wins the approval of the domestic science teacher. From an apprehensive and unhappy girl, she is transformed into an ambitious and hopeful one. An unattractive young woman, to whom fate has been unkind so far as endowment with good looks is concerned, sets herself the task of cultivating personal character traits such as genuineness, sympathy, cooperativeness, and the like, and experiences the great satisfaction of attracting to herself a large number of warm and faithful friends. A widower whose wife has been strongly interested in a certain local philanthropy, and has supported it faithfully by her work and her gifts, continues after her death to give it the same financial and moral support that his wife was accustomed to do, and in burying himself in its affairs adjusts after a fashion to his bereavement by ministering to others in need.

Dangers in Compensating Behavior. There is, however, a danger in compensatory activities against which one must be on his guard. Having made the substitution, it is essential for the individual to accept it in full equivalent for the thwarted objective and permit no lingering animosity or jealousy or rebellion to spoil the soundness of the adjustment.

If, for example, the mediocre student, who substitutes for the original desire to go to college the furthering of his vocational proficiency by transferring from an academic high school to a technical school, allows himself to lament the necessity for his transfer and to develop an envy of all college-bound students, he may continue to be maladjusted to his surroundings as he was before. If the plain young woman, while striving to substitute for good looks—which she lacks—a fine personality—which she can bring to pass—develops also morbid and unpleasant jealousies of good-looking young women whom she knows or meets, and rebels against the harshness of fate in making her own features plain, she may not only fail to achieve her substitute goal of a winsome personality but she may likewise fail in general adjustment to life. If the widowed husband continues to support the favorite philanthropy of his wife after her death but never identifies himself whole-heartedly with it, he may remain embittered toward Providence, or else so introvertedly lost in soul-harrowing reminiscence of his dead wife that he cannot find solid ground beneath his feet again.

Adjustment by substitution is efficient and hygienically salutary only when the individual who does the compensating is willing to cultivate in himself the fine art of wholesome appreciation of those who have not been thwarted as he has, and of wholesome and complete acceptance of the substituted objective, to the attainment of which he has transferred his energies and desires.

Overcompensation. Another danger in compensation is that the thwarted individual will go to extremes of conduct and *overcompensate*. As we have noted heretofore, all of us are motivated by a strong urge to be superior, to impress our ego upon those about us, to win attention and recognition. In their efforts to achieve these things, not a few individuals make the mistake of becoming artificial, ridiculous, or extreme. Thwarted in securing the attention or approval of their fellows, such people sometimes seek to compel recognition by the unconventionality of their conduct. Individuals who throw dust in the eyes of their associates by the tall stories they can tell; who dress extravagantly or perhaps immodestly; who put on airs and affect the mannerisms of the gentry; who strike poses or attitudes; who express "advanced" or daring opinions; who cover up their meager intellects by a volubleness of speech; who conceal their ignorance under the cloak of an assumed great learning: these are among the hosts of people who crave recognition and the limelight of attention and approval, yet who do not know how or are unable to earn them by direct attack. Instead of the pleasing and genuine recognition which some simpler and more natural substitute behavior would win for them, they achieve a type of notoriety which can rarely bring them satisfaction and happiness. Such adjustments as these are, as we shall observe presently, negative rather than positive.

Positive Adjustment and the Student Nurse. For the nurse, as for every other individual, direct attack is the most wholesome of all adjustments. Complete and sustained identification with the task ahead is taken for granted by her teachers and supervisors. They assume and expect that she has embarked upon a career in nursing, and that she has the purpose of preparing herself for the profession of her choice. Direct attack means for her, at the moment at least, the determination to follow through until she has arrived at her goal as a graduate nurse. It means no evasion of duty or responsibility; it involves the mastery of a large amount of technical information and professional and manual skill; it presupposes a readiness to sacrifice whatever other interests or plans she may have that might interfere with her efficiency as a student nurse; it implies perseverance, faithfulness and quiet determination.

It is an excellent plan for the nurse to make a thoughtful inventory of her personality, character and physical traits, with the purpose of identifying frankly such limitations as she may have and of deciding upon whatever revision of her habits and attitudes may appear necessary or desirable. Specifically, she might consider the following:

Do I tend more to be:

    Dominant, or submissive?   Optimistic, or cynical?
    Industrious, or lazy?   Serene, or apprehensive?
    Resourceful, or helpless?   Alert, or muddled?
    Cooperative, or selfish?   Courageous, or cowardly?

Facing reality, or adjustment by attack, implies that the individual must take into account her shortcomings as well as her redeeming qualities. Many people find it distasteful to attempt any kind of self analysis; the sensible person, however, is eager to know her liabilities, along with her assets, in order that she may adjust intelligently to her opportunities.

The list of oppositional traits suggested above can be greatly extended by anybody who is seriously concerned with improving her own chances of successful achievement. If the student finds, for example, on self analysis, that she is an apprehensive, gloomy, foreboding sort of person, she needs no psychologist to suggest to her that these are poor attitudes to build into a harmonious personality, and that a rational optimism is to be desired in everybody. Or, if she finds other negative propensities or attributes in her makeup, she should set about a personality housecleaning that will help to release her from such influences.

The point here is, of course, that closing one's eyes to her shortcomings and imperfections is dubious behavior for anybody. One must face her limitations, admit them to herself, and then attack. If they resist her best efforts at dislodging—few of them will if she persists—then she will be compelled to accept the inevitable and find some promising means of compensating for them. If, for example, she finds that her eyes are too far apart, her ears too large, or her height too great or small to suit her, she must accept these conditions as inevitable, forget about them promptly and cultivate such compensating traits of mind as will more than make up for these liabilities.

Adjustment by Flight. Many people in the world have failed in direct attack upon their obstacles, have not been able or willing to accept substitute objectives or plans, and in consequence have hauled down their colors and taken to their psychological heels. By fleeing from the harshness of reality and the bitterness of failure and thwarting, they have arrived at a kind of adjustment, known to the psychologists as *introversion*, which ought properly not to be called adjustment at all: it should better be called a pseudo-adjustment or even a maladjustment.

This psychological fleeing from obstacles and failures is a curious and interesting form of response. The person who flees would never admit to herself that she has failed or that she cannot carry the struggle any further. One must maintain her self-respect and her faith in herself at all costs. In consequence, she must adopt some plausible excuse by which to explain away her failure and her subsequent flight from the thwarted objective. In its more extreme form, adjustment by flight is seen in the hermit who chooses to shut himself away from his fellows; in the tramp, who takes to the road to escape from an uncomfortable environment; in the psychotic individual who finds in insanity refuge from a situation which he cannot or will not face.

In its less extreme form, adjustment by flight is observable in people who close their eyes to the actualities about them, who will not fortify themselves to meet the problems ahead, who refuse to accept the implications of events around them, or who evade or sidestep the harsher things. These and numerous other adjustive types will occur to the reader to illustrate those who are fleeing from their proper objectives instead of pushing forward toward them. To these flight forms of adjustments to thwartings psychologists have given the term *mechanisms of introversion.* There are several of these mechanisms, only a few of which will be examined here.

Mechanisms of Introversion. 1. *The Sour Grapes Mechanism.* The term "sour grapes" has been borrowed from the well known fable and applied to the method of introversional adjustment adopted by many people who are thwarted in the achievement of their objectives. After making an initial unsuccessful attempt to reach a desired goal, they turn aside, like the proverbial fox, and content themselves with the consolation that the thing they desired was not worth having, anyway, or perhaps that further efforts to obtain it would not be worthy of the seeker. Here is a neat little way of *adjusting to defeat.* It does not require that the individual shall admit either her own inadequacy or her lack of perseverance in attacking; it does not necessitate indulgence in regrets or self criticism. The thing just is not worth the having. Common examples are the unsuccessful candidate for a position who decided that the job would have been too taxing, anyway, and that he didn't care for it for that reason; or the poor man who did not desire wealth because riches were not worth the bother; or the childless man who expressed himself as being glad that he had no children because they are always a responsibility, and often even a liability; or the unpopular woman who is thankful that she does not care to purchase popularity by indulging in the silly or extravagant conduct of those who are popular.

The fact is, of course, in all of these illustrations, that the boasted satisfaction one derives from his failure to possess the boons mentioned is not satisfaction at all. Just as Mr. Fox would have preferred to have the luscious grapes, so the unsuccessful applicant would like to get the job, the poor man would dearly love to be possessed of riches, the childless man would give almost anything for children of his own, and the unpopular woman would like to be admired and sought after.

The sour grapes mechanism is not, then, a rational form of adjustment but a deceptive one. One adopts it to protect her ego and to defend herself from her own censuring. To acknowledge failure in achieving one's desires is not pleasant if one recognizes the reason for that failure to be in her own laziness, sloth, improvidence, or shortcomings; but if one explains away her lack of achieving by the sour grapes logic, that it is silly to strive for things that are worthless or perchance even dangerous, she can continue to respect her really unrespectable personality and live very comfortably with herself.

Other people, however, may not fare so well at her hands. The circumstance that the person who has been thwarted in the attainment of some desire or goal observes that others have achieved similar things, renders her extremely liable to develop traits of suspicion, jealousy, envy and other unlovely attitudes toward successful individuals who have "arrived." No doubt if Mr. Fox had observed that a neighbor of his who could jump higher or who had a longer reach had succeeded in knocking down and devouring the grapes, he would have been thereafter very unsocial toward him. If we look out upon the social and industrial and economic and material world about us, we can identify countless examples of the envy and dislike of those who have failed for those who have succeeded.

2. *The Blaming Mechanism.* It is more flattering to one's ego if instead of censuring herself for her carelessness or inadvertence, she is able to lay the cause of her failure to somebody else, or some material object. Here is a method of adjusting to thwarting quite as commonly to be observed among people as is the sour grapes mechanism. The student, for example, who fails in a test blames it upon the instructor's cantankerousness instead of upon her own negligence or faulty preparation; the motorist who has collided with another car blames the other driver for the accident; the illegible penman lays his poor writing to a scratchy pen; the bungling workman condemns his tools; the defeated political candidate, the weather, or the indifference of the electorate, or the unfair tactics of his opponent; the young student nurse, censured for being slow, may attribute the difficulty to her patients' many demands.

All of these and other common examples of the blaming mechanism indicate how prone we humans are to impute to others the cause of our embarrassments and failures. The urge to safeguard the ego is so tremendous in most of us that we seize upon this attractive and always-at-hand mechanism as a ready means of self justification. Blaming serves as a great self deceiver, and while we sometimes "see through" ourselves when we stop to think about it, the fact remains that for many people this type of adjustment is quite as unconscious as is the sour grapes mechanism.

3. *Other Forms of Introversion.* There are several other kinds of introversional adjustments to thwarting of our desires and ambitions. *Rationalization* is adjustment by a sort of one-sided reasoning in which the maladjusted person protects her ego from self censure by marshalling "good" reasons for her conduct and closing her eyes to the actual reasons. Thus, a woman who can ill afford a fur coat, yet who covets the attention which the possession of such a coat would bring her, explains that fur coats are much better protection for "this climate," that they wear enough longer to be cheaper in the end, or convinces herself by some other false argument that she ought to have a fur coat. And following out this line of reasoning, she proceeds to purchase one, or at least to pay down enough to get one into her possession.

Identification, or the tendency to reduce the poignancy of one's thwartings by seeing herself in the creditable achievements of others, is another form of defense mechanism in which the individual appropriates to herself the esteem which others enjoy. Thus, the unlettered and toil-worn scrub woman, whose lot in life is none too rosy, identifies her questing personality with that of the actress before her who possesses wealth, power, beauty, or all three together, and for two or three hours she loses her identity as she is absorbed, body, mind and soul, into the personality of some character of the silver screen.

In this sense, identification is not distinct from *daydreaming.* The latter, however, sometimes called *fantasy,* may not be instigated by objective stimulation. More typically the fantasy mechanism is aroused subjectively, and the dreamer gives full rein to her own dreams.

A common form of childish fantasy is the *conquering hero* introversion, in which the thwarted youngster imagines himself to have achieved in actuality the things he desires, and is in fancy being applauded by those who have prevented him from attaining his goals. Thus, the boy who has been failing in his school work or in his social endeavors in fancy sees himself now grown to man's estate returning in triumph to the scenes of his boyhood, with an equipage of splendor that dazzles the blinking eyes of his detractors. As a true conquering hero, he passes them by with head held high, never deigning to bend to their now proffered friendliness and adoration. Many a child—and probably, too, many adults—have those introversional moments of fantasy in which one's shortcomings have been swept away and replaced with success and achievement.

Opposite the conquering hero is the *suffering hero*, who achieves his heroism through the fantasy that because of the harshness or fault of his relatives, friends, associates or neighbors, he has been compelled to sally forth into the cold world to battle it alone, and in doing battle has lost his life in the unequal struggle. Now, in fancy, he beholds the flattering spectacle of all those associates of yesterday doing homage before his bier, prostrate with remorse that they were so cruel, and now appreciating only when he lies dead before them the worth of a real hero. Many a child and youth thus looks in upon his own obsequies and thrills with a satisfaction that he cannot experience in reality.

Still another defense mechanism is to be noted in various *ailments* and indispositions which are often associated with failure and thwarting. If one cannot achieve his goals by the expenditure of the efforts of which he is capable or which he is willing to put forth, he may by simulating disease or defect escape the criticism that he has failed in his objectives. Such symptoms of physical impairment are not trumped up consciously as a means of escape; typically they are hit upon by unconscious trial and error and, by incapacitating the victim, save him from the stinging humiliation that he is a failure. Psychoneurotic people commonly find salvation in this mechanism. Thus, a poor pitcher develops a cramped right arm; a mediocre singer, a chronic throat affection; a failing student, severe migraine or perhaps failing eyesight; a lazy person, gastric distress. Often the ailment form of escape started as real enough; later on, when thwartings appear, the individual, recalling the sympathy and attention he received when he was ill, may now unconsciously resort to the former ailment and find in it escape from blame and self criticism. Hysteria, as the psychiatrist knows it, is usually a psychic condition at root, though it may be reflected widely in an impaired muscular system or in a balky organism.

THE MEANING OF INTEGRATION

We have been discussing in this chapter the problem of mental conflict in the individual. We have noted that conflict arises when one is thwarted in attaining one's desires and goals, and that, since relatively few people ever achieve all of their purposes, there is likely to be existent in most of us some degree of conflict. When we are thwarted, it is imperative in the interest of our mental health that we make some form of adjustment that will bring us satisfaction. Adjustment by attack is the most rational, provided of course the goal is not beyond our reach, in which event adjustment by some sort of substitution remains the sensible alternative. Unfortunately, many people run away and seek to adjust to their failures by escape into some form of introversion or fantasy. Such a procedure is not in line with good principles of mental hygiene, if for no other reason than that it fails to promote integration of the personality. What, then, is integration?

From its root meaning, it is obvious that integration has to do with "integer," or "oneness," as opposed to disintegration, meaning "twoness" or "manyness." Psychologists refer to the integrated personality as the personality that is tolerably free from conflict, for conflict if it remains long unresolved will eventually set the personality at such cross purposes with itself that serenity and peace will be impossible. A personality that is constantly at war is a sick personality because it is a disunified, disintegrated personality. Emotional stresses are so opposed to one another that the strain upon the personality may almost if not quite reach the breaking point. In the disordered and disjointed mind of the insane person one sees disintegration at its worst.

The integrated personality is, then, the personality which, instead of serving as a battleground for conflicting purposes and goals, for unattainable desires that have not been compensated or sublimated, for discouragement and regret, for thwartings and rebuffs, has succeeded in drawing together all its purposes into a coordinated pattern into which all the constituent parts fit smoothly and easily. The integrated personality has found its level, has adjusted satisfyingly to its major thwartings, and has set itself upon the pathway to the achievement of whatever goals and purposes of life and conduct it has adopted as desirable and achievable. Rankling regrets, jealousies, envies, fears and misgivings, resentments have yielded to the unifying and purposeful momentum of a psychic drive that holds the individual upon his predetermined path. There is small place for conflict in such an integrated and unified personality because the energies of which the individual is possessed are coordinated in driving him to his goal. The contrast between such a personality and one in which the psychic energies are dissipated by turmoil and conflict is tremendous.

THE NURSE AND INTROVERSION

It is perhaps necessary to warn every young person of the dangers of introversion. To a limited extent, of course, one can justify resorting occasionally to fanciful imaginings that she has achieved her objectives. When one is weary from well doing, or when she is resting for a renewed attack, to indulge in a wee bit of fantasy in which one has actually reached the pot of gold at the foot of the rainbow does no particular harm, *provided* she brings herself back to earth and resumes her efforts at real achievement. The spectacle which she has gained of herself victorious may serve as fresh motivation to drive her forward. For the most part, however, we do not advance by introversion; we advance, as we have seen, by attack.

Like everybody else, the nurse may be inclined to spend more time and effort than is wise in rationalizing her failures or in imagining her successes. She should therefore cultivate the practice of facing reality as it is, of unmasking the "sour grapes" disguise and the "blaming" disguise and all the rest, and of looking at herself and her tasks naturally and honestly. She will do well to cultivate a healthy suspicion of tendencies she may have to indulge in such mechanisms as we have been considering in the last few pages. Instead of fleeing from things-as-they-are, blaming her shortcomings and failures upon others, or of daydreaming herself into happiness, let her rather strive rationally and openly toward the achievement of her goals—personal, social, professional. Let her struggle to eliminate discordant notes of conflict and rebellion and seek to attain to the priceless boon of an integrated and harmonious personality. Real satisfaction and happiness lie only in integration; in disunity and disintegration, by the same token, lie discomfort and misery.

It is important, too, that the nurse comprehend the subtle role which flight and introversion mechanisms play in the psychology of her patients. There is no question that the unwillingness to face their limitations and failures bears no small contributory relationship to the ills of body as well as mind that fasten themselves upon people. The person who is running away from life or who is rationalizing his failures is subjecting his personality to a tremendous amount of mental strain and even torture, which may and frequently does lead to psychosomatic ills. Furthermore, when he becomes physically ill, whether from this or from other adequate cause, the inner, unsolved conflicts become more acute and disrupting than normally and consequently render the problem of caring for him far more complex and baffling.

The man who, for example, is suffering from gastric or digestive malfunctioning, and who is at the same time torn with inner turmoil regarding a business incompetence which is coming to be more and more obvious with the years, presents a far more difficult problem for his nurse than he would if his trouble were purely physical. Whether or not his mental conflict was a causative element in bringing on his digestive disorder, it is patent that it will be a factor to be reckoned with in his restoration to health.

THOUGHT PROBLEMS FOR THE STUDENT

1. Can you point to any real conflict going on within your own personality at the present time? Is it likely that you will eventually arrive at a peaceful solution? How seriously are you seeking for a solution?
2. Cite several examples known to you of sound and satisfying adjustment to thwartings or failures.
3. What are the advantages and what are the dangers of adjustment by substitution? Suggest instances of substituted goals which have been effective, and several which have been doubtful in outcome.
4. Have you ever made use of the sour grapes mechanism? Of the blaming mechanism? In what sense may these forms of introversion be salutary? In what respects are they likely to be decidedly unsalutary?
5. Present illustrations of rationalizing that have come to your notice. What purpose does the mechanism of rationalization serve in aiding a person to adjust to thwartings?
6. Do you recall any occasions in your childhood in which you resorted to the conquering hero form of introversion for the satisfaction of thwartings? To the suffering hero form? Explain.
7. Do you have any special reason to believe that the ailments of which individuals complain may sometimes be defense mechanisms rather than true symptoms of organic disease or deficiency? Explain.
8. Read Reid's "The Great Physician" and Wald's "The House on Henry Street." Contrast and compare the methods of meeting conflicts as illustrated by these two outstanding persons.
9. Carefully analyze your own behavior for twenty-four hours and label the adjustments you tend to make to such situations as:
    (*a*) Criticism by a supervisor.
    (*b*) Greeting unacknowledged by a senior.
    (*c*) An uncooperative patient.
    (*d*) A class scheduled on your half-day off duty.
    (*e*) Inability to answer when called on in class.
    (*f*) "No letters today."
    (*g*) Need of working overtime to finish assignments.
    (*h*) Failure to receive invitations to dances.
    (*i*) The blundering recitation of your best friend in the psychology class.
    (*j*) The arguing of a classmate whose opinion always differs from that of the other students.
10. Can the nurse with a vivid imagination place herself in the patient's place to the extent that many conflicts may be averted for the patient? May she also serve to direct a good adjustment by her understanding of the patient's conflicts? Give illustrations.
11. Illustrate, by diagram, conflicts which are common at various age levels and consider how you could help patients belonging in these different groups to develop positive habits of adjustment.
12. Discuss the adjustment of the student who reminds her coworkers at frequent intervals that she is considered a fast worker; of the supervisor who weaves into conversations the statement that tolerance is her great virtue.

SUGGESTED READINGS

1. Bullis, H. E., and Kelly, C. W.: *Human Relations in Action.* New York, G. P. Putnam's Sons, 1954.
    Read especially these chapters:
    Chapter 3, "When Emotions Conflict."
    Chapter 9, "Do You Get Along Well with Yourself?"
    Chapter 11, "Relax—Take It Easy."
    Chapter 13, "Morale."
    Chapter 14, "Don't Dodge Emotional Problems."
2. Munn, N.: *Psychology.* 2nd ed. Boston, Houghton Mifflin Company, 1954.
    This widely used text contains a considerable amount of material relevant to the present discussion. Refer to the index for good leads.
3. Ruch, F. L.: *Psychology and Life.* 4th ed. Chicago, Scott, Foresman and Company, 1953.
    In Chapter 14, "Personal Adjustment Problems in Group Living," will be found an excellent presentation of such topics as problems of marriage, group dynamics, cooperation, competition, etc.
4. Shaw, F. J., and Ort, R. S.: *Personal Adjustment in the American Culture.* New York, Harper and Brothers, 1953.
    An attempt to relate personal adjustment to the social environment.

Chapter 14

*What unknown seas of feeling lie in man,
and will from time to time break through.*

H. W. LONGFELLOW

EMOTIONAL STATES AND TENSIONS

THE PSYCHOLOGIC CONCEPT OF FEELING

Popular Misuse of Term "Feeling." There are few words in the English language that are more loosely and inappropriately used than is the verb "to feel." We say, for example, that we "feel" sleepy; we "feel" warm; we "feel" cold; we "feel" that something is about to happen; one has a "feeling" that he has been in a given place before. We speak of a "feeling" of need, of a "feeling" of friendliness, of a "feeling" of respect. A man "feels" well or ill; he "feels" certain or uncertain, excited or serene; he has a "feeling" of sympathy, of pity, of disgust. In these and in diverse other connections we employ indiscriminately some form of the verb "to feel" whenever we wish to convey ideas of perceiving or judging, and often quite without any reference to essential physical conditions of agreeableness or of disagreeableness.

What Feeling Really Is. Psychologically speaking, the concept "feeling" must be limited to the subjective awareness of a general bodily state either of pleasantness, on the one hand, or of unpleasantness, on the other. In general, those stimuli that make for a general feeling of pleasurableness arise when the organism is comfortable and functioning smoothly, as, for example, when one is comfortably relaxed and resting or when one is warm and sleepy. Unpleasurable feelings are experienced, on the other hand, when the organism is uncomfortable or functioning inadequately, as when one is hungry and cannot appease his hunger, when one is nervously wrought up and tosses sleeplessly on his bed, or when one is cold and cannot get comfortable.

Contrast, for instance, the feelings experienced in the two following situations. (1) The student nurse has finished her studying and her

292   CONFLICT AND TENSIONS

ward duty for the evening and finds herself with still an hour upon her hands before time to retire. She recalls a most interesting book that she was unable to finish last week when she had some idle time, and she gets the book down from the shelf, ensconces herself comfortably in an easy chair by a warm radiator, finds the place in the

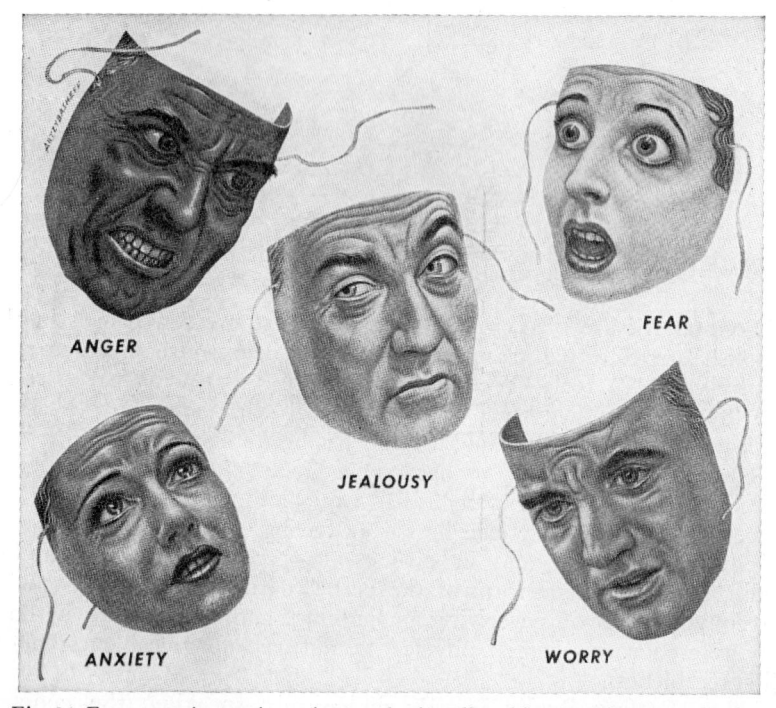

ANGER

JEALOUSY

FEAR

ANXIETY

WORRY

Fig. 34. Every one knows how these and other disturbing emotions can play havoc with our mental poise. But not everyone realizes that such emotional disturbances can also make us *physically* ill. For we can actually worry ourselves into stomach ulcers, high blood pressure, allergies, and other disorders. And, of course, if we already have any of these disorders, nervous distress can make them worse. (Reproduced by permission of Parke, Davis & Company, Detroit.)

story where she left off, and proceeds then to follow the interesting narrative. (2) She retires an hour earlier than usual, in the hope that an extra long night's rest will relieve her of a headache that she has been experiencing throughout the afternoon and early evening hours. While ordinarily she drops off promptly upon retiring, she finds tonight that sleep simply will not come. She tries her best to relax, but no sooner does she get a bit quiet than a throb in her head brings her wide awake again. She rolls and tosses for an hour. Exasperated, she rolls and tosses for still another hour, and when the midnight bell rings in a steeple far in the city she is still awake.

There is no question about the nurse's *feelings* in these two situations. In the one case, there are pleasantness, serenity, an awareness of well-being; in the other, there are unpleasantness, an awareness of stew and pother. In the relaxing-reading situation, there was a general sensation of tranquillity and placidity; the nurse was unruffled, unperturbed. In the tossing-wakeful situation, there was a general sensation of restlessness and irritability.

There are, of course, organic *sensations* which inform us of the condition of the various organs of the body. It may well be that feelings are a complex in which agreeable or disagreeable sensations from the inner organism play a prominent determining part. Usually pleasant stimuli are biologically beneficial while unpleasant ones are apt to be harmful to the organism.

Interestingly enough, there are no special receptors or sense organs that report feeling to us, as there are to report sensations. Our feelings are vague and diffuse; they seem to spring from a general organic condition of well-being or of ill-being which may be in part specific organic sensations but which is principally unlocalized. Pleasant stimuli throughout the body are interpreted as positive and agreeable; unpleasant internal stimuli are interpreted as negative and disagreeable. One strong source of pleasant or unpleasant feelings is to be found in the smoothness or the tardiness, respectively, with which nerve action, especially brain action, takes place. When ideas follow one another easily and without hindrance, we tend to feel satisfied and agreeable; when they are inhibited and halting, we tend to feel uncomfortable. A conversation, for example, that runs on easily and interestingly we find pleasurable; one in which our thoughts do not flow freely and we find it difficult to express ourselves or to participate readily we find unpleasurable.

Another source of pleasant or unpleasant feelings is to be noted in the familiarity or the unfamiliarity of the social environment. In the bosom of one's family, one finds it easy to be himself, to talk without restraint, to bear his share of the give and take of living; the familiar things are the agreeable ones. Put the same individual in a novel environment, however, in which he is compelled to rub elbows with strangers and to participate in conversations and in customs which are foreign to him, and you will likely find his conversation dwindling down to the bare minimum, homesickness for the known and the familiar becoming overpowering to him. For most adults, to keep the status quo of life unaltered is to continue in serenity and content; to alter it is to experience a strong desire to escape back to the known and the enduring.

It is true, of course, that through long habituation the familiar may become stale, especially when brought into conflict with ego-projecting urges. In such circumstances, the untried and the unfamiliar and unknown may come to be intriguing and alluring. Age is doubtless a strong factor in this connection, the younger individual tending to find his thrills in change and novelty, the older one finding his in the maintenance of the status quo. In any event, regardless of age or of the status quo, every individual reacts pleasurably to some stimuli, unpleasurably to others.

The Feeling Scale or Range. We may set off the range of the pleasantness-unpleasantness tone on a feeling scale, as in Figure 35,

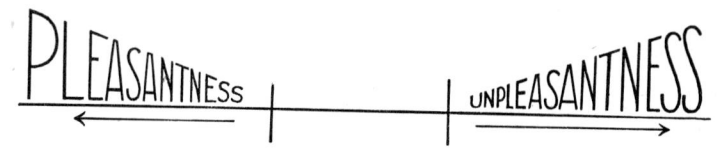

Fig. 35. Feeling scale for pleasantness and unpleasantness.

in which pleasantness is located at one extreme and unpleasantness at the other. Midway between the two is a neutral zone in which there is neither pleasantness nor unpleasantness, the existence of which may be accounted for by the fact that some of our experience is such as to arouse no particular feeling, either of agreeableness or of disagreeableness. The relative heights of the letters in the figure suggest the diminishing amount of pleasurableness and the increasing amount of unpleasurableness as one moves from left to right. Somewhere on this pleasure-unpleasure scale we could perhaps rank every feeling experience possible to us. Those falling near either the extreme left or the extreme right, *i.e.*, the most pleasant and the most disagreeable experiences we have or could ever expect to have, would in most instances pass from the realm of feeling and press upon the domain of the *emotions*, to a consideration of which we shall shortly turn.

Feeling Tone and the Nurse. Any nurse will find life and its experiences taking less toll of her physical and mental resources if she can train herself to cultivate positive and agreeable feeling, rather than the reverse, in connection with the routine occurrences and duties of the day. As a nurse, she will have no less need for husbanding her physical and spiritual resources than do other professional workers. It is important during the early months in nursing situations that she should form the habit of meeting her daily problems and obligations with serenity and satisfaction. It is easy to fall into the habit of reacting to the petty details of everyday living and working with annoyance and irritation, and she who makes the mistake of so doing becomes a source of much discomfort both to her associates and to herself.

If we will observe the facial expressions of people, we will note a difference in the feeling tone which characterizes them. Some persons rarely feel irritation but discharge their duties with cheerfulness and a pleasant face and make interesting and well liked companions. They are cordial, genial, and their company is highly acceptable. They know how to be good-natured and charming without being frothy and shallow. On the other hand, some persons are chronically irritable or are in a temper so much of the time that one never knows when they are going to take off a head. Their tasks jar upon them, and they perform them with obvious displeasure. They criticize subvocally or vocally everything and everybody.

If the nurse falls into this habit of easy irritation, or of reacting disagreeably to the common rounds of everyday toil and circumstance, it is to be regretted. Her dominant feeling tone ought to be in the direction of the pleasant end of the feeling scale rather than of the unpleasant end. It may require a good bit of determined self analysis and self discipline to lift herself up bodily from the place where she has settled toward the latter end and deposit herself somewhere toward the former end, but she will be gratified and ultimately will feel amply repaid for the efforts expended. She should try to find a modicum of pleasurableness in the duties of every day; to substitute for the quick frown the quick smile; to develop interest in other people, sympathy for her patients, respect and appreciation for her superiors, eagerness for and enjoyment of her profession. She should not rest content with herself or with her efforts at rehabilitating her personality until she can feel a dominant and secure satisfaction with life and the things it brings. In other words, *she must not be a disagreeable person to have around; she must be an agreeable one.* She must cultivate positive feeling; she must uproot and banish negative feeling.

THE EMOTIONS

What Emotions Are. As we have seen, whenever a mild awareness of pleasantness or unpleasantness is aroused internally, we experience feeling or feeling tone. Suppose, however, that the experience becomes so intense or exciting as to stir up the entire organism, notably the viscera, as occurs in fright, rage, passion, hate, anger or ecstasy. Our condition is then recognized as an emotional state. An emotion is always associated with a deep and profound arousal of the muscles and the viscera. Whenever there is strong innervation by the autonomic nervous system, more adrenalin is secreted into the

Fig. 36. The facial expressions characteristic of several emotions. Name them and compare your judgments with those of others. (Ruckmick.)

blood, causing in turn a rise in blood pressure, a quickening pulse, release of liver sugar, the inhibiting of digestive processes, and improved muscle tone.

Whether this widespread disturbance in the visceral organs causes the emotion or whether the emotion causes the visceral disturbance is for the moment beside the point. The significant thing is that whenever we experience an emotion there go along with it turmoil and ferment in our deepest organism. An emotion is not a mere series of ideational acts by the brain, originating within the skull and terminating there: an emotion is associated without question with the most widespread internal reverberations of any mental or physical reaction that we can possibly make. There are of course mild emotions as well as mild feelings; even in the mildest emotion, however, if it is true emotion there is a definite excitation throughout vast areas of the organism.

How Emotions Affect People. One has but to pass in review some of the common instances of emotional behavior observed among humans to realize how greatly they are affected by their emotions. An angry person may bang a door, become profane, say bitter things, refuse to speak at all, refuse to eat, "throw things," shout aloud, even raise his hand against his fellowman and strike him down. A frightened individual may lose his appetite, cover his face, take to his heels, cry out, curse, strike blindly, even take the life of his antagonist or take his own. An accepted lover will modify his whole life pattern, build or establish a home, share his possessions, redouble his efforts to make good, deny himself for his wife and children, and renounce old ways.

The tremendous power of the emotions over human conduct can perhaps best be seen in the behavior of the mob. The influence of the presence of other people upon the acts of men is extremely potent. Wherever and whenever a mob gathers, there is no way of predicting what may happen. Heretofore law-abiding citizens may often, under the social stimulation of the mob, conduct themselves in ways so utterly different from their wont as to amaze all who know them. Especially when there is present in the group a strong leader, it is possible to inflame men to the most extravagant conduct. Unleashed emotions inspire the mob to destroy property, menace law-abiding citizens, and even commit acts of fiendish brutality. In time of war, clever propagandists whip up anger and indignation in one national group against the nationals of some other country, and fire them to commit mass murder and prosecute the wholesale destruction of the richest fruits of civilization. Dictators by the assumption of otherworldly power or prestige may attach millions of their fellowmen passionately to themselves and to their cause, and by aggrandizing their own country, by playing up the indignities which they have "suffered," or by calling upon the spirit of the sacred past, succeed in inflaming their fellows either to hatreds of other peoples or races or to a false and empty nationalistic frenzy that knows no satiety until it finds it in the spilled blood of men or in the annexation of foreign soil.

Classic Interest in Emotions. The literature of all ages has abounded in accounts of men and women who have been driven by emotion or passion to this or that extraordinary conduct. Indeed, one of the most remarkable of all the classic tales is that recorded in Homer's *Iliad*, the principal action of which arises from the wrath of the Greeks against the Trojans because the king's son had abducted the wife of Menelaus, king of Sparta. The Trojan War as depicted in the *Iliad* was a struggle of vengeance for this dastardly act of the prince of Troy. Not only literature but history itself during four thousand years of recorded events has been in good part the story of the anger or the fear or the lusts of men.

It is not surprising that from the earliest times philosophers also, in common with the romanticists, have been intrigued by the power of the emotions. Classic psychologists were concerned primarily with an enumeration of all the various affective states that could be thought of and with introspective descriptions and critiques of each of them. Lengthy comparisons and classifications were undertaken by them, and the results of their analyses filled volumes. For a long time students of mental life assumed that every emotion was not only distinct in its patterning from every other but that it was innate.

Naïve Observations of Emotional Behavior Not Trustworthy. Naïve observation as a method of studying emotions has been used along with introspection. Nothing is simpler than to observe that a man is angry if he kicks a family cat, that a lover is jealous if he makes belittling remarks about his rival, that a boy is gleeful if he laughs and shouts, or that a girl is sad if she weeps. These obvious forms of physical expression of emotional states need no explanation. The tone of one's voice, the expression of one's countenance, the look in one's eyes, the curl of one's lip, the tilt of one's head, the smile, the laugh, the frown, the tear—these all indicate something rather definite about the emotional condition of the subject. It must be admitted, however, that a good actor or actress—whether on the stage or anywhere else—learns to dissemble and to "cover up" the true emotions. You cannot always tell that the woman who smiles is happy, or that the man who curses is angry. Naïve observation will not get us far in the scientific study of emotions.

Beginning of Experimental Methods: J. B. Watson. The modern experimentalist has been able to throw light upon the nature of our emotions. One of the earliest was Dr. J. B. Watson, who dismissed the notion that all our emotional reactions are innate and unlearned. Watson was able to establish the existence of but three distinct emotional states in infant behavior: fear, rage and love or sex. He succeeded in demonstrating that the only stimuli which would arouse fear natively in a young child were (1) loud noises and (2) loss of support. When a very loud noise was made near the child or when he was dropped vertically through 2 feet or so of space, he showed signs of fear. He could find only one stimulus that would evoke anger or rage in the child: restraint of movement. When the infant's arms were pinned down at his sides, or when he was otherwise restricted closely in his moving about, he struggled and exhibited a clear and unmistakable pattern of rage. The love or sex emotion was aroused when the infant was patted, rocked, or tickled. In a great number of test procedures Watson demonstrated that outside these three categories there were no original stimuli or situations that elicit emotional behavior in infants. In further experiments he was able to show, as we have pointed out previously, that the numberless fears that obsess the consciousness of most children and of many adults are in all cases learned or *conditioned.*

Discovery that the fear emotion is attached to its arousing objects, or events by actual learning or conditioning does not, of course, reduce the significance of fear as an emotion. Regardless of whether our fears are innate or acquired, we have them just the same and they play often destructive roles in our lives. Whereas the simple and sensible fears, such as those of crossing a busy street, catching a contagious disease, drinking polluted water and eating spoiled food, are beneficial and constructive, the complex and irrational fears and *phobias,* such as *morbid* fear of disease, of disaster, of accident, of crowds, of water, or of death, play no useful part in our lives and we should be not only much happier but quite as safe if we could eliminate them completely.

Are Fear and Rage Identical in Pattern? Watson succeeded in cutting down the number of native stimuli that could be shown to be adequate to arouse fear and rage. Still other experimenters have gone so far as to raise the question seriously whether there is any difference, so far at least as visceral and muscular upheavals go, between fear and rage. It had always been assumed that one could tell easily enough when a baby was angry or when he was frightened from the nature of his crying, his breathing, his struggling activities. An ingenious experiment by Dr. Mandel Sherman, however, makes it somewhat problematic whether, apart from learning and experience, the same organic and muscular patterns may not underlie both fear and rage.

Sherman filmed the activity of several infants, all under twelve days of age, under varying conditions of pain, hunger, loss of support, restraint, and the like. The films were then exhibited to nurses, medical students and graduate students in psychology, who were requested to interpret the several emotional states indicated by the infants. The results were amazing. In one group, for example, the anger response, aroused by hampering and restricting the movements of the infants, was identified 13 times as anger, 14 times as fear, 11 times as hunger and 8 times as pain. To check up, the experimenter caused the films to be "scrambled"; that is to say, they were cut and spliced in such a way that, for example, following the painful stimulus of a mild prick from a pin, the response to the stimulus of sudden dropping was substituted; amazingly still, the subjects detected nothing incongruous in the spliced film.

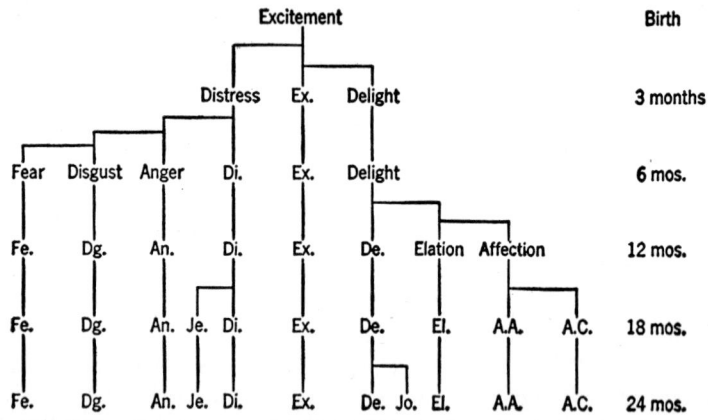

Fig. 37. Approximate ages of differentiation of emotions in early childhood. (From Bridges, K. M. B.: Emotional Development in Early Infancy. *Child Development,* 1932, Vol. 3.)

Reasoning from these and other experiments, the investigator concluded that it is more or less idle to attempt to set up two different original emotional patterns for rage and fear in the young subject who has not yet learned to employ characteristic adult forms of expression or control. Rather, it is apparent from such investigations as these that there is a general pattern of exciting emotion which expresses itself indiscriminately. Especially is this the case with very young subjects. The earliest emotional response in the visceral organs is a mass reaction.

Interesting research into the nature of early emotion in infants, which somewhat corroborates the work of Sherman, has been reported by Bridges. The original emotion in infants, from which all other emotions later split off, is alleged to be *excitement,* which is aroused in the earliest weeks of extrauterine life by such varied stimuli as bright sun in the infant's eyes, being suddenly taken up or put down on the bed, pressure of the bottle nipple into the mouth. The excitement emotion is evidenced by tightening muscles and arms, quickened respiration, kicking movements, opening eyes, and arching upper lip. Bridges finds this original emotion to be general, mass and undifferentiated, both with agreeable and with disagreeable stimuli. Shortly, however, a new emotion, which he calls *distress*, can be observed splitting off and becoming specific in such situations as mucous-blocked nostrils, long lying in the same position, lying on a wet diaper. By six months the distress emotion breaks down further to denote *fear* and *anger;* by twelve months, *disgust;* and by eighteen months, *jealousy.* Coincidentally with the splitting off of these distress emotions, there is found by Bridges to be the parallel emergence of *delight* emotions, which further ramify by twelve months into *affection* and *elation,* and by twenty-one months into a definite emotion of *joy.* Figure 37 shows chronologically the development of the early emotions from the original one of general excitement.

Experimental Techniques to Measure Emotion Objectively. Since the autonomic nervous system is thrown into activity by emotional states and since it affects so profoundly certain visceral and organic functions, it follows that one of the fruitful ways of investigating emotions consists in studying these internal processes as they are excited by emotional states.

The Electrocardiograph. Among other functions, the circulatory system is affected by emotion, as everybody knows who has felt his heart pound or his face flush in a moment of rage or fear. In times of excited emotion, the bore of certain arteries is diminished and the blood pressure rises. The force or magnitude of the heartbeat can be measured by the electrocardiograph, and the variations in the amount of blood can be determined by attaching a *plethysmograph* to the forearm. When either or both of these pieces of apparatus have been connected mechanically with a kymograph, it is possible for the observer to read and to record the variations in pressure and circulation during the period in which the subject is under the experimental effects of emotion.

The Pneumograph. Respiratory changes are also characteristic of emotional states, and hence some experimental work has been done with the pneumograph. Whereas the inspiration-expiration ratio of the laboratory subject during periods of calm is typically about 1 to 4 (*i.e.,* he takes about one quarter as much time to inhale as he does to exhale) it may rise to a ratio of 1 to 1 in states of sudden fright.

We experience this phenomenon in the tendency to breathe more rapidly, or even to pant, when we are frightened. The pneumograph records these variations in the respiration rate and depth.

The Psychogalvanometer. Interesting also have been the experimental investigations of the effects of emotion upon the ability of the skin to resist electricity. The body's resistance to electricity is considerable and it is the skin which normally keeps the resistance to this force high. Under certain conditions, including emotional conditions, the degree of this resistance changes, and to this change the term *psychogalvanic reflex* or *galvanic skin reflex* has been applied. In emotional states, there is likely to be a hyperactivity in the sweat glands and more moisture is thrown off on to the surface of the skin. This moisture makes the skin more pervious to electricity. Whereas the calm, unmoved subject will not ordinarily react to 4 or 5 volts of current, he will under stress of emotion react to a lesser voltage. The degree of oscillation of the needle of the galvanometer indicates momentarily the changing resistance to electricity and so, indirectly, affords a measure of the emotional upheaval of the subject.

The Free Association Test. While not strictly an objective method, the free association test is commonly used in conjunction with some of the apparatus above described, and so may be regarded as at least partially objective. In administering the test, the experimenter first prepares a list of stimulus words—100 is a common number—some of which are "innocent" words and some of which are "critical." After the list has been completed and scrambled, the examiner gives the subject some such directions as these: "I am going to pronounce aloud to you one at a time, a list of words, and you are to respond as promptly as you can with the first word that comes into your mind. If, for example, I were to say 'black,' you might immediately answer 'white'; or if I were to say 'man,' you might say 'woman.'" The particular value of the word association test lies in the fact that while the noncritical words will ordinarily suggest simple and immediate responses, perhaps no more than a second or so elapsing between the experimenter's pronunciation of the word and the subject's response, *critical words will arouse repressed or incriminating ideas which the subject will wish to conceal,* and in attempting so to do he will either require an overlong time to react, he will repeat mechanically the stimulus word while sparring for time or he will ask to have it repeated, or perhaps if he is clever he will make an abnormally prompt reaction with some irrelevant word which he has ready for critical occasions which might otherwise embarrass him.

The examiner who uses the free association test keeps a careful record of all reaction-times and whenever it is apparent that something is interfering with the naturally smooth and easy flowing of the subject's associations, he has a right to assume that the critical word has touched off some emotional disturbance or complex. The free association technique has been used extensively by psychoanalysts in

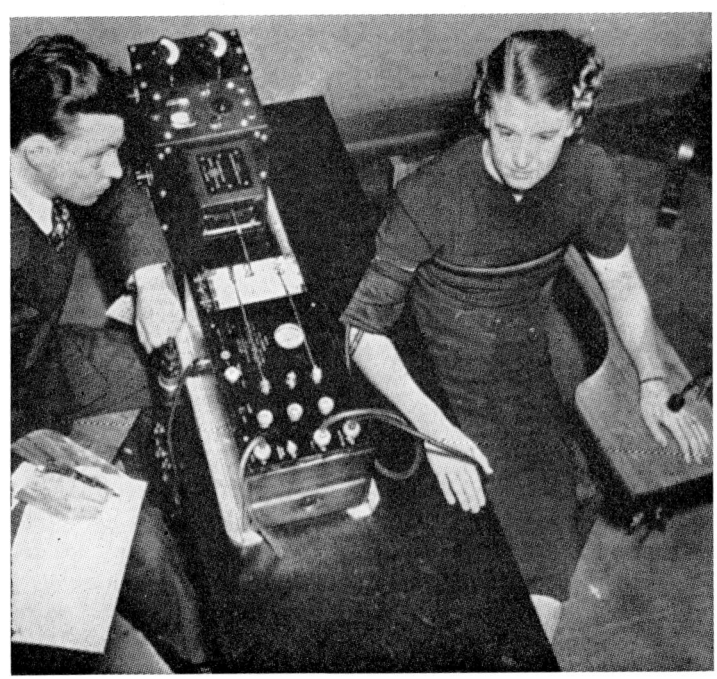

Fig. 38. In the Chicago Police Scientific Crime Detection Laboratory, Paul V. Trovillo demonstrates the polygraph, or lie detector, which was developed by the laboratory. (An office employee poses as the "criminal.") This apparatus measures respiration rate, blood pressure and galvanic responses. However, lie detectors do not always record this particular combination of physiological responses. (Ruch: Psychology and Life. 3rd ed. Scott, Foresman and Co.)

getting at repressed or forgotten emotionally charged experiences in their patients and by clinical examiners in ferreting out the connection of a suspect with the crime with which he may be charged. The word list is made up by the examiner to fit the particular case and circumstances in which it is to be employed.

The "Lie Detector." Figure 38 illustrates the combined use of the mechanical contrivances described above and the free association test in studying the emotional behavior of an individual. A criminal may cover up his knowledge of a crime by responding to critical words with harmless responses, or by hesitating and feigning not to understand the stimulus word he may even, if he is a clever crook, school himself so to control his muscles under all circumstances that there is no "give away" observable outwardly in his reactions to the stimulus words. The cleverest criminal, however, can hardly control the organic processes of his own body, and consequently the record on the kymograph reel may give him away in spite of himself. In the hands of a careful operative this technique has been found in many cases reliable in detecting the guilt or establishing the innocence of a suspect. The combined apparatus—including the pneumograph, sphygmograph, plethysmograph and psychogalvanometer—has been popularly and somewhat misleadingly termed a "lie detector." Its scientific name is the "polygraph," so called because it records or graphs many things. There are several varieties of polygraphs, some of them using all of the different pieces of apparatus described in this section, others of them using one or two of them only. Use of the polygraph is not yet approved by most courts of law, but at the request or with the consent of any person undergoing trial, it is frequently used. It is easy for one to see the possibilities which inhere in it as a means of testing the guilt or innocence of an individual through physiological variations going on within his organism which are tied up intimately with his fear emotions and over which he has no voluntary control.

Theories of Emotion. 1. *James-Lange.* Our emotions are so intricately bound up with our physiological and visceral functions that it is difficult to work out cause and effect relationships between emotion and organic reflex. Suppose, for example, that you are walking through a deep wood and come suddenly upon a rattlesnake, coiled ready to strike. What is the *first* response you make to the encounter? Is it physiological or psychological? Do you feel a great fright, *followed by* a blanching or a flushing face, a depressing sensation in the abdominal organs and a wildly pounding heart? Or is the reverse the case: *i.e.,* is your *first* reaction a reflex blanching or flushing of the face, occurring simultaneously with sinking sensations from the viscera and your "heart in your mouth," *followed by* a conscious awareness of fright? In other words, *is* the emotion you experience merely a feeling or an awareness of the physiological changes which occur upon perception of the rattler and hence a result rather than a cause? The classic question is often proposed: Do you run because you are afraid, or are you afraid because you run? Or, one might ask, in the third place, does the organic upheaval occur *simultaneously* with the perception of the stimulus, the former being neither an antecedent to nor a resultant of the latter, but rather a concomitant with it?

More than half a century ago, two men, William James, a psychologist, and Carl Lange, an anatomist, formulated independently of one another and approximiately simultaneously, the former in America and the latter in Denmark, a theory that has since been known as the *James-Lange theory of emotion.* It takes the position that emotion *is* the awareness of a stirred up condition of the organism and of the internal bodily changes which take place immediately upon perception of the exciting object or situation. Instead of speaking of these variations in organic functioning and facial pattern as expressions of emotion, adherents of the James-Lange theory believe that we should speak of them as the emotion itself. One of the reasons why it is so difficult either to accept or reject this theory is the obvious fact that the psychological experience of an emotion and the organic correlates of it occur extremely closely together. It is almost impossible, even for the most experienced introspectionist, to declare whether the immediate response to an exciting situation is a psychological awareness of an emotion or whether it is a profound and widespread variation in the visceral reflexes.

The James-Lange theory has suffered considerable loss of support in recent psychology. Not only is it next to impossible to prove its validity introspectively, but the fact that all emotional response is basically the same viscerally makes it improbable that any given instant of inner upheaval and turmoil could be immediately perceived and identified consciously as an anger upheaval, a fright upheaval, or a jealousy upheaval. Moreover, the total amount of sensory experience arising from visceral and organic changes is hardly sufficient to provide a conscious basis of emotion.

2. *Cannon's Theory.* In a series of interesting experiments, Dr. W. B. Cannon has found striking evidence which seems to run counter to the "peripheral" James-Lange theory and which leads him to suggest a "central" theory of emotion. In experimenting to determine whether there might be a brain center that controls emotion in a dog, Cannon began at the forebrain and removed bit after bit of it, without, however, inducing any loss of emotional behavior in the animal. But at length, when a small area in the posterior part of the *diencephalon* was removed, all emotional disturbances ceased suddenly. Reasoning from this discovery, Cannon supposes that there is in the brain a center which presides over emotion and that this center is located in the thalamus. The theory is interesting, particularly when one reflects that in a brain disease like sleeping sickness (encephalitis) the emotions are profoundly checked and that the seat of the infec-

tion is in the brain stem in the same general area that Cannon found to control the emotions in his experimental animals.

Recent experimentation with the electroencephalograph done by a number of laboratory workers* serves further to confirm the belief that emotion is profoundly conditioned by autonomic factors within the brain stem. There is good evidence that the reticular system in this subcortical area activates a general excitability under certain conditions and reduces it under others. This belief that cortical tone is maintained, increased and diminished according to the nervous processes flowing through the reticular formation is now well established. When lesions are made in the reticular activating system of the laboratory animal, a cortical condition resembling sleep is induced. On the other hand, under conditions of emotional arousal, apprehension, unexpected sensory stimulation, anxiety, etc., the reticular network is excited and unquestionably sets off wide collateral arousal throughout the brain.

A most interesting contribution of Cannon has been another hypothesis which he has advanced regarding the *purpose* of emotion. Cannon has done pioneer work in identifying the bodily changes which take place under stress of emotion; *e.g.*, the discharge of adrenalin into the blood, the release of liver sugar and the discontinuance of digestive functions. To account for these widespread and dynamic changes in visceral processes during emotion, he suggests an "emergency theory" of the utility of emotion. In the jungle animal and in the primitive human being, there was constant danger from attack or destruction by forces in the environment too strong to be met when the organism was in a state of relaxation. When a strong animal or a strong man attacks, the victim must have at once available all the physiological and muscular resources of his organism to meet the emergency. Survival therefore means, for the jungle animal and for the primitive human alike, the marshalling of all available defenses of muscle and blood and viscera. Emergency situations call forth warlike responses, in contrast with what might be called peaceful responses to such normal and favorable situations as eating, digesting food, resting and carrying on the vegetative functions generally.

Human life outside the jungle has existed but a short span of generations when compared with the age-long precivilized existence of man on the earth, and there has not yet been time enough for the powerful emergency organization of our nervous system to be super-

* Cf. especially the work of D. B. Lindsley, H. W. Magoun, R. S. Snider, *et al.* References to the experiments may be read in *The Journal of Clinical Neurophysiology*, 1950, II; also in The Biology of Mental Health and Disease (Milbank Memorial Fund, No. 27).

seded by an organization better adapted to civilized living. The warlike reactions are still potent. Perhaps in another fifty thousand years we shall possess organisms better adapted to the fine art of living than the present complement of fear-rage emotion makes possible.

How Are Fear and Rage States Distinguishable in Adults? We noted above that Sherman and others have concluded that the original emotional patterns of fear and anger are identical, at least so nearly so as to be indistinguishable to experienced observers. We noted also that Cannon's emergency theory suggested at least a fundamental similarity in fear-rage patterns in that we are prepared in an emergency for either fight or flight. How then does it come about that we are able to distinguish one of these exciting emotions from the other in our own experience? Surely no one would insist that he is unable to tell whether he is angry or afraid.

The emotional expression of the infant and the very young child is largely unspecialized, and even the mother or nursemaid cannot always tell whether the baby is in a tantrum or in a fright. As maturation proceeds, however, and as the social experiences broaden, differentiation of original mass behavior takes place, and there come to be specific patterns for a large number of emotions. The child soon learns what situations are dangerous and to be avoided and what situations are vexatious and to be attacked. Consequently he comes shortly to build up one pattern of fear response and another one of anger. He reacts characteristically to being alone, and to withheld food, uncomfortable clothing or a new infantile usurper in the home. Fear becomes finally for him, as for all of us, the basal expression of the mass response coupled with various learned or conditioned responses of avoiding or withdrawing. Anger becomes similarly for him, and for everybody ultimately, the original mass response coupled with learned or conditioned responses of attacking or struggling. Thus, in all our experiencing of these two emotions there is the mass, original, undifferentiated component and there is also the particularized, learned, differentiated component. It is no doubt the latter component in each case that enables the adult subject to differentiate fear from anger. We come sooner or later to experience recognized emotional patterns. At the extremes of strong emotion, such as blind rage, craven fear and intense pain, these learned components drop out and the original undifferentiated component alone remains, making all strong emotions organically almost identical.

Other Emotional States. Fear and rage are two emotions that have been systematically studied by psychologists. In addition to these two, there are of course a great many other emotions, among them the following: disgust, shame, awe, tenderness, joy, grief, jealousy, pride, apprehensiveness, ecstasy, remorse, excitement and worry. In all of these and other emotional experiences to which all of us are at times subject, the general underlying factor of a stirred-up condition of the organism seems to be fundamental. In our experience of disgust, there is a bodily condition of tension which may express itself externally in characteristic facial contortion and internally in highly uncomfortable visceral innervation. In tender emotion, on the other hand, there is a more pleasurable tension which expresses itself in facial beaming, in fondling and caressing, and in agreeable sensations from the deepest organism. Sometimes the organic accompaniments of emotion are pleasurable, sometimes they are unpleasurable; sometimes they are mild, sometimes they are profound; sometimes they run their course swiftly; sometimes, as in the case of worry, they may be prolonged over extended periods of time.

Abnormalities of Emotion. If by some supernatural pass of a wand emotion were to be removed completely from our lives we should find living to be prosaic and unintriguing. With no fear, there would be no prudence and foresight; with no anger, there would be no righteous indignation and no urge to win the world for the powers of good; with no love, there would be no family life, no stability, no sacrifice; with no shame, there would be no moral control, no modesty; with no reverence there would be no aspiration for the high, no communion with God; with no joy, there would be no lightness, no lift of the soul.

Our emotions are potent forces, and they motivate us with tremendous and dynamic energy. When kept under reasonable control and within normal bounds they contribute to the satisfactions and the accomplishments of life. When they pass beyond our control or when they become abnormally intensified, they may wreak great havoc in us.

Abnormalities of emotional expression do not wait, however, to make their appearance in the *adult* lawbreaker. In the early life of the child in the home the foundations are laid for adequacy or inadequacy of emotional control. Consider for example the common *temper tantrums* of childhood. Incensed because he cannot do as he wishes, the small child flies into a passion of rage and rebellion. Unless the first outbreak of this nature is properly handled, the youngster may find in it a device for frightening his parent into granting him the coveted privilege, and if it works he will use it thereafter with decisive effect. Some parents are "led around by the nose" by their own children to whom they have yielded so consistently as to have made them impossible tyrants.

Normally we should expect the rage tantrum to decrease with the years, according as the child finds it to be unprofitable. When, however, it is continued gratifyingly beyond the first experimental trial or two, the individual is almost certain to grow up with the notion that he can always get his own way by merely resorting to his paroxysms, or perhaps by sulking and remaining aloof until those about him will dance to his music. To grow into adulthood with this sort of abnormality of emotion is certainly to face life and its problems later on with slim chances of happiness and good adjustment.

Unfortunate emotional attitudes may be established in children whose parents overpraise them, who display their abilities or accomplishments, who are careful to guard their offspring from everything hard, or who themselves indulge in tantrums. Parents of this ilk can hardly fail to encourage the establishing of an insufferable self-centeredness in their children and to promote their negative emotions in ways that will prove unfortunate from the viewpoint of adult social adjustment ten and twenty years later.

The fear emotion may also be exaggerated in childhood and so come to play an overprominent part in the adult. One little girl grew up in such continual fear of her father that she transferred her fear of him to fear of all men with loud voices. Often parents themselves create enduring fears in their children by threatening them with the "bogey man," the "dark closet," and the like; or they may overdo their solicitous warnings against strange dogs and strange men, to the extent of arousing needless fears. Often a child acquires a conditioned fear, as of thunderstorms, of cats, of contagion, and because the mechanism of conditioning is not recognized, there is a failure to recondition promptly, with the result that he may grow up with abnormal dreads of situations which should be dismissed as casual. Sometimes the individual's efforts at repression of fear which has been built up in him serve to intensify his maladjustment and make him still more nervous and apprehensive. This is likely to be the case when he cannot go with confidence to a parent or some other person whom he respects and have his fears and worries sympathetically handled.

The love attachment likewise may suffer serious maldevelopment in childhood. Normally, we expect the child to develop in his emotional relationships as he does in his social, physical, moral or intellectual. If, however, he is kept infantile by parents who will not face the circumstance that their child is growing up, or who are themselves love-starved or mismated and who consequently seek to attach to themselves the heartstrings of their offspring, he can hardly be expected to evolve normally in this sense. A mother who rebels against her marital lot and does not hesitate to represent to her young adolescent daughter the miseries of married life is hardly paving the way for her child to react with normal emotion to the whole problem. Excessive fondling, kissing, petting and endearing of the offspring are likely to create in the object too complete attachment for the parent and prepare him poorly to develop a normally evolving love behavior.

The love goal of every adult is, of course, the establishing of a new family circle. Unfortunately, one finds parents who overstress the completeness and perfection of the child's home circle, and still others who would prolong the infantile love behavior up through adolescence. Both these types of parents innocently set the evolving individual emotionally against ultimate withdrawal from the present "ideal" circle. When he grows up, he will find it extremely difficult to adjust to and derive satisfaction in the new family circle, which in the natural order of events it should be his some day to establish.

Unconscious Emotional Factors in Behavior. In the preceding chapter we devoted attention to emotional conflict arising out of thwartings and of failures to achieve objectives. It remains at this point to pay some attention to conflicts in an individual that have their basis in his unconscious or subconscious mind. Here we shall be concerned with a brief consideration of the concepts of Dr. Sigmund Freud, the late Viennese physician and founder of the school of *psychoanalysis*. *Freudianism*, as Freud's general philosophy of mind is called, emerged as a system from the actual clinical experience of a medical practitioner who came to the conclusion early in his career in medicine that there is far more to the motivation of human behavior than appears on the surface, and that many ills to which mankind is prey are not explainable in terms of conventional medical and psychological practice.

Much as the principal bulk of a floating iceberg is beneath the surface of the ocean, so the bulk of the human mind is below the surface of consciousness. This unconscious mind, as it is termed, is in the nature of a vast storehouse for the forgotten and unworthy and emotionally unexpressed experiences of life, even from earliest childhood onward. Into this subterranean dungeon, according to the Freudians, we repress such ideas, thoughts, wishes and desires as run counter to the approved and acceptable in conduct. Driven from the conscious mind, these vague unfulfilled purposes rankle and seek continually for some kind of overt expression. A "censor," which may be thought of as presiding over the trap-door into the unconscious realm, prevents all unworthy or unapproved impulses and desires from escaping back into the conscious mind.

Much of the psychic energy of the individual must be used to hold the repressed content of the mind in confinement. In dreams and reveries, however, when the censor is a bit off guard, these repressed desires and purposes may disguise themselves sufficiently to deceive the nodding censor and parade forth once more across the threshold into the conscious mind. Dreams thus are interpreted as being wish-fulfillments. Strongly dynamic, a repressed purpose or motive or desire may also substitute for its normal outlet a type of expression quite far removed from its original nature, *e.g.*, nervousness, hysteria, neurosis, tension, and the like. The physical strain and tension resulting when repressed unconscious drives can find no legitimate outlet are placed by Freudians at the basis of maladjustment and conflict.

Libido and Ego. Fundamental to Freudian psychology is the theory that the sex motive is a basic one in human beings. Here is a force that characteristically undergoes repression from earliest childhood, and it is not unthinkable that its failure to receive fitting satisfaction at each stage of the development of the individual may set off deep-rooted conflicts that reverberate throughout the entire personality, accounting not only for restlessness and a feeling of futility but also for the neuroses and psychoneuroses. The struggle between the ego (*i.e.*, the conscious self, out of which "conscience" develops as an expression of social approval) and the sex drive—the Freudian *libido*—begins in infancy, and much of the psychoanalytic technique consists in tracing back adult hysterias and neuroses to their childish origins in unfulfilled sex curiosity or repressed and forbidden sex interest.

It should be recognized that Freud's interpretation of the term *libido* makes it include not only the sex drive as such but also the love life and pleasure life and achievement life of the individual. In this connection, it is contended that the creative work of the artist, the investigation of the scientist and the ceremonial of the religionist are all expressions alike of an underlying sex motive. Through such channels and by such means as these, people adjust satisfyingly to the drives of the libido.

Those who cannot adjust and whose personalities hence become battlegrounds of conflict between the ego and the libido, manifest, according to Freud, various forms of "nervousness" and tension. Psychoanalysts are interested in the interpretation of the dreams of their patients, finding in them, after they have straightened out the distortions imposed by the censor upon them, a disguised expression of the unfulfilled desires of the libido. They are also interested in slips of the tongue, slips of the pen, forgotten errands and engagements, and the like, which in turn they attach to the unconscious motives of the individual.

Psychoanalysis Today. A tremendous amount of psychoanalytic work is going forward today, not only in mental hospitals and in the psychiatric wards of general and veterans' hospitals, but in the offices of professional practitioners to whom come people who suffer from all degrees of conflict, tension, frustration, and psychic impotence, on the one hand; and on the other, innumerable individuals who, though reasonably well adjusted, are searching for greater release from their inhibitions and inferiorities and a more wholesome and dynamic way of personal living. Indeed, in certain quarters and among certain people, to be "psychoanalyzed" has become almost a fetish providing fuller and richer achievement. Extreme Freudian psychoanalysts still place great importance upon repressed or forgotten experiences of infancy or childhood as being at the root of maladjustment and conflict in the patient. They see in the early associations the infant has with his parents and with his brothers and sisters the greatest possibilities of the genesis of unfortunate conditioning. They see in his early interest in and exploration of his body and sex organs, in mishandled instances of exposure to sexual acts, in the punishments and warnings and threats dealt out to him on occasions of his own autoerotic acts, the lingering basis for later anxiety and the guilt complex that divert their adult energies from happy and positive participation in the vast arena of life and sluice them into dark, swift channels of fear, apprehension, guilt and neurosis. To the Freudian's way of thinking, relief of patients who are struggling in such psychic maelstroms as these is to be had through concentration upon their unconscious feelings and memories until they can be recalled, identified or recognized, and then reintegrated into the total psychology of the individual.

Other and less extreme psychoanalysts have felt that, while early experience cannot be set aside, sex is only one of several powerful human needs which the more radical Freudians have played up out of proper proportion to the total psychic drive. They believe it to be far more practical and promising to aid the patient to accept himself as he is and help him to better methods of adjustment to his present situation. They are convinced that there is in everybody, along with possible personality distortions that hark back to childhood, a tremendous will to live, to be healthy and strong, to conquer, and that these fundamental drives can, if emphasis is rightly placed upon them, become the dynamics for new life and hope in any individual. We have already devoted some attention to the various techniques used by psychoanalysts and psychiatrists to help the individual to overcome his emotional and personality difficulties and achieve a better adjustment (see Chapter 2).

Freudian Psychology and the Nurse. However much the psychologists may find to criticize in the theories of the Freudians, most of them admit that the concept of the unconscious mind has validity in the treatment of much functional disorder and neurosis. The literature of modern dynamic psychology is so filled with the therapeutic values of psychoanalysis as an instrument in helping unadjusted people to adjust that all of us—psychologists and laymen alike—will do well to recognize the Freudian contribution.

From the standpoint of nursing, it shoud be helpful for those who minister to the sick to understand the presence of vague, restless tensions that so commonly sap the energies and undermine the integration of their patients. The actual physical ailment or indisposition with which a person is temporarily stricken is not always a sufficient basis to account for his symptoms, and it is important that the nurse realize that his whole unconscious mind may be contributing to his total condition. When his physical health is impaired and he cannot fulfill his conscious and usual functions, it is not too far-fetched to suppose that his repressed, half-understood or actually misunderstood and unrecognized motives crowd a bit closer to the surface and markedly influence his general condition. While the nurse is not expected to be a psychoanalyst, she ought to understand that there are hidden mechanisms at work in the deep unconscious mind of many a patient who, when physically well, can carry on his life without too much interference from them but who, when ill, may suffer tension and physical upheaval from them.

If she is handling a psychiatric case, the nurse will understand not only how much more profoundly these undercover motives are influencing the present behavior of the patient, but that disturbances among them may well have been the original causative factor in bringing about his condition of maladjustment.

Emotional Transfer. A familiar figure is the man who comes home at night worried over some business transaction of the day, only to "take out" his mood upon his wife or his children. This kind of emotional transfer from the originating situation to an innocent and irrelevant situation is extremely common. A woman loses consistently all afternoon at the bridge party, only to vent her spleen when she returns home upon her maid whose indiscretion was the fact that she was the only person available in the house when her mistress entered. A student in a pother over a poor grade received in an examination launches into a tirade against her friend who has received a higher grade. A rejected suitor transfers his affections to the first person of the opposite sex that he sees after his rejection.

Many of our ingrained prejudices result from emotional transference. Thus, a certain man of middle age has a most pronounced hatred of tobacco, an aversion which he appears to have had since boyhood. The underlying explanation seems to be that his father was an inveterate user of tobacco, and that the house was interminably reeking with stale pipe smoke, while every room in it had its cuspidor for the man's convenience. The boy grew up detesting tobacco in every form and prone to look at every smoker somewhat askance. Perhaps a partial reason for his pronounced conditioning was the fact that his mother also detested her husband's tobacco habits and was always chiding him about them. Today, this man is ill at ease when anybody is smoking in his vicinity and becomes nauseated at social gatherings in which there is much smoking, absenting himself from occasions which would be interesting to him because he foresees the clouds of tobacco smoke that will assail him if he is present. It is extremely difficult for anybody who has a strong emotional prejudice to weigh matters objectively and sanely. Sometimes we are unjust in our judgment of an individual because we suspect in him—wholly without reason, it may be—some behavior or trait which we despise in ourselves. This sort of emotional projection may be disastrous to the equanimity of all concerned.

Education and Control of the Emotions. One of the earmarks of the adult individual is the fact that he has learned to govern his life by intelligence rather than by emotion. The implication is not that our emotions are of no consequence: it is rather that without intelligent direction the emotions may lead us far astray. In the well managed home in which children are growing up, it is essential that the offspring shall be developing progressive control of the naturally strong emotions of childhood. Of the anger or rage emotion especially there is strong need for discipline. The child who gets into the habit of grumbling, scolding, flying into a passion, harboring resentments, heaping abuse upon his mates, is making a poor start. He needs to be taught that other people have rights like himself, that expressions of anger and rage are unprofitable, and that those who give way to them are likely to become insufferable to their comrades. He should be helped to understand that anger and the expression of anger have their place in the world, but that place is not in the ordinary give-and-take relationships of the home and the playground. He should be encouraged to reserve his rage behavior for situations where somebody is suffering unjustly, where there is cruelty or deceit, or where men are tricky or mean or hateful in their dealings one with another.

The fear emotion requires also much discipline. The world has little use and less comfort for those people who are timid and given to fright and apprehension. Consequently it is important that parents guard their offspring from the development of unnecessary fears as solicitously as they guard them from the germs of contagion. The environment of childhood should be so ordered that fear will have little place in it. The parent who calls fear to his aid in disciplining a child makes in so doing tacit confession of his own inadequacy; by appealing to fear as an ally, he aspires to make his child conform because he dreads something or somebody. It is a dubious technique for an adult to summon such negative and often disastrous assistance in dealing with a child. When a fear has been once established in a child, on in anybody else, it is often extremely difficult and sometimes impossible to uproot it. We may reasonably persuade ourselves that our fear is absurd, but that will not help much in ridding us of it. We may admit that the thing we dread is powerless to harm us and yet go right on dreading it as heartily as ever. Psychoanalysts often find in those who seek their counsel long ingrained fears and phobias that yield stubbornly if at all to their skill in diagnosing and uprooting. It is far more sane to prevent the development of fear in a person in the first place than it is to attempt to correct or cast it out afterward.

MOOD AND TEMPERAMENT

Mood. When an emotional condition endures for some time, it is called a *mood*. Our moods change noticeably in the course of an ordinary day, depending upon the changing stimuli to which we give attention and the consequent variations in feeling tone. At one period we may feel greatly depressed because of some unpleasant experience we hear about, some bit of grim or uncomfortable reflecting, or some present malfunctioning of the body. At another period, we may feel elated, gay, "top-o'-the-mornin'," because of some cheerful occurrence, some bit of happy memory or anticipation, or the unspoiled beauty of a landscape. We speak of a happy mood, of a jovial mood, of a black mood, of a testy mood; all of us have experienced every one of them at one time or another.

There are wide individual variations in the nature and duration of our moods. Some people pass rapidly from one mood to another; they are now all smiles, now all tears; like an April day, they swing back and forth between sunshine and cloud. In manic-depressive insanity we observe this changeability of mood in its most exaggerated form. Some people, on the other hand, are much more stable in their fundamental moods. While they commonly experience depression and exaltation, just as their more rapidly vacillating fellows do, the alternation of mood is less rapid and the extremes may be less intense.

Temperament. Two ancient physicians, Hippocrates, of Greece, and Galen, a Greek who practiced in Rome, were responsible for the early classification of human beings into four types of temperament: the *sanguine*, the *choleric*, the *melancholic* and the *phlegmatic*. It was their belief that everybody was possessed of a characteristic mood which persisted more or less unchanged as long as one lived. This theory has exerted a strong influence in philosophy and psychology down almost to modern times. Nowadays, however, while we recognize the fact that one person is characteristically an optimist while another person is as characteristically a pessimist, we deem it unprofitable to attempt to divide all the people in the world into separate and distinct types, for there is so much optimism in the most pessimistic and so much pessimism in the most optimistic that hard and fast classification is impossible. About all we can say with conviction in this matter is that many if not most people incline rather characteristically toward one dominant mood, with variations. Modern physicians commonly ascribe mood to endocrine peculiarity or to other organic or physiological or hereditary factors not yet understood.

THOUGHT PROBLEMS FOR THE STUDENT

1. Make two parallel lists: one of the principal situations and experiences in which you customarily feel pleasurableness; and one of those in which you generally feel unpleasurableness. If possible, make a third list of situations which arouse neither type of feeling tone.
2. Do you interpret your own characteristic feeling tone as one of pleasurableness and cheerfulness? Or as one of out-of-sortness and easy irritation with your work or surroundings?
3. Analyze the next real emotional experience you encounter and try to decide whether the visceral and muscular turmoil precedes the "emotion" itself. Of course, your analysis must be made simultaneously with the arousing situation, and you may forget to make it until it is over. If you forget the first time, try again.
4. Collect several newspaper clippings of unfortunate acts which were probably the result of emotions. Explain the possible drive or drives behind each one of them.
5. How successful are you in "covering up" your emotions? Observe and question your close friends to find out how successful they are in dissembling.
6. Spend some time at your convenience in observing the emotional behavior of a young child. Is there evidence of "covering up"? Does there appear to be an identical pattern for fear and rage? How does the child manifest his love behavior?
7. Cite some family known to you in which you have reason to believe that the children's emotions are being abnormally expressed through tantrums or useless and pointless fears. What correctives or reeducational techniques would you recommend?
8. Of what objects, persons or events were you afraid in childhood? Can you account for the origins of your several fears? What is their present status?
9. Can you recall childhood experiences of rage or tantrums? Do you have any tendency today to seek to get your own way by sulking, anger or by tantrums?

10. Read Dr. Heidbreder's Chapter X and write an epitome of Freudian psychology.
11. The characteristics listed below in pairs receive consideration when reports are made on the practical work of student nurses; when present to a marked degree, we consider the student one who can be relied upon, whose behavior is motivated by sound reasoning. Discuss how emotions would modify these characteristics, taking one pair at a time
    (a) Alert and accurate.
    (b) Thoughtful and openminded.
    (c) Poised and self-confident
    (d) Industrious and systematic
    (e) Adaptable and constructive.
    (f) Purposeful and honest.
    (g) Informed and skilful.
    (h) Capable and cooperative
12. What physical symptoms may appear due to prolonged worry and anxiety? What is the nurse's function in the prevention and alleviation of such symptoms?
13. Observe your own emotional reactions for two days. What is your method of meeting mental conflicts when you are on duty? Off duty? If there is a difference, how do you account for it?
14. (a) Observe a patient who fears the operation or treatment she is about to undergo. Describe facial expression and bodily movements.
    (b) How would you handle such a situation?
    (c) If you also are fearful for the outcome of the operation, is your face likely to tell the patient?
    (d) Discuss the best method of adjustment to such a situation.
15. Fear plays a very important part in the lives of all people; psychologists list as one of its chief motivators uncertainty of what lies ahead. Accepting this premise, list some fears of the patient; of the student nurse; of the head nurse; of the intern.
16. May reactions of apprehension sometimes be dispelled by physical treatments such as prolonged warm baths, vigorous exercise or sound sleep? How do you explain these changes?
17. In your observations, have you found that illness affects emotional control? In your experience, have you found that fatigue affects emotional control? In the light of your conclusions, suggest what the nurse can do to minimize emotional upsets in the sickroom.
18. Distinguish between mood and temperament. Why is it unprofitable to divide people into separate and distinct types according to temperament?
19. In this chapter we have noted that fear plays an important part in motivating human responses. Discuss some unreasonable fears, such as the fear of people in authority—head nurses, supervisors, etc.—and consider how such fears may be conquered. Contrast with these some reasonable fears, such as fear of making a mistake in the administration of medicine, and consider what precautions you must take to avoid such errors.

SUGGESTED READINGS

1. Bernhardt, K. S.: *Practical Psychology*. New York, Blakiston Division of Mc-Graw-Hill Book Company, 1955.
    This book in general provides a good guide for wholesome living. It is scientifically sound, yet refreshingly readable and practical.

2. Hall, C. S.: *A Primer of Freudian Psychology*. Cleveland, World Publishing Co., 1955.

   A presentation of Freud's fundamental ideas with reference to the organization and development of normal personality as distinguished from his better known views in abnormal psychology and psychoanalysis.
3. Heidbreder, E.: *Seven Psychologies*. New York, D. Appleton-Century Co., 1933. Chapter 10, "Freud and the Psychoanalytic Movement."
4. Pitt, W. J., and Goldberg, J. A.: *Psychology*. New York, McGraw-Hill Book Co., 1954.

   Well illustrated, this book is oriented to the social and personal needs of the individual and his role in his home, his school and his community.
5. Ruja, H.: *Psychology for Life*. New York, McGraw-Hill Book Company, 1955.

   Especially good in its discussion of the developing of social skills, control of fear and anger, and the cultivation of a healthy mind. Read especially Chapter 6, "Emotions and Health."

Unit 7

In Pursuit of Mental Health

Chapter 15

The air of paradise did fan the house, and angels officed all.

WILLIAM SHAKESPEARE

MENTAL HYGIENE OF THE FAMILY

THE ADEQUATE HOME

Supreme Importance of Home. Beyond all question, the most powerful factor in shaping and molding the individual is the home in which he is nurtured. To whatever degree it may fail in the fulfillment of its high functions, the fact remains that throughout the ages the home has been the place of nurturing the young in those traits and attitudes which have been and are still deemed desirable for perpetuation in the oncoming generation.

The concept of home has probably not altered greatly in thousands of years. From the half-savage, half-human mother who defended her brood with instinctive fierceness against all molesters and who taught them to follow her and learn of her, to the strictly up-to-date human mother who devours the latest literature in child psychology and child training in the quest of light to guide her in her task, motherhood at its best has continued unaltered. Sociological institutions have changed; habits and points of view and goals have changed; but home and motherhood have remained fundamentally unaltered and unchallengeable. Throughout the animal series the den, the nest, the burrow, where the litter of young has been deposited, become sanctuaries which no marauder may desecrate and which the parents will defend to the last ditch. Any person, group or doctrine that would presume to deny or minimize the indispensability of an adequate home, presided over by two parents committed to the high task of rearing their children to be worthy men and women, would indeed display bold ignorance.

Earmarks of the Adequate Home. What makes an adequate home? What makes two persons—a male and a female—adequate parents? We have, on the positive side, the testimony of social workers, psychologists, psychiatrists, sociologists and other workers in the broad general field of human engineering, all of whom are in agreement concerning certain basal features of the adequate home and the adequate parent. On the negative side, we have the testimony of the judge, of the probation officer, of the juvenile court, of the correctional institution and of others who must deal with the product of the home after it becomes a menace or liability to the community at large. These latter persons and institutions are likewise in good agreement concerning what makes the *inadequate* home and the *inadequate* parent.

The adequate home is a home where there exists a harmonious and sympathetic understanding between parent and parent, and between parents and children; where, after the economic stability of the family has been provided for, the role of guidance of the young becomes the supreme role of the adult members; where a happy mean is maintained between freedom and repression; where love and protection of the child are invariable and unfailing, without becoming obstacles to his complete personal and social evolution and his complete individualization; and where there is a wholesome community of interest, purpose and spirit among the members.

Earmarks of the Adequate Parent. Serving as the guardian of such a home, the adequate parent may be characterized as the parent who finds satisfaction and happiness in the mate; who looks upon his function of parenthood as requiring of him deep concern in the welfare of his offspring, interest in their interests, pride in their achievements, sympathy in their problems; who recognizes the psychological necessity for the younger generation to face its problems and make its way without needless parental restrictions; who is ready and anxious to guide and advise and lend a listening ear, without feeling constrained to dictate, "nag" or prohibit; and who realizes that the best and most satisfying outcome of parenthood is the rearing of one's children into young men or young women of good habits, good morals, good controls, and possessed of individuality and a degree of self reliance and self completeness sufficient to guarantee a strong likelihood of successful achievement in future adult affairs. Still a part of the ancestral hearthstone, the new individual is by way of becoming emancipated not only physically from its restrictions, but also socially and emotionally, and is being made ready to build for himself a new hearthstone and a new family organization in which he will himself in turn play the part of parent, and so perpetuate what is unquestionably the greatest of all human institutions: the family. The family is a small world in itself, and hence those who control and direct it need both to know a great deal and to possess many and varied skills.

EDUCATION FOR FAMILY LIFE AND HOMEMAKING

Most Couples Poorly Prepared for Homemaking. While there is good evidence in certain quarters that some of the more intelligent and best-intentioned parents are seeking to equip themselves to discharge all the functions and responsibilities of parenthood and homemaking, it is unfortunately still a fact that by far the largest percentage of married persons have had no premarital training in the responsibilities of marriage and parenthood, and they do not commonly seek it postmaritally. It speaks well for the fundamental common sense and adaptability of human beings that no more than 25 out of every 100 marriages go on the rocks, or at least end in the divorce courts, while some 75 of them continue in force throughout the lifetime of the contracting parties. Certainly there is little in the typical sort of preparation and background of most young couples as they stand at the altar that might be supposed to prepare them for establishing a home and maintaining it against strains and stresses for a lifetime.

Most couples when they marry have but the dimmest notions of any philosophy of the family and the home, hardly a remote appreciation of their historical evolution, and next to no comprehension of the emotional and personality adjustments which they will be compelled to make if their lives together are to be mutually satisfying and harmonious. They are likewise in the grossest ignorance of the physical growth and development of the organism from the time of conception to the close of adolescence, and they have only passing information regarding the problems incident to child training, shared play and adventuring, and the cultivation of the esthetic and the religious. More often than one would believe, they possess no proper information regarding the marriage relationship, no reasonable understanding of the biological structures and the physiological processes of the organism, and little knowledge of sex hygiene. In only a few, but fortunately an increasing number, of the states does society take any precautions to guarantee physical health and mental soundness in those who assume the bonds of wedlock.

Need of Training for Family Life. One of the most neglected areas of our social organization is that which comprises the institution of the family. It has been rather commonly assumed that the family can run itself and that parenthood is something for which nature automatically equips and prepares every adult individual. Nothing could be farther removed from the actualities of the matter. True, nature endows most adults with the biological capacity to sire or bear children; but she does not by any means endow every person temperamentally or emotionally to rear them and to preside over the unfolding and maturing of their personalities. Neither does she equip them natively with the information and the background to train them intelligently during the formative years of infancy, childhood and adolescence. Every parent needs careful and systematic preliminary preparation for assuming the functions of parenthood, child-rearing and family life if the home is to be the sort of institution it should be.

Education for family life and homemaking has not yet proceeded very far with us. We deem it needful to train for almost every other occupation and profession: for practicing medicine and law, for teaching, for cooking, for farming, for office work, for salesmanship, for plumbing and for most of the thousands of other occupations into which the work of the world divides itself. In preparing for the most fundamental of all occupations, however, that of homemaking, only sporadic efforts have been expended. Sociologists, social workers, psychiatrists, educators and psychologists alike all feel keenly the importance of adequate training for family life and child-bearing.

The National Council on Parent Education and the National Council on Family Relations have been for some years committed to the promotion of this important phase of adult education; they have assisted many local, state and national agencies to organize and carry on courses in child development and family relationships in voluntary study groups of parents; they have been successful in getting courses in these subjects introduced into some secondary and college curricula.

The unfortunate part of such effort is, of course, that those parents most in need of the help offered in voluntary courses never seek enrollment, only those well-intentioned individuals who are ambitious to do their best by their children and by themselves ever electing to pursue them. Courses offered to under-graduates in those few high schools and colleges that sponsor them are often negatived by the sensational, half-satirical manner in which the public press calls attention to them. The work of such organizations as the National Council on Parent Education and the National Council on Family Relations is to be commended and supported in every possible way by all professional workers who are brought into intimate contact with home life and who have opportunity to observe the profound need in this field.

THE DISHARMONIOUS HOME AND ITS EFFECTS

Maladjusted Husbands and Wives. As was pointed out in Chapter 12, one of the outstanding earmarks of the mature individual is the evidence that he has been weaned emotionally from the childhood family circle and can stand four-square to the world. To the married relationship many an individual brings an immature emotional hangover from childhood which unfits him or her for well adjusted participation in the mutual task of building the new family. The infantile woman in particular is likely to suffer keenly. Product often of a pampered home in which she was perhaps kept dependent and immature by her own selfish parent or parents, the emotionally unweaned woman enters the married state with an inadequate idea of what a real partnership of two mutually conditioned people should mean. She may also have been shielded by fastidious or thoughtless parents from an understanding of the role of sex in human life, and she may have approached its experience in the marital state, with misgiving and even with shock or disgust. Only psychiatrists and consulting psychologists know how numerous are the families in which because of inadequate preparation for marriage on the part of the wife the happiness and adjustment which ought to attend every marriage are never realized.

Likewise the husband, if he is the product of a self sufficient home and has been pampered and babied by his mother up into adult life, may find it difficult if not impossible to transfer his affections and allegiance to the mate. Being still under the emotional dominance of his mother, he may compare his wife unfavorably with her and find the new relationship not adequate to satisfy his idealistic childish conceptions. The senior author has met cases in which, because of the emotional and infantile attachment to the mother, the son has grown up unadjusted and has steered clear of matrimony because he could find no mate who could replace the mother image.

The home life and family relationships of parents, either or both of whom are emotionally unweaned from the childhood home, are most distressing not only to the two mates but to the children as well. Suppose, for example, that the mother has been spoiled as a child and has grown up selfish and dominating. Finding it impossible to hold a club over the head of her husband as she had been able to do over her parents, and being disillusioned regarding matrimony, such a woman assumes a compensatory sort of childish petulance and self pity that express themselves in fault-finding, nagging and "nerves," which may be either voiced or eloquently unvoiced. There results a mutual misunderstanding between herself and her husband, with the attendant strain and stress. The cordiality and fine forbearance which should obtain between husband and wife are lost and each tends to seek compensatory means to find the satisfactions of life, the former becoming more and more engrossed in his business, his club, or his golf, and the latter in her children, her whims, or her neurosis.

One common form of compensation which such an infantile woman seeks is an emotional domination of her son or daughter. The urge to be the center of the scene is there, just as it was in her girlhood home, and finding herself thwarted in the attempted domination of her adult spouse she turns naturally to somebody whom she can certainly victimize. Sometimes she plays a consistent game to attach her child's loyalties to herself and to insure that they shall not be attached to her husband. It is of course a selfish procedure, but such a woman is a selfish person through her training and background. Her motive is perhaps not blameworthy, for it is in all probability a subconscious purpose that moves her to achieve domination. The desire has been so firmly built into her personality and character that she is not altogether responsible.

But the result is inevitable. The personality of the offspring becomes submerged in the overpowering personality of the mother. If a son, he becomes a "mama's boy" type, if a daughter, she grows up to reflect in her own attitudes those in which she is schooled by her mother. Listening to the chronic fault-finding and fussing which her mother carries on regarding her husband, the daughter's natural inclinations toward the latter are held in restraint and she sometimes experiences an intolerance of him which is likely to spread to include the entire tribe of males. As she becomes more and more identified with her mother, the adolescent daughter hears frequent denunciations of her father and philosophizing upon the intolerableness of marriage and the wisdom of keeping away from the opposite sex. All men are alleged to be alike, with the implication that all of them are bad. If the mother has found herself unprepared emotionally or informationally for the duties and responsibilities of a wife, the effect upon her unwholesome attitudes is enhanced, and her daughter may develop an intensified mind-set against men and marriage. Thus does the emotionally immature woman succeed in passing on to her daughter the same unfortunate attitudes and the same infantilisms and inadequacies that she herself possesses.

Somewhat akin to those parents who endeavor to attach their plastic-minded young children to their own personalities are those other parents who project themselves overwhelmingly upon the personalities of their children. In their misguided affection for them, born of the pride of parenthood and the selfish desire to dominate them, this type of parent spends his days in solicitude for their every condition, in surrounding them with luxury and possessions out of keeping with their needs, in shielding them from contacts with other children, in defending them from teachers, mates and from the consequences of their own misdeeds, in aiding and abetting them in their perverseness, in inventing excuses and explanations for their non-conformities, and in rationalizing their conduct and behavior.

Such parental protestations prepare children poorly for life later on. Instead of learning to care for themselves, the unfortunate young persons continue to be psychological dependents; instead of learning the lessons of thrift and frugality, they learn only lessons in extravagance; instead of being fitted to live harmoniously with others, they are trained to be social misfits; instead of the lesson of cooperation, they learn selfishness and nonconformity; instead of self-control, they are schooled in a kind of license and untamed freedom that augur poorly for the future. Still other products of homes that are made to revolve concentrically about the growing young people within them include aimlessness and purposelessness of character, unrest and rebellion, moroseness, emotional conflict and delinquency. No home can baby its members, condone their lapses and prolong their period of dependence without breeding a host of negative and dangerous potentialities.

Interparental Conflict. Even though interparental difficulties may be less acute than those which arise out of an infancy prolonged up into adulthood, whenever and wherever they occur they make for an inharmonious and unsatisfying family experience. A happy mutual adjustment between the two mates is indispensable to the adequate family. Wherever there is strain or antagonism or incompatibility, there is the inadequate family. In some family circles there exists a good deal of bitterness and animosity. It is a part of human nature to be selfish, and when two individuals in the married state are not able to learn and practice the lessons of forbearance and restraint there is sure to be unhappiness and suffering for all concerned. To live together in harmony and comfort is not something which is an innate gift to mankind; cohabitation, if it is to be congenial and mutually enriching, is something which has to be cultivated, like any other fine art. To achieve such harmony and serenity requires on the part of both partners definite and persistent effort and loving and sympathetic purpose.

Where there is not the skill or the will to achieve such harmony and understanding, cohabitation of a woman and a man in the married state too often degenerates into a sort of irritable toleration which frequently breaks out into quarreling and reproachfulness. Those families are legion in which there occur daily misunderstandings, disputes, threats of separation or divorce, and unlovely personal criticisms, until home becomes anything but a place of sympathy and concord. If one will call to mind the most ideal middle-aged couple he knows, he will after a few moments' reflection probably conclude that the one thing which makes for stability and charm of the union is the simple and consistent respect which each partner has for the other.

Poor adjustment between two individuals leads inevitably to conflict. They disagree more or less vigorously and consistently regarding the details of family management, of bringing up the children, of spending their money; they cannot agree on questions of discipline; they dispute over all sorts of matters that are not worth the breath it takes to argue them; they fuss over choice of friends; where to go, how to spend their leisure time or their vacation; they become explosive over besetting weaknesses, over choices and tastes, even over the moves of a family game! Instead of being brought more closely together by the common daily experience, they tend to be thrust still farther apart.

Effects upon the Children. The effect of discordance and strife between two adults is bad enough upon the personalities of the two individuals themselves; it is more disastrous upon the personalities and the mental health and serenity of the children of the family. We have the combined testimony of psychiatrists, social workers and sociologists to the effect that the majority of the behavior and personality difficulties of problem and delinquent children in our clinics can be laid definitely at the door of the homes from which they individually come. Consciously or unconsciously, a child who grows up in a family where there are instability and strain in the relationship between the father and mother perceives the underlying condition of insecurity and antagonism which exists in the home and tends to become filled with vague fears and anxieties and with a sense of uncertainty and of personal insecurity. A good deal of unhappy conflict results.

The effects are particularly bad upon a child who happens by nature to be impressionable and emotionally responsive. The whole present outlook of many a high-strung and sensitive child is blackened by the suspicion or the certainty that all is not well between the parents, and with this condition constantly suspended over his head he passes out of childhood into adolescence fearful and apprehensive of the future, both as it relates itself to his home and as it relates itself to his own chances of serenity and happiness. Often the parents are able to keep their differences from the public ken, and they may actually pass in the community as well mated and happy. Only the worried and apprehensive children may be undeceived as to the true situation.

Many incompatible parents become love-starved; that is to say, they do not reciprocate a gratifying emotional love experience with the mate; hence they may divert their normal affections for one another upon the helpless and unoffending children. Love thus restrained from finding its natural release upon the mate may center itself upon its filial substitute until he (or she) is totally absorbed into the personality of the parent. It is the same kind of compensating affection that the emotionally infantile parent, about whom we spoke above, seeks to concentrate upon an offspring, and it has in it the same potentialities for evil to the unfolding personality and individuality of its young object. He tends to grow up aloof from other children and to be distrustful of himself. He may feel himself inferior to other boys and girls who have full and abundant opportunity to enjoy the give-and-take of normal juvenile contacts. Instead of putting himself forward and establishing a place for himself in the group, he becomes reticent, secretive and avoids social intercourse with people outside the home. His attachment for his parent is such as to discourage friendliness and comradeship with others. He becomes parent-centered and hence incapable of gaining adequate perspective of normal extra-familial relationships. In school he continues aloof and is inclined to avoid the conventional and commonplace activities that play so important a part in the social experiences of the pupils. He may become a bookworm, perhaps even a prodigy, devoting entirely to his books those energies which should in part be given to social participations and good comradeship.

Some of the more self-assertive, "hard-boiled" children who are thus made the selfish center of parental affection react quite differently from those who are naturally tractable and easily influenced. Instead of reciprocating the selfish love of the parent they may, as they grow older and pass up through the elementary school and into the high school, rebel against the suffocating parental fixation and break away, becoming leaders among their mates and indulging in extravagant or wayward conduct that shocks the uncomprehending parent beyond measure. Quite different from the introverted type of offspring upon whom the love-starved parent showers his miscarried affections, this type of child is strongly extroverted: he is not introspective, fearful, apprehensive; rather, he is bold and venturesome. His personality cannot be absorbed by that of his love-starved parent; it seeks to be self-determining. If such a high-spirited child keeps himself out of delinquency, it is no thanks to the parent who by attempting to smother him actually drove him forth to seek normal emotional experience for himself.

THE BROKEN HOME AND ITS EFFECTS

Divorces and Broken Homes. While of course not all delinquency and waywardness in children is due solely to broken or inadequate homes, it is a significant fact that problem children in general are known to come far more commonly from such home backgrounds than they do from normal and happy home environments. Frequently, a maladjusted husband and wife may resolve to "stick it out together for the sake of the children" and refrain from a divorce. While on the face of it this resolve may appear commendable, its effects upon the children may be anything but salutary. Differences that are "patched up" for the children's sake are usually such as to keep the entire family in turmoil. Partnerships that are thus maintained in name only in order to shield the children are productive of much unhappiness and suffering on the part of all concerned. The atmosphere is continually tense and disturbing, and the growing personalities of the children may be damaged seriously. The author is not an advocate of easy divorce, or indeed of divorce in general; he has seen so many children and adolescents, however, whose misery and inadequacy were due principally to the circumstance that they were compelled to live in homes where there was incompatibility between the two parents, that he feels the wisdom of relief for such unfortunate young sufferers if the conditions in their homes are such as to resist all hope of amelioration.

A deficient home, in other words, is not alone a broken home over which the spectre of divorce constantly hangs, or upon which it has actually fallen and brought about a separation; a deficient home is perhaps as often as not one in which there are disharmony and incompatibility without open rupture. We have no satisfactory way of estimating how numerous these failing homes are, for sociologists and welfare workers have given much more attention to and research upon the definitely broken home as it relates to delinquency and waywardness than they have to the inharmonious home. Such homes are certainly common and their negative influences over their children are too profound for sociological complacency.

Effects of Separation upon Children. Parental separations, with or without divorce, do not always relieve the emotional situation. Not infrequently they create baffling new problems of adjustment in the children concerned. As we have said before, one of the essential aspects of an adequate home is the feeling of security and enduringness which it provides its children. When that security, even though at best it has never been too certain, is completely taken away and the young person sees his home crumble around him, the effect is likely to be disconcerting and in some cases terrifying. The readjustment which he makes may be difficult indeed for him. If he goes to live with a relative in another locality, away from the scenes of childhood, much will depend upon the sympathy and understanding which the foster parents assume toward him. If he remains under the chaperonage of one of the divorced parents, it is not unlikely that subtle psychological influences will be exerted by that parent to turn him away from his other parent and to develop toward him (or her), if he did not feel it before, an antagonism which may endure for the rest of his life. He may be encouraged to blame this absent individual for his own present unhappy state and for that of the other parent with whom he lives, and so nurture a strong animosity toward him (or her).

Regardless of what disposition is made of him by the courts or by his parents, the child of divorced or separated parents has lost his sense of security, and with it have gone those loyalties to the home and those protective and reassuring sentiments which can be taken from a child only at the cost of his happiness and peace of mind. The sufferings of the adolescent, bereft of the security of home and family loyalty, differ in degree rather than in kind from those of the younger child. Bitterness, shame, mortification, resentment, anger, reproachfulness—these unfortunate emotions may share place alternately or mutually in his inner behavior. They may drive him into cynicism, laziness, an extravaganza of inner conflict, or into open delinquency. The need for guidance and helpful older companionship in such times of deep inner stress as this cannot be overstated.

IGNORANT HOMES

Many homes are not in imminent danger of shipwreck; many of them are neither broken nor disharmonious; in great numbers of them the parents are only ignorant and uncomprehending. Entrusted with the care and tutelage of children, they have not the background of understanding or information or insight to discharge their duties constructively. The bulk of adult individuals have had little formal education beyond the eighth grade and practically no specific preparation for the cares and responsibilities of rearing children. The homes which these ill-prepared parents preside over are rife with limitations and shortcomings. In a study carried through some time ago by the National Committee on Visiting Teachers, the following undesirable home conditions were listed as obtaining most frequently in the homes of the children included in the inquiry:

Attitude toward the child:
: Too indulgent.
: Too severe.
: Lack of supervision.
: Partiality to particular children.

Attitude toward the school:
: Lack of cooperation.
: Lack of ambition.
: Overambition.

Conditions in the home:
: Lack of harmony.
: Improper diet.
: Lack of opportunities for study.
: Lack of opportunities for play.
: Inadequate opportunities for sleep.
: Broken homes.
: Immoral conditions.
: Alcoholic parents.

Family status:
: Chronic poverty.
: Periodic economic strain.
: Maladjustment due to foreign-born parents.
: Temporary economic strain.

Most of these indictments against the home spell *ignorance*. The combined effects of them, or of any number of them, are of course serious upon juvenile members. Too much indulgence spoils the child and keeps him infantile and introverted; too much severity overrepresses him and either makes of him a family robot or else drives him into rebellion and escape; lack of parental supervision encourages the development of habits of idleness and perhaps waywardness; partiality to a particular child stifles him and arouses conflict and resentment in the siblings; parental noncooperation with the school encourages in the child attitudes of disinterest and criticism; lack of parental ambition for the school success of the child leads to neglect and the adoption on his part of a casual and detached relationship to it; too great school expectations may engender worries, fears, nervousness, or perhaps truancy, rebellion and hatred; physical limitattions of the home in the matter of the dietary, facilities for study, play and sleep may injure the health of the child or encourage him to seek companionship outside; immorality, drunkenness, and so forth, may disgust, injure or debase the child; economic strain, whether recurringly periodic or temporary, by drawing a pall of gloom or resentment over the elders, enshadows also the juvenile members of the family and ill fits them for normal and healthful attitudes toward the workaday life of the world. The presence in the home of foreign-born parents, while a situation which belongs in a different category, undoubtedly does frequently result in developing inferiorities and perhaps rebellious conduct in the children, who become increasingly aware of the contrast between their own and the parents and homes of other children.

Though written thirty years ago, the words of an early investigator[*] in the field of family relations are equally applicable today. Miss Reynolds, reporting the results of a survey of the home and family backgrounds of 400 problem children, found that "more than half the parents of these children were too ignorant to live understandingly in the world of common life," and that "80 per cent of the children failed to find adequate home care, including training in conduct for living with other people." She raised the baffling query: What can be done about it? To quote this investigator:

"When we, as a people, care supremely for the upbringing of our children, care enough to provide training for young people in parenthood as carefully as in reading, writing and arithmetic, when we believe in play enough to see that no child misses it because of the accident of living in a city wilderness, when we learn enough about living together to prevent our quarrels from embittering our children's lives, or our foolish love from sapping their vitality, then perhaps we shall be fit to be the guides of the children of the future."

THE PROBLEM OF DISCIPLINE

In no area of family life perhaps is there greater ignorance and futility than surrounds the problem of discipline of the young. Resort to fear, to whippings, to scolding and upbraiding, is still a common means of enforcing family law. The schools have learned the futility of fear and force as redemptive or guiding agencies, but parents still resort in great numbers to threatenings, to tongue-lashings and applications of the strap. Much of the inefficacy of such attempted methods of discipline in the home arises from a failure of the parents to realize that a child is a child, with childish values and perspectives, and not an adult with adult values and perspectives.

In the ordinary home those situations which call for disciplining of a child include chiefly the following: (1) disobedience, in which the small offender wilfully sets aside the parental command and does the thing prohibited; (2) untruthfulness, in which the child deceives the parent regarding what he has been doing or where he has been; (3) forgetting to do as he had been told (often ascribed to heedlessness by the parent), expressing itself commonly in failure to remember the details of an errand; (4) the neglect of small responsibilities, such as keeping the room orderly, hanging up clothing or

[*] Reynolds, B. C.: Environmental Handicaps of 400 Habit Clinic Children. *Hospital Social Service*, 12, 329–336, Dec. 1925.

doing homework; (5) rudeness, impoliteness or sauciness, or other forms of behavior in which the dignity or the seniority of an adult is offended, or in which the rights, the person or the feelings of another child are disparaged; and (6) thoughtlessness, which manifests itself in playing noisily, disturbing others, teasing, and the like. While of course there may also occur disciplinary situations arising out of immoral or vicious conduct, these are by no means typical of the offenses that call for parental correction. Most of the common ones are included in the listing above.

From a perusal of these six primary disciplinary situations, it is obvious that the common underlying factor that sets them off is the immaturity and inexperience of the child offender when viewed in contrast with the maturity and the sense of propriety of the adult disciplinarian. Whenever the conduct of the child is noted to be at variance with what from his adult vantage point the parent understands to be right and proper, the ordinary adult loses patience, indulges in an outburst of temper and metes out some sort of spur-of-the-moment punishment calculated to be effective; perhaps it will be only a scolding; perhaps it will be a threat of future punishment; perhaps it will be heated language of reproof; perhaps it will be a thrashing. Much will depend upon the present mood of the parent; but in any case the chances are good that whatever disciplining is done will proceed from the mistaken supposition that children are activated by the same motives and see through the same eyes as adults. Grownups know (though they may not practice) the importance of obedience, of truthfulness, of faithfulness in discharge of obligation, of politeness and thoughtfulness, but they forget that children do not know these things and hence may be expected to make many mistakes and lapses in learning them. Wise discipline takes into consideration the unwisdom and the lack of perspective and experience of the offender, and is therefore imposed understandingly and with the sympathetic will to help him in building up gradually those standards of conduct which are good and acceptable to the family and the group.

In some homes there is disagreement between the parents in matters of discipline of the children. One parent may be "easy" and the other may be strict; one may permit a child to do almost anything he asks, while the other always says "No." Sometimes when there are grandparents living in the family, the difficulty becomes serious, especially when the child learns to play off the grandparents against the parents. Children are quick to learn which grownup in the family is most easily twisted around one's little finger, and they incline to seek favors from the most indulgent adult. Often the more strict parent criticizes the more lenient, and if the child is present to hear the conversation he grasps the fact that there is disagreement over matters of discipline in his household. As soon as he makes that discovery, he is in position to capitalize it and to play thereafter a winning hand in securing privileges and permissions.

If discipline in the home is to be reduced to a minimum of friction and unpleasantness, it is essential that the adult members shall agree privately upon the standards of conduct to be permitted in the children, that they shall not put themselves into a position to be played off against one another, and that there shall prevail an atmosphere of understanding and good adjustment without family strain and tension. Departures from the approved or permitted are to be pointed out courteously and the adequate amends suggested kindly and firmly. When a child finds out that his parents are not scolding, fault-finding and quarreling infants, but that they are consistent, invariable masters of themselves, he will not venture far from the conventional conduct expected of him. Where the child is set down in a family of grown-ups who are still infantile in their emotional evolution, poor conduct and inadequate discipline are frequently to be noted.

IMPORTANCE OF THE EARLY YEARS

Psychologists make no mistake when they insist that the years of infancy and early childhood are the most important years in an individual's life, for it is during the first three or four years that the fundamental physical and emotional habits are formed that are likely to endure throughout the subsequent lifetime. Most parents make the mistake of failing to appreciate the significance of this period and the importance of getting their children off to a good start emotionally. Miss Bassett has epitomized* excellently some of the personality weaknesses that are promoted by thoughtless parents in their young children:

"The strong emotional response of adults to the beguiling appeal of infants and young children tends to make it exceedingly difficult for them to regard this important period in the developing personality of the child with due seriousness. It seems to them utterly impossible that present idiosyncrasies in the behavior of such cunning, ridiculously amusing and cuddlesome creatures could have any very great significance in determining future adjustments. Their usual optimistic and sentimental opinion is that the child 'is just a baby,' he 'doesn't know any better,' and he 'will outgrow' any of the characteristics which a more objective and informed view might consider as meriting serious attention. The obstreperous infant is thus pampered, coaxed and laughed at so long as he is small enough to be cute, and parents, after several years of fond indulgence to the tyrannical whims of their

* Bassett, C.: *Mental Hygiene in the Community*. New York, The Macmillan Co., 1934, pp. 176–177. By permission.

offspring, suddenly awake to the fact that their child has many disagreeable traits which seriously interfere with their comfort and which disorganize the life of the home. He refuses to eat and the whole family goes through long daily sessions in which the child is prodded, coaxed, scolded, bribed and punished in an effort to induce him to satisfy the anxious desires of the parents. The child dawdles, he revels in all the excited attention focussed upon him and he continues to eat just what and when he pleases. He 'refuses' to take his afternoon nap and the harried mother decides that he probably doesn't need so much sleep after all. He often continues to soil and wet himself until school age and at bedtime there is another struggle in which the triumphant child successfully postpones the hour of his retirement from the scene by such kicks and screams that neighbors are forced to complain. He is jealous of any attention given to the other children in the family and insists upon usurping the spotlight in any situation. If his slightest desire is thwarted, he falls into formidable temper tantrums which soon compel the terrified parents to relent and he blissfully gains his way. As a result of all the nervous tension, the constant bickering, turmoil and conflict, the child becomes 'high-strung,' irritable and whiny. He wears an anxious, ill-tempered expression which seems sadly out of place on a baby's face. The parents 'can't do a thing for him,' and they decide that for some mysterious reason he is an innately 'bad child' and from now on will have to be treated with due severity, his 'will' will have to be 'broken' and he must be rudely shown 'who is boss.'"

For these and many other reasons it is apparent that many children start out in life with sharp emotional and personality limitations and physical and mental habits that are certain to interfere seriously with their subsequent happy adult adjustment. Unfortunately we do not commonly, "outgrow" deeply implanted attitudes and habits as we grow older; rather we tend to become still more emphatically what we started out to be in infancy. Barring accident or miracle, the child is literally father to the man. The whining, ill-tempered, selfish, sulking child is metamorphosed by the passing years only into the whining, ill-tempered, selfish, sulking grownup. There is an inevitableness and a consistency of growth and development, whether it is physical, mental, emotional or moral which promotes straight-line evolution. If parents and others who are charged with some part in the care and disciplining of young children could appreciate this fact, and could realize that poor beginnings make for poor continuings, much of the subsequent disillusionment and remorse of parents whose children turn out to be social or moral liabilities would be spared them.

THE NURSE AND THE FAMILY

The nurse whose duties call her into the home must expect to find the family "as is," not the ideal family that the sociologist, psychologist, or mental hygienist might wish every family to be. She will find it with all its tensions; its fears, superstitions, and conflicts; its marital maladjustments; its resentments and bitternesses; its worries over children, neighbors, obligations; its paternal preoccupation over problems of finance and material welfare; and its maternal preoccupation and perhaps rebellion over unwanted pregnancy and its dread and often fear of childbirth. She will find unstable and neurotic mothers and perhaps also fathers in kind; she will find ignorance and poor judgment in handling the children, in planning the dietary, in buying necessities and luxuries; she will find poverty and hopelessness. All these and many other disconcerting and near-tragic things she must expect on occasion to encounter. It is her province to meet such unpleasant and unfavorable conditions not as a critic or as a moralizer or judge, but rather as a professional individual who understands human weaknesses and who understands also the helpful ministrations which her skill and philosophy may apply to them. She must face these unadjusted family situations with a cheerful and matter-of-fact professionalism which proceeds with its ministrations actively and convincingly. Often her manner and spirit of good will and cheer will go quite as far in relieving the distressing mental and emotional aspects of the situation in a family as will her applications of professional skill and information. After all, the human values are the most fundamental; a nurse's expressed or manifest interest in a sick child, in a rebelliously pregnant woman, or in a tubercular husband and bread-winner, may well be and frequently is the contact that succeeds in reconciling a family to its afflictions or in helping it to adjust to what may eventuate as a blessing and a benefaction.

Fortunately for the continuing peace of mind and happiness of the nurse, her mission will call her also into the happy and the well adjusted home where she will find love, respect, forbearance and good fellowship, marred it may be temporarily by the illness or discomfort of some of its members but giving good evidence that after the storm passes there will be brightness again. Professionally minded, capable and intelligent, she gives of her best skill to restore those who are suffering; human, friendly, interested in the things that loom large on the horizon of the family or the individual, she contributes to the atmosphere of the sick room and its anxious watchers an encouragement and a faith and hope that dissipate much of the foreboding and apprehensiveness and substitute a refreshing and inspiring gleam. To exert such influence as this, however, she must be possessed of plentiful springs of inner wisdom and a strength and stability of character that can result only from long and patient cultivation. She must, in other words, have the ability to make intelligent use of the knowledge and information which school and life have brought her.

THOUGHT PROBLEMS FOR THE STUDENT

1. Write out an appreciative analysis of the best home you know. Perhaps it will be your own home; perhaps it will be that of some longtime friend or neighbor: its identity is unimportant.
2. Write out a similar analysis of some decidedly poor or inadequate home which you happen to know about. Try to show the specific ways in which it is failing. Again, of course, identification is unimportant.
3. Call to mind items of instruction that you personally had in the elementary school and in the secondary school which were calculated to make you a better informed and more capable homemaker. What criticisms or suggestions have you to offer?
4. Show by citing some example known to you how the personality and the emotional maturing of a child have been influenced unfavorably by a family circumstance in which the father and mother were maladjusted to one another.
5. Report upon some inadequate home known to you in which the basal difficulty is neither parental incompatibility nor parental disharmony but rather simple ignorance of the fundamentals of family care and nurture.
6. Suggest five rules of discipline which any adequate family might well follow. Suggest five other rules which, if followed, would be likely to harm seriously the normal emotional and personality development of the children concerned.
7. Select one of your younger patients and make an investigation of her family background. What can you find out about the parents? Were they reasonable and natural in their relations with each other and with their children? Did their sense of values and interests parallel the best thinking of the time? Did they direct the energies of their children to the interests which would tend to give most lasting satisfaction? Did they control their own behavior so as to present to their children worthy patterns of conduct? Does the end-product, the present patient, reflect the answer you would expect from your findings? Discuss fully.
8. In every class of students that enters a school of nursing there are usually some individuals who have difficulty in adjusting to the new environment. Sample cases will be cited; read them carefully, then indicate what in their family lives may have contributed to the present development of these individuals, bringing about the type of behavior described. Indicate what you can do as a member of the same group to help these individuals to better adjustments:
    (a) Miss A, although in the school now for three weeks, cries herself to sleep at night. She is shy and does not respond to the friendly advances of her roommate. Her classwork is of passing quality, but she is awkward in doing nursing procedures. She is twenty-four years of age and had two years of college work before she entered this school, living at home, however, during that time.
    (b) Miss B had two years at a girls' finishing school previous to her entrance at the nursing school. Here she badgered the instructors during lecture periods with irrelevant questions, assuming an air of confused interest. One after the other the instructors suggested that she note down her questions and ask them after class. Miss B, however, did not ask her questions after class, but sulked in class and spoke loudly and continuously out of class about the lack of helpfulness of the teaching personnel.
    (c) For one week, Miss C and Miss D have been roommates. Miss C has come to realize that Miss D is embarrassed by the undressing which precedes

going to bed, that she disapproves of the girls in the class who smoke, that she is shocked at the unconventional attitudes expressed by some of the other students, that she is also inclined to withdraw when men friends are mentioned, that she is apprehensive of the day when she will be expected to be the subject for nursing demonstrations of bed-bathing.

(d) Miss E is a college graduate. She assumes an air of subservience before her instructors but tries to impress her classmates with the fact that she never studies, that she is tired of listening to reiterations in class that one and one make two. She is not clean in her personal habits, weeps when suggestions for improvement are made by instructors.

(e) Miss F feels that the grades she receives in class are never quite fair, and always compares her papers with those of several classmates; then she proceeds to call on the instructor.

(f) Miss G is never sure of her own knowledge but asks help from everyone with whom she works.

(g) Miss H has received failing grades on the first two weeks of class work. She feels that the class program is too heavy, that there is not adequate time for study, that the place set aside for study is not suitable, that it is impossible to sleep in the home because of the street noises, and that the teaching personnel use poor methods and give impossible assignments.

(h) Miss I resents all criticism by assuming a sphinxlike expression from the first word to the end of a conference. She then continues with an air of determination to repeat the error upon which criticism was offered.

(i) Miss J's pet enthusiasm is fortune tellers; she goes to the Gypsy Tea Room once a month to find out about the new thrills which are to come into her life.

(j) Miss K expresses a distaste for marriage. She insists all men are selfish, and she has yet to see the family life which illustrates the advantages for increased happiness over that of a well ordered career.

(k) Miss L finds life amusing; she ridicules her classmates, the airs of older students, the importance of the interns, the clothing of the faculty members and the ignorance of the subsidiary groups.

(l) Miss M is boisterous until a restraining influence is encountered; then she becomes sarcastic. After she has made caustic remarks about various acquaintances and situations, she isolates herself and, if advances are made by anyone, she indulges in a temper exhibition.

(m) Miss N is always in disgrace because her room is so untidy. Everything is left where she drops it; her dresser drawers are in confusion; her study nook is cluttered up with candy bar covers, letters from home and snapshots; her toothbrush is left on the edge of the basin and her bedroom slippers in the middle of the floor.

9. List ways in which the nurse may assist the family in its efforts to establish good health.
10. List authentic sources of information which are procurable and nontechnical enough to be used by the average family for the promotion of better health.
11. What nursing skills would you consider to be indispensable to every mother of a family?
12. Name some periodicals and books which you would recommend to young parents, should an opportunity to give this help present itself to you.
13. One of your patients is the mother of two daughters, aged eight and thirteen; she asks you how she should proceed to give these children the necessary sex

instruction. She says that she herself, although a college graduate, never received any, and she is desirous of giving her daughters this rightful help; but, as she has not been sure how to go about it, she has kept putting it off. She feels confident that you are the person to help her. What are you going to tell her?
14. List five problems you have encountered which you believe were the outcomes of feelings of insecurity in the home lives of the patients in your care.

SUGGESTED READINGS

1. Cruze, W. W.: *Psychology in Nursing.* New York, Blakiston Division of McGraw-Hill Book Co., 1955.

    Written with the needs of students of nursing in mind. Chapter 15, "Mental Hygiene and Sane Living," is particularly well done. So also is Chapter 13, "Social Relations."

2. Karn, H. W., and Weitz, J.: *An Introduction to Psychology.* New York, John Wiley and Sons, Inc., 1955.

    Chapters 9 and 10 deal with personality problems. There is considerable valuable material in them, including the integrated personality, family influence, school influence, etc.

3. Katz, B.: *How to Be a Better Parent.* New York, Ronald Press, 1953.

    Practical help for rearing well adjusted children—centered on better understanding by parents both of their offspring and of themselves.

4. Lindgren, H. C.: *Mental Health in Education.* New York, Henry Holt and Co., 1954.

    Excellent material for the young student interested in the meaning and importance of mental hygiene as it relates to learning and teaching.

Chapter 16

I believe that the next developments in education will come not from philosophy and pedagogy, but from psychology—the science of human minds and emotions.

JAMES MARSHALL

MENTAL HEALTH IN SUCCEEDING LIFE STAGES

MENTAL HEALTH IN INFANCY AND THE PRESCHOOL AGE

The Need for Security. From his earliest months of life, the infant craves security. If one has any doubt about this, all that is necessary is to observe the baby as he turns from the stranger and clings to his mother; or the older toddler, as he runs to her for soothing and indulgence; or the five-year-old, as he spars for her favor. As a matter of fact, throughout the preschool life of the child, the youngster thrives on parental and familial affection almost as much as upon the physical sustenance he receives. Emotionally he turns, like the sunflower to the sun, to the warmth and stimulation of the adult personalities in his immediate environment. A comforting feeling of belongingness pervades him, and he appears to look out upon his small kingdom as a monarchy in which he is central but in which also the other familiar personages are indispensable.

This flattering feeling of security and belongingness needs to be safeguarded in every family where there are children growing up. Sometimes when a new baby makes his appearance, the little monarch's security may be challenged, and he may resort to extravagant conduct to register his resentment. To win back to himself the affection and solicitude which his jealous fancy convinces him have been transferred to the necomer, he may exhibit consuming jealousy, display tantrums, avoid the rival with studied determination, or otherwise seek relief in weeping, wetting, and the like.

At such periods in the evolution of the family, the mother and father will need to make special efforts to reestablish the security of the disgruntled member and take him actively into partnership in caring for and loving the new arrival. Thus, a situation which bade fair to be nothing short of dreadful in its shattering effects upon the first child's feeling of belongingness may, wisely handled, be made to contribute to his sense of importance and to the total family security. Affection within a growing family circle has a way of increasing as it is shared successively with the new individuals that take their places within it.

Wider Meaning of Security. Security, however, is a far more complex thing than the mere physical and emotional serenity that arise from awareness of parental protection and familial *esprit de corps.*

Contributing richly to the child's feeling of security is the confidence which he builds in the process of discovering and ordering his universe. To the grownup, the surrounding world in which he passes his days may come to be commonplace, or even boring. To the toddler, however, the environment hums with captivating and intriguing possibilities. His background is initially so meager and his curiosity so consuming that he throws himself into the fascinating adventure of discovery and the search after satisfying meanings. Making the accidental but exhilarating discovery that a block which he pushes off the table will *fall,* he pushes it off over and over again in amazement and vocal delight. Passing his hand over a bit of smooth cloth, he crows with happiness at the feel of it and looks about him for others to share in his joy.

As he progresses through the earlier childhood years, this drama of sense perception proceeds in mounting tempo. Fortunate indeed is the youngster who is provided with sand, dirt, water pots, clay and other plastic media through which he can learn about his physical environment and upon which he can work freely his creative will. In these years he must be expected to be investigative, enthusiastic, consumed by curiosity; to know no limits to the excursion of his fancy; to seek in every area sensory satisfaction. If he sways in trees, delves into dirt banks and snow banks in season, plucks off flies' wings and grasshoppers' legs, roams and leaps and throws and pulls apart—it is all to be expected, for he is studying his universe and familiarizing himself with the forces that underlie it.

Not only should he not be restrained needlessly in his furtherance of this dynamic purpose: he should rather be encouraged and abetted in it by his elders. It is a mistake for them to fret and fume because he comes in from his adventurings dirty and disheveled: the glow in his eyes should reconcile them and hearten them to strive patiently and honestly to answer his incessant "Why?" questions. He is an indefatigable researcher, and as such needs free opportunity and cooperative advice and assistance. It is for him tragic if, instead of receiving patient understanding and helpful advice and interpretation at their hands, he finds his elders only bored and unimpressed with his overwhelming problems that clamor for solution.

Our young quester, too, must not be expected to control and repress his naked feelings as he passes along his fascinating pathways. His world is fresh and new, and the mind that he turns upon it is fluid and seething. Self restraint is unthinkable in such circumstances. Vociferous surprise as he comes upon a solution, loud and dramatic action as he masters a new skill, excited verbalization as he recounts his adventures—these are to be expected and encouraged.

The principal caution with which parents and nursery or kindergarten teachers need to be concerned as they manipulate the stage upon which the dramatic activities of childhood take place is that the young actor shall experience successful achievement rather than failure. If the tasks undertaken are too hard, so that he experiences frustration and defeat, they are unfit for his level of maturation and should be eliminated. Feelings of adequacy and status develop naturally and logically from efforts that eventuate in goals successfully achieved; on the other hand, defeatism and insecurity arise quite as obviousy from undertakings that have turned out negatively. Here is a fundamental principle of mental health in early childhood that must be constantly kept in mind by adult guides of children in the preschool years. It continues to be operative also, as we shall see, in subsequent periods of developmental history of the individual.

Three Factors in the Driving Force. 1. *Basal Drive.* The motivating force at any given moment in the behavior of the young child will comprise, first of all, the basal protective and projective urges. (See Chapter 5.) Restricted or hampered, for example, in his physical movements, he may be expected to struggle in anger against the restraint and to strive to escape; jealous, he may be expected to throw himself against the usurping agent; hungry, he may be expected to demonstrate his discomfort insistently; intrigued, he may be expected to engage in manipulating and appraisal activity. These patterns of response are unvarying, since they are rooted in innate mechanisms. It goes without saying that many of them will require redirection before the child can fit into approved social behavior.

2. *Conditioned Emotional Patterns.* In the course of his intimate association with the other members of his family—particularly with his mother, and to a lesser degree with his father—the child develops a number of emotional attitudes that flavor his behavior and conduct. His reactions at any given moment and in any given situation will therefore reflect this early conditioning. He may have been so thor-

oughly spoiled as to be completely undisciplined. Unrestrained by adoring adults who "love" him too much to curb his whims and impulses, such a child is bounded by no limits in his range of self expression. On the other hand, his parents may so repress and restrain him that he is made timid and unsure of himself.

Conditioned behavior patterns are as inevitable as they are cogent in their influence over the present and future conduct of the youngster. By the time he enters school, he will have achieved a total personality that will tend to be resistant to change or reeducation. Habits and attitudes of selfishness, domination and egocentrism, on the one hand; or of timidity, secretiveness and aloofness, on the other, may be seen already fixed in the personalities of primary school children whose home conditioning has been unfortunate, and their teachers face the considerable task of unconditioning them and freeing them for more wholesome development. Young school braggarts and bullies, swaggerers and show-offs, evaders and withdrawers, whiners and fretters are the unfortunate victims of unwholesome emotional conditioning in the preschool years. Predisposed thus, they react characteristically to the situation of the moment, whatever it may chance to be.

By the employment of various projective techniques, mental hygienists and clinical workers are able often to discover the identity of the individual or individuals responsible for the abnormal behavior of an unfortunately conditioned child. Through his play or his imaginative dramatizing, or through his reactions to pictures, plastic materials, stories and toys, the child unconsciously gives to the analyst the clue to the underlying conflicts and complexes that are responsible for his emotional conduct. Working subsequently with the adult personality or personalities identified in this revelation, one is often able to achieve therapeutic results both in the child concerned and in his adult associates as well.

All of this adds up to the fact that much of the kindergarten and early school behavior of a child is but the reflection of his emotions toward personalities outside the school setting. Fortunately for the mental health of children, many of these emotions and feelings are of course wholesome and commendable.

3. *Personality Type: Dominant-Submissive.* The motivating force behind the behavior of the very young child will be determined to a degree by his unique personality pattern. There appear to be two opposed types discernible among children and, of course, adults as well. At the one extreme is the "outgoing," dominant, aggressive pattern of personality; at the other is the "in-going," submissive pattern. Those who fall in the first category exhibit traits of leadership,

social perception, companionableness; those who fall in the second tend to be aloof, secretive, submissive. The aggressive child dominates, plans, executes, leads the way; the submissive one avoids, repels, assays merely to follow. Aggressors are attackers, take the offensive, ride off full-tilt into the joust; submissives are dreamers, dwellers in the realm of fancy and imagination, inclined to be on the defensive rather than the offensive. In their quest after status and security, most children fall more or less naturally into one or the other of these two personality styles.

The aggressive child is likely to get on fairly well in his world. In the main, he can sail his own boat, fight his own battles, safeguard his own ego. It is more commonly the withdrawing, submissive child who needs help in establishing and maintaining his security and status. It is less easy for him to gain in self confidence and assurance than it is for his more aggressive cousin. With extra effort on the part of the nursery school or kindergarten teacher, however, tremendous gain may be made by the shy, reticent, awkward youngster.

It is necessary in such procedures to beware that one is not attempting premature forcing of a nonascendant child into the behavior pattern of the ascendant type. The present state of maturation must be taken into consideration in working out any program of correction; otherwise, failure may occur. To help a nonascendant child to increase his self confidence, without running the risk of exposing him to failure and so building in patterns of defeat, requires keen analysis and judgment on the part of the teacher and parent.

In this connection, too sharp condemnation can hardly be made of overscheduling and overplanning the daily life of the young child. As L. K. Frank puts it, the little person needs "time to sit under a tree—ripening, so to speak." Undoubtedly no small part of the thumb-sucking, wetting and other manifestations of regressive behavior represents a throw-back of the harassed and overdriven youngster to find release from a difficult present in the security and familiarity of an easy and understood past.

Blame, scolding, censure for these reappearing infantilisms are ineffective, at best; at worst they may be harmful to the child. What needs to be done rather is to reexamine the whole present situation, in order to discover the actual malady of which these emotional extravaganzas are but symptoms.

MENTAL HEALTH OF THE SCHOOL CHILD

Adequate Social and Emotional Experience. As we found to be the case with the younger child in the preschool period, the older child requires likewise the security and self confidence that accompany successful achievement in the everyday routine of life. Lacking these satisfactions, he is likely to develop into the so-called "problem child," and, in extreme cases, to fall into waywardness and delinquency. If he fails in his strong bid for status through the safe and ordinary channels of experience, he will be impelled to seek release and compensatory satisfactions in socially disapproved conduct. Status and success he must have, however he achieves them.

Some Sources of Inferiority. Nothing inhibits the normal achievement of status and faith in oneself as does the feeling of inferiority, once it gets rooted in the child's personality. During infancy and the greater part of his preschool life, the child is not brought too obviously into competition with other children, so that any peculiar personal lack or deficiency he may have may remain unrecognized. As he participates, however, in the give-and-take of the playground and the schoolroom, he is likely to become conscious of his limitations and his lacks. Observing himself and his capacities and potentialities against the background of the juvenile group of which he is a social part, he discovers those elements in his makeup in which he was—or fancies he was—"born short." A feeling of inferiority is likely to be an emotional accompaniment of this discovery.

Prominent among the deficiencies that give rise to inferiority in a child is an unsatisfactory physical status. This may be reflected in such things as birthmarks, deformities, limbs shrunken or shriveled by disease, poor musculature, impediments of speech, facial blemishes or disfigurements, extreme plainness or actual homeliness. The boy with the harelip, or the girl with the freckled face and the pug nose, may be resentful of fate and find it difficult to adjust calmly and sensibly.

It is to be taken for granted that other children will refer—sometimes thoughtlessly, sometimes pointedly—to the physical abnormalities of a playmate. It is inexcusable when one finds grownups, and sometimes parents themselves, referring even jestingly to the "ugly duckling" of the family. Any child who by virtue of physical peculiarity is "different" from the ordinary run-of-the-mine of children needs to have his good points so wisely kept in the foreground that he finds it not too difficult to accept and face up to his bad ones. The proper technique should be for the adult to ignore any physical peculiarity in a child. Therapeutically, much can be done by keeping his mind and muscles so occupied with activities in which he can achieve creditably that he may come to accept, if not actually to forget, his deficiencies. Awareness of success and of goal-reaching is a potent antidote for a child who is below par in certain physical areas.

Of significance also in arousing feelings of inferiority and insecurity in the child is poor school accomplishment. The juvenile population in any schoolroom is a heterogeneous group, including along with the "good" students a liberal sprinkling of those "not so good." Inasmuch also as many schools expect a standard amount of achievement for each individual in each succeeding grade, it is obvious that there will be children at each level who fall behind schedule and fail to discharge their obligations.

Even as low as the first grade, the amount of pupil failure is amazing. Thus, many children get off to a poor start and experience defeat and discouragement almost from the moment when their feet first cross the threshold of the school. Lacking an adequate background for beginning reading, they are set at reading prematurely, with the result that they are forced into remedial reading classes, often for years, calling painful attention to their failures in this most basic of all schoolroom skills.

Held to standards of accomplishment beyond their capacity or their present degree of maturation or readiness, children are thus compelled to taste the bitterness of failure and defeat at the outset of their school career. Comparison of their poor records and performance with those of the pace-setting children in their classroom focuses the attention of these incompetent individuals the more sharply upon their own poor status and develops their feelings of inferiority and futility. Striking back blindly, many a child resorts to compensatory behavior that is not infrequently unwholesome and sometimes lawless. One should be justified in suspecting poor school achievement and adjustment in any child who becomes an attention-seeker, a show-off, or a teller of tall stories. Still more, one should suspect it as the invisible motivator often behind the acts of the rowdy, the vandal and the potential or actual delinquent. Without doubt, the activities of the more predatory type of boys' gang may spring from the compensatory urge to success and security which conventional school experience has failed to supply.

Not all boys, by any means, are gang-minded; socialization for many of them can be effected satisfactorily through single contacts with one boon companion or friend. We have reason to know that some children experience inferiority and frustration, even in gangs, because of their immaturity, their personality lacks, or anachronisms of age, interests and capacities. Moreover, children are sometimes harmed by continuing gang membership through the ever-deepening thrall which such contacts hold for them, and they may remain in the gang stage all the rest of their lives. Thus boy gangdom may become synonymous with arrested social development, instead of being a promoter of it.

Emotional Suppression. E. K. Wickman's study of the schoolroom evaluation of children's emotions presents a rather strong indictment of those teachers who overlook the damage done to their charges by abnormal suppression. Queried as to what behavior traits in children they regarded as most serious, the teachers reported stealing, heterosexual activity, obscenity, untruthfulness, lying, and masturbation as most reprehensible. Clinicians, likewise interrogated, placed these misdemeanors low in the scale, and judged the most damaging traits instead to be unsocial and withdrawing responses, suspiciousness, unhappiness, depression, resentfulness, and fearfulness.

The teachers, in other words, saw no reason to include withdrawing traits among serious juvenile faults, but were prone to regard as serious those associated with sex interest and dishonesty. These last are undesirable traits, of course, and children exhibiting them need much guidance. From the standpoint, however, of long-time damage to the personality and the adjustment of the children, the unsocial-depression traits are believed to work the greater havoc. The teacher-rated misdemeanors are incidental to development and will in most cases be outgrown and forgotten in due time.

The unsocial-depression traits are, however, dangerous because they indicate failure on the child's part to gain adequate social and emotional experience. Somewhere along the line he has found himself lacking in the achievement of status and security, with the resulting tendency to retreat into introversion.

Possibly his teachers, possibly his parents—perhaps both—have by their handling of him crowded him rather in the direction of suppression than in the more wholesome and normal one of expression. The traditional teacher-parent technique of sarcasm, ridicule, appeal to fear, is likely to arouse emotional tensions that keep their victim uneasy and secretive. Needless severity of adult mentors, impatience at slowness and uncertainty, glowering threats and warnings, contagion of adult tensions and nervousness—these all tend to create in the juvenile personality fearful and negative reactions, particularly in the case of the less assertive children.

MENTAL HEALTH OF THE ADOLESCENT

As we have intimated in the two preceding sections of this chapter, adjustment is a cumulative thing. The degree of perfection of one's mental health in any life period reflects the condition of one's mental health in the period or periods preceding it. A preschool child who experiences security and successful achievement, and whose emotional development has been wisely conditioned, passes over into school age and its challenge with the strong likelihood of continuing good adjustment. Similarly, the school child who achieves healthful social and emotional experience stands an excellent chance of passing on into and through the adolescent years satisfyingly.

Fundamental Needs of Teen-Agers. 1. *Complete Psychological Weaning.* Each life period presents its own peculiar pitfalls to the individual passing through it. Adolescence is in many ways the most trying and critical of all periods. It is the young person's last hope in his preparation for a wholesome and well integrated adulthood. In infancy and childhood, mistakes may have been made; guidance may have been inadequate; conditioning may have been unfortunate; teachers and parents may have been inept and bungling; difficulties of adjustment may have piled up. Consequently, the youngster may bear in his personality the scars of mishandling when he crosses the borderland between childhood and youth. The challenge which this circumstance presents to parents, schools and all other agencies concerned with the evolving personalities of adolescents is tremendous.

Fundamental among the needs of teen-agers is the need for psychological weaning from the protecting and the shielding that have characterized their earlier years, both in home and in school. This emancipation of the adolescent individuality is not easily achieved. Childhood has been secure, safe, a dependable mooring place. But now, childhood is waning; one's craft is bearing away from the sheltered haven and putting out into the untried currents.

At times the youthful skipper is bold and fearless; life is good; there is much to anticipate. At other times, the future looks disturbing, insecure. Gone temporarily are the confidence and assurance, the pride and the venturesomeness, that were so impelling yesterday. At such times of apprehensiveness and self distrust, the youth manifests behavior traits that are in strange contrast with those that loom so prominently at other times. Reverting blindly to infantile patterns of conduct, he may become careless and indifferent, display marked confusion and self consciousness, be riddled with fear, appear shy and reticent.

Only the grownup with insight can appreciate the vast readjustments going on in the personality of the youth as he changes from a child status to an emerging adult status. At this particular juncture, parents particularly, and teachers and counselors only to a slightly less degree, need to be sympathetic with the discouragements and frustrations which the youth is experiencing. It is a time when one must employ the wisest discrimination and be guided by the keenest insight in directing the life and activities of the young person. To be clever enough to encourage on his part the assumption of increasing independence and self government, yet at the same time to be cognizant enough of his limitations to realize that occasional failures will come, requires a rare and understanding heart in him who would aid in regulating the affairs of the teen-age person.

Most disturbing of all problems of juvenile adjustment perhaps are those centering in the psychosexual area. Continence and celibacy for youth are, in our culture, demanded by the mores. Society frowns upon premarital relationships and insists that girls shall remain virgins and males shall remain continent until marriage takes place. This postponement of sexual gratification places a burden upon youth, who are biologically mature and ready for it years before it can be countenanced. To magnify in the young person those spiritual and psychological values that accompany continence and chasity, and to provide at the same time outlets for the psychosexual energy into healthful and satisfying channels, is a task to which every counselor of adolescents must turn his attention seriously if he is to meet his full obligation to them.

The harvest of suffering, disillusionment and ostracism which is commonly reaped by those young people who have had no adequate guidance in the control and sublimation of the sex drive is so tragic that it behooves all who concern themselves with the guidance and training of youth to pay attention to this aspect of psychological weaning. We have done too little to help young people to gain an ordered and satisfying control of the psychosexual aspects of life and to build into their minds those ideals and purposes that will be needed both in observing the mores and in making the choice of a mate with whose life one can at length happily and fulfillingly join his own.

2. *Adequate Physical and Recreational Programs.* Few of our communities have felt the need of providing adequate opportunities and facilities for teen-agers to indulge in wholesome physical and recreational activities. They have left this important service too much to commercialized amusement promoters and to a few, often poorly supported, private or semiprivate agencies, with the result that young people are often led to dissipate much of their time in "hanging around," and their energies in carrying on nondevelopmental activities.

In the world of today one of the problems of widest and most crucial concern is organizing our neighborhoods for the highest possible adolescent welfare. Filling the leisure time of youth with satisfying and stimulating physical and recreational activity is a problem that every locality will have to face and make concerted attempts to solve if adolescents are to have a chance to build good mental as well as good physical health. Only as their days are filled with constructive and challenging recreational programs, including the physical, the athletic, and the competitive in prominent role, will adolescents find safe journeying across the years into rich and satisfying adulthood.

3. *A Feeling of Being Needed: Loyalties.* The 1930's were a lost decade for American youth. Depression years reduced recreational and educational opportunities, restricted the activities of agencies catering to the health and guidance of youth, threw hundreds of thousands into migrant ways of living. At the time when the adolescent population of the dictator nations, likewise caught in world depression, was being regimented into impassioned nationalistic organizations, the democracies largely overlooked the powerful urge present in every idealistic young person toward identification with and enrollment in a great cause. Consequently, while the youth of the former nations were swept along with the popular socio-political currents of the day, young people in the latter countries were being provided with too little leadership and challenge. Without adequate outlet for their seething and dynamic idealism and restless energies, they drifted into idleness and delinquency. In every city and town was enacted the stark tragedy of the street corner, with its vice; of the spa, with its gambling machines and its crooks; of the cheap poolroom, with its fringe of criminal hangers-on.

During the 1940's—the war decade—our national economy improved, of course, and the status of the adolescent generation was decidedly changed. With the nation engaged in a fierce struggle to safeguard our American way of life, the zeal and the commitment of their elders was caught by teen-agers, to whom was presented something arresting and compelling in the way of patriotic service and ideals. Thus, the rising young generation was brought face to face with something bigger than self to which to be loyal and devoted.

During the 1950's, with continuing international stress culminating in a sort of armed-camp world situation, and with the requirement of universal military service always facing them, the adolescent generation requires on the part of schools, and adult society generally, a new and stronger effort to build into youth security and dedication to tomorrow. A fuller, richer meaning of citizenship, a personal emotional commitment to democracy and the democratic way of life— these things youth now needs to experience with new power and determination.

Democracy must be glamorized in the minds of young people in the schools, precisely as communism is glamorized through indoctrination in the minds of millions of youth in the Eastern Hemisphere. Its institutions, ideals, purposes, future—all must be presented with realistic vision if our youth are to know and feel its pull in their lives. Generous and sympathetic study of our past as a nation in a great democratic experiment will help. But most of all, youth must *live* and *practice* democratic citizenship in the school and community. Lip service to democracy and the passive acceptance of it will not suffice in the present circumstances. True and meaningful citizenship must inevitably be *participative* citizenship. Democracy will have to be *lived;* classroom procedures will have to be organized around it; deeds and actions in school and out will have to spring from it; in practical demonstration as a dynamic way of juvenile life, it will have to be salvaged from the conventionally academic and frozen, and established warmly in the fluid and the energizing. The best teachers will find their highest challenge in helping youth to create a transforming and consuming faith in and commitment to the principles of democratic citizenship.

For the time being, war whips up an artificial zeal and purpose. But when peace comes, where shall youth turn for its loyalties and inspirations? The answer which society provides for this question will comprise the acid test of a nation's ability to understand adolescent psychology and to capitalize the dynamics of youth's idealism and set them at work in evolving a more wholesome and challenging human society.

MENTAL HEALTH OF THE ADULT

The grownup, too, like the child and the youth, needs security and self realization. Unfortunately, men have tended to confuse power with security, and while they have achieved the former they have been in grave danger of losing the latter.

Power and Security Not Synonymous. This principle stands forth both in the evolution of the individual and in that of the mass or group. In world history, misguided nations have not infrequently assumed that by adding to their possessions and their military strength they could achieve security. The lesson of the ages teaches, however, that security never comes from accumulated power alone. Sooner or later power finds itself in conflict with the strivings of other groups, and wars impoverish and destroy the labors of the centuries. Thus do blood-lust and the lust for might combine to topple the security and the prosperity of men.

The case is no different with individuals. He who makes the error of supposing that through aggression and the trampling of his fellows he can win for himself peace and safety, sooner or later is disil-

Fig. 39. Moments of relaxation.

lusioned. "With all thy getting," advise the Scriptures, "get understanding," *i.e.*, wisdom and a sensible philosophy of life. Wisdom and a sensible philosophy of life are not to be achieved through unbridled struggle for power and preferment.

Security Through Self Realization. Genuine satisfactions experienced in the decades of one's maturity are the creators of stability. Man's mental health is tied in with his contentments and his satisfactions. The simple pleasures and delights of his home, his family, his children; the reassuring contacts with his work associates; the stimulation of his job; his hobbies; the pleasurableness of identification with churches and social groups; the pride in his accomplishments; the sureness of his friends' loyalty and understanding—these are the foundations of a person's security. In these, there is no inordinate bid for power, no disregard of the rights or feelings of one's fellows.

Modern society has failed to provide people with the means of achieving this comforting sense of importance, of belongingness, of self realization. Cogs in the industrial machine, too many lose their perspectives and sink down into its noise and clatter. Too many lack the resiliency to spring back, after the day's labor at the machine is over, and lose themselves—or perchance find themselves—in the lessened tempo and the more reassuring experiences of life in its byways. Self realization is hard to achieve if one's personality resources are limited and there are no rich fields of comradeship and spiritual adventure to be cultivated.

> "Around my fire an evening group to draw,
> And tell of all I felt and all I saw."

In such circumstances as are suggested by these lines, the questing mind of man finds satisfaction and self realization. Turned for the time being aside from the pursuit of the material, it applies itself to the immaterial, the social, the philosophical. The ethical purpose in life thus rises to the surface, and men can find pleasure and satisfaction in tracing its pattern and in emulating it in their own strivings and search for values.

Buoyed up by this awareness of one's status and one's continuing self realization, the stable adult avoids much of the petty and sapping emotional gaucherie of his poorly adjusted fellows. He keeps himself in the main out of depressions; he dissipates little of his energy in fretting at life; he shuns sullenness and ready anger, cultivating in their stead good cheer, control and interest in his fellows. Socially-minded and reasonably well extroverted, he schools himself to take time for reflection and for reexamination of his values, finding inspiration and help in what Jastrow so aptly termed "the lost paradise of solitude."

Adjusting to Emergency Situations. A reliable index of a person's mental health may be seen in the smoothness with which he adjusts to new or emergency situations. If an undue amount of friction is generated in the process, so that adjustment is either partial or wanting, a low degree of mental health is indicated. Conversely, if adjustment occurs with the minimum of friction and lost motion, a high degree of stability is apparent.

The conscripted soldier provides us with an excellent illustration of ability or of disability to adjust to emergencies. Uprooted from his established way of life, he may present all the symptoms of the true psychopath, finding it intolerable to abandon his freedom of person, forsake his family, forfeit his income, risk injury or death. To protect the armed forces from the induction of such individuals is one of the most essential services rendered the country in times of war by the Army psychiatrists.

The well adjusted inductee, on the other hand, confronted with identical problems and uncertainties, achieves a highly satisfactory status and suffers the minimum of personality and emotional damage in the harrowing experiences through which he is compelled to pass.

The roots of healthy and of unhealthy adult adjustment lie, as we have seen, in the experiences and the training of the earlier life periods. Security, fortunate emotional conditioning, satisfying social experience, proper emotional expression, psychological weaning, adequate physical and recreational and avocational programs, loyalties —these things bear abundant fruit in well adjusted and stable adulthood and in the ability to adapt to whatever circumstances one may encounter along the way. Lack or absence of them points to psychopathology, and to an undeviating personality that shipwrecks when the breakers roll in.

These types of adjustment have been demonstrated not only in conscripted soldiers, but in the wartime civilian population as well. Under bombings and the scenes accompanying them, some civilians were magnificent; others were immediate emotional casualties.

Identical types of stability and of instability are to be met with on every hand in times of peace as well as in times of war. There are those who crack up when the going gets rough; there are those who rise magnificently to the occasion and become towers of strength and examples for their less militant fellows.

MENTAL HEALTH OF SENESCENCE

Since senescence represents a life period of particular importance for the nurse who in the natural course of events will be called upon to devote much of her professional time and skill to the aged, we shall devote the entire next chapter to this general problem.

THOUGHT PROBLEMS FOR THE STUDENT

1. Observe for a half hour the behavioral activities of a very young child to discover evidences of his desire for security.
2. What opportunities have you had to note the ways and means through which young children struggle characteristically to win back their sense of security if and when feelings of security have been challenged or lost?
3. Record examples to show how close to the surface are the feelings and emotions of the very young child.
4. Review some of the activity channels through which a child expresses his ego-projective drive.
5. Present several instances of what seems to be unfortunate emotional conditioning in a very young child; others of sound emotional conditioning.
6. Investigate further the "projective" techniques employed by child guidance workers in probing the emotional conflicts of small children.
7. Contrast the behavior of two children known to you: one, an aggressive type, the other a withdrawing one. Is each equally well adjusted for his age or stage of maturation?
8. List as many physical defects and abnormalities as you have observed in children. To what extent might a comprehensive program of health and the correction of defects have mitigated or actually have done away with some or all of them?
9. What is the psychology back of the readiness with which children will call attention to or make sport of the physical deviations or peculiarities of their mates?
10. Suggest as many as possible of the intraschool and the extraschool compensations to which children resort who feel their inferiority to the group.
11. Contrast good and bad features of boys' gangs. Do girls also combine in natural groupings similar to boys' gangs?
12. With which conclusions in Wickman's study do you find yourself the more sympathetic, those supported by the teachers, or those supported by the psychiatrists? State your reasons.
13. Try to put into your own words the meaning of the term "psychological weaning."
14. In what ways have our schools failed in the promotion of independence in youth? In what ways have they succeeded?
15. Estimate the adequacy with which your own community is organized to further the welfare of its adolescent youth.
16. Do you believe it is possible for democratic nations to enlist the zeal of their young people in great public and national causes as effectively as totalitarian ones are able to do? Why, or why not?
17. Enumerate other common life experiences, in addition to those mentioned in the chapter, through which adult individuals commonly achieve self realization.
18. Look up accounts of effects of aerial bombings of cities upon the morale of the citizens.
19. Recount as many of the relevant details as possible in the mental or emotional "crack-up" of some particular individual with whom you are acquainted and who, in an emergency or crisis, showed himself to be a psychoneurotic.

SUGGESTED READINGS

1. Lehner, G. F. J., and Kube, E.: *The Dynamics of Personal Adjustment.* New York, Prentice-Hall, Inc., 1955.

    Shows the interaction of personal needs and social influences in the lifelong educational process.

2. Munn, N. L.: *Evolution and Growth of Human Behavior.* Boston, Houghton Mifflin Co., 1955.

    Cf. especially Chapter 17, which discusses the development and changes in personality from adolescence until senescence.

3. Schneiders, A. A.: *Personal Adjustment and Mental Health.* New York, Rinehart and Co., 1955.

    Makes a very practical approach to personality adjustment. Evaluates the leading theoretical viewpoints.

4. Thorpe, L. P.: *Child Psychology and Development.* 2nd ed. New York, Ronald Press, 1955.

    Trace down in the index the following: emotional factors in development, personality and character formation, parent-child relationships, mental hygiene of the child, psychosexual development.

Unit 8

Special Problems of Adjustment

Chapter 17

Grow old along with me!
The best is yet to be,
The last of life, for which the first was made.

ROBERT BROWNING

THE PSYCHOLOGY OF THE AGING AND AGED

UNFORTUNATELY, the sentiment expressed in Browning's poem is far from realization on the part of most people in the upper age brackets. For many elderly people, old age is instead a period of anxiety, insecurity, and great dread. For them, the best has already been, and in contemplation there appears only the worst ahead. As health fails and infirmities grow, they find it difficult and often impossible to know either serenity or comfort.

Some Significant Statistics Regarding Old People. There are no fewer than 14 million people in the United States, according to the Bureau of the Census (July 1954), who have passed their 65th birthday. At no time heretofore has there been such a high ratio of older people in our total population. Statistics indicate that during the past fifty years life expectancy has been increased almost 40 per cent. Since the turn of the century, eighteen years have been added to human life.

At the time of the Civil War, by contrast, 7/8 of our population was under forty-five years of age; only 3 per cent ever reached or surpassed sixty-five. The Bureau of the Census estimates that by 1960 almost 10 per cent of our people will be sixty-five or over. Within the decade 1940 to 1950, the increase in percentage of the aged was five times that of the general population. Better infant and child care has cut down the infant death rate and given more babies a chance to grow up and grow old; improved public health and sanitation have reduced the plagues and epidemics that once decimated the populace, permitting more and more people to live out a lengthened life span; modern advances in surgical techniques have saved hundreds of thousands of older people from the afflictions which proved fatal to so many in later life; greater medical knowledge and skill, aided by the availability of wonder drugs, have similarly delayed the coming of the final chapter of life for old people; improved hospital and nursing facilities provide better treatment; social welfare agencies afford better care. The net result of all these and other developments in recent decades has been an extension of the life span far beyond any limits previously known.

SOME PROBLEMS OF AGING AND THE AGED

In a changing society such as ours, it is inevitable that any modification of ratios of the aged to the total population will have wide reverberations in the social scene. It will be helpful at this point to

DEATHS PER 100,000 BY DECADES AFTER FIFTY-FIVE YEARS OF AGE

Disease or Defect	Ages 55–64	65–74	75–84	85 and Over
Diseases of the Heart	713.5	1,723.5	4,233.7	8,313.0
Cancer and other malignant tumors	369.6	695.2	1,161.0	1,319.0
Cerebral hemorrhages	212.8	569.2	1,451.7	2,540.8
Nephritis	177.1	459.0	1,233.4	2,485.4
Pneumonia and influenza	98.7	226.4	691.2	1,929.9
Diabetes	87.2	189.3	274.6	214.4

scrutinize some of the problems created by the sharp increase of elderly people among us.

Physical. 1. *The Problem of Disease and Infirmity.* With the coming of the sixth decade of life, as is to be expected, organic defects are likely to begin to appear, functional processes to "jam" and infirmities to multiply. It has been estimated that 25 per cent of those who arrive at sixty years of age without chronic illness will develop such ailments within the next five years. It is an unfortunate fact that chronic forms of illness are still largely unconquered by the medical profession. Probably no fewer than 25 million persons in the United States are suffering from chronic diseases; of this number between one and two millions are chronic invalids. As many as seven million people are disabled by diseases of the heart and arteries; two millions have degenerative arthritis of old age; five millions have rheumatism.

The sharp rise in mortality rates from the principal of these diseases and debilities of old age after fifty-five years may be seen strikingly in the table on page 359.

2. *The Problem of Deteriorating Sense Organs and Tissues.* While large numbers of the aged escape the hazards of organic disease and chronic illness, at least until the last decade of their lives, many do develop impairment of sense organs and deterioration in tissue elasticity and vitality. Presbyopia and other ocular interferences limit visual acuity and comfort. Deafness makes it difficult to maintain satisfactory conversation and enjoy normal auditory stimulation. Appetite diminishes, digestive complications occur, and there is likelihood of the development in the aged of nutritional deficiencies. Tone of the heart muscle deteriorates, causing palpitation and breathlessness and necessitating care in avoiding overexertion. Body weight diminishes, subcutaneous fatty tissue disappears and stature lessens. The eyes appear shrunken as fat is withdrawn from the ocular orbits. Gums shrink and teeth often loosen. Nutrition of hair roots falters, pigment blanches out, and the hair becomes gray or disappears. The skin becomes wrinkled and dry from loss of fat and general dehydration. As the blood withdraws more and more from the skin, there comes to be less tolerance of cold, and the elderly person is likely to require a higher room temperature than is agreeable to younger persons.

Psychological. Disconcerting as are the physical and physiological changes and problems that confront the older person, the most discouraging ones are psychological or behavior adjustments. In many ways, also, these are more difficult to resolve.

1. *Changes in Attention and Memory.* The aging individual often finds it impossible to hold his attention to a particular subject or stimulus. His mind may wander away from the subject at issue and it is not easy for him to control it and bring it back. With loss of attentive powers, it is not to be wondered at that memory, too, should be fickle and untrustworthy. The experiences of a long lifetime get jumbled in the mind of the old person, and he finds himself uncertain of their relationships. This appears to be true of the more recent experiences that he has had; earlier ones are commonly still properly associated. Forgetfulness is apt to grow; sure identification or recognition of other people, even though they may be close relatives or intimate friends, cannot be always relied upon. Inability to remember where one put his glasses, whether he has taken his medicine, whose letter it was that was read to him, or what day it is, and hosts of similar items, are characteristic of failing mental functions in the aged.

2. *Irritability and Peevishness.* The nurse must understand that

people beyond the sixth decade of life are likely to develop a peculiar psychology of their own. Restricted by physical deficiencies and limitations, they smart at the curb placed by the advancing years upon their former spryness and self sufficiency, and even after they have grudgingly accepted the fact, and have developed a routine of their own along which to pattern their days, they are often annoyed when other members of the family or household fail to fall into the pattern. Pursuit of routine has become almost an addiction with them, and they may oppose strong resistance to change, even in such ordinary matters as food, place at table, room, clothing, companions, and the like. Peevishness and querulousness are apt to be shown when their schedule is broken, as, for example, when noisy grandchildren scamper past them in boisterous play, or when the dinner hour is deferred by callers or company. If the passing years have brought also physical discomfort or organic impairment, as is likely to be the case, the irritability and peevishness of the aged may be increased.

3. *Moroseness and Depression.* One of the most satisfying aspects of maturity is the use and enjoyment of skills and abilities that have been cultivated in the workaday world. Middle life finds one's capacities at their height; vocationally, one is able to render a full day's work for a full day's pay; socially, one is able to mingle with friends and acquaintances with whatever ease and gracefulness he may have achieved through the years; leisure time activities challenge one's abilities. With the encroachment of age, however, there come restrictions. The hands are no longer steady; work is bungled; skills are waning; social engagements are losing their zest; avocations may no longer challenge. In consequence, the aging person tends to become morose and gloomy, compelled unwillingly to behold his own mounting shortcomings.

The reverberations of this decline of physical capacities are felt keenly in the sex life. Women approaching fifty ordinarily pass through the menopause, which they may find to be a very trying time. Those of them who suffer no striking physical discomforts or disorders during the period may manifest strong psychological disturbances. Realization that one's powers to bear children have been lost sometimes makes for melancholia and depression.

Aging men, while their sexual capacity lingers longer than that of women, come also to the realization that here is a function that no longer brings satisfaction. Since the sex function has been for half a century their assurance of virility and strength, its final decline is likely to set off considerable personality disturbance and emotional disconcertedness. On the other hand, it is unquestionably true that many men experience quite keen sexual satisfactions in the sixth and seventh decades of their lives, and it is by no means unusual to find octogenarians still virile and potent sexually.

4. *Unemployability and Insecurity.* Although employment managers are coming increasingly to feel that it is a mistake to dismiss workers *en masse* at 60, 65, or even at 70 years of age, it is unfortunate that the practice still persists far too widely. Over against the 60 per cent of male workers between 65 and 69 who continue to be gainfully employed, 40 per cent between these ages are not working. Between 70 and 74, the condition is reversed, employment having dropped to 40 per cent in those years and dismissal having risen to 60 per cent. Beyond 75, 20 per cent are still working.

Employers of elderly people rather consistently reach the conclusion that, while it may take somewhat longer to train them for their jobs, once trained, older employees are likely to prove more dependable, are absent fewer days in a year because of illness, and watch the hands of the clock less intently than is often the case with young workers. The oldsters tend as a group to be steady, conscientious, efficient, and capable of turning out a creditable amount of work.

The unfortunate "shelving" of men who are still able and competent to do a creditable day's work makes for psychological distress among the aging. To see younger men replacing them at the bench and at the machine, to realize that society reckons them now to be of little economic worth, is hardly calculated to flatter their egos and implement their former feeling of security and worthwhileness. Odd jobs about the house, strolls down the street, hearing the "shop talk" of younger persons in the family who are employed and earning, and such other experiences as the worker who has been "let go" is for the rest of his days subjected to, may make his later years anything but happy ones.

The aging worker, because of his longer and richer experience, may have better and sounder judgment than the younger individual; his memory may be somewhat less tenacious, but his interest and motivation are likely to be so keen that this depreciation is of small hurt; his speed of reaction at a machine may slow down, but patience and endurance may be great. Police officials report the automobile driver over sixty-five to be a better and safer driver than the twenty-year-old at the wheel. The industrial accident rate among sexagenarians is no higher than it is among workers in the lower age brackets, indicating that one of the compensations of aging is greater carefulness. It was not only gratifying but of enormous economic significance that during the difficult years of the Second World War upward of half a million workers sixty-five years of age and over, who had been shelved or retired earlier, were reabsorbed into industry.

A recent study indicated not only that of 500 top business executives, 44 per cent were over sixty years of age, but also that older workers tend to perform more evenly and turn out fewer substandard products. Facts such as these implement a fact well known to psychologists and neurologists, namely, that the central nervous system ages more slowly than the rest of the body structure does. Therefore, if the kind of employment of which they are still physically capable can be made available to elderly people, there is no reason why many can not continue to be self-supporting in whole or large part for a long period of time.

5. *Loneliness.* The unhappiness of old age is greatly aggravated if, as so frequently happens in the later decades of life, death removes the mate of the years. It is a statistical fact that 50 per cent of those over sixty-five years of age are either single, widowed or divorced. For the male who has lived single all his life, there is probably not much more loneliness in the sixties and seventies than in the earlier decades. But for the man who married in his youth and has lived with his wife over a span of forty or more years, bereavement may make for the greatest possible upheaval of emotion, and the years of loneliness that lie ahead stretch away in fancy almost interminably. When the love and the years of care and devotion and sympathy that a man has known all his adult life are suddenly swept away, it is small wonder that the surviving husband feels himself to be little more than a lost soul.

In some ways, adjustment after the death of the mate may be still more difficult for the woman than for the man, if she is left without adequate means of support and a competence that will enable her to continue to live independently. Although in recent decades married women have been increasingly engaged in working outside the home, Occidental mores have traditionally made the husband the breadwinner, the protector of the home, while the wife tends to play the somewhat more passive part of homemaker, comforter, and helpmeet. When the masculine stay and the perennial object of her comforting and helping is withdrawn, the bereaved widow may lack the aggressiveness and indeed the background in training and experience to make the necessary readjustment to her new status.

6. *Preoccupation With Self.* For all these and other reasons, older people are frequently thrown back upon themselves. Feeling the advancing infirmities of age in their physical bodies, dismissed from the occupational world, aware that their children are now in homes

of their own and needing the parental presence no longer, circumscribed in their capacities and limited in their physical powers, they find it easy to retire within themselves and interpret all values in terms of immediate self reference.

In such circumstances, there may be a growing disinterest in their surroundings, indifference to the affairs of the world, and distaste for social and civic participation. So profound may this detachment from earlier interests and activities become that the aging person may lose pride in personal appearance, dress, cleanliness, and the like, and have recourse to the unfortunate condition of "just waiting to die."

Feelings of self importance, however, often die hard, and in their efforts to retain their status, aged people may frequently be observed to resort to the "blaming" technique. If he is being cared for in the home of a married son, the aged parent may chide his son for devoting himself more to his wife and children than to his father, or for the unsatisfactoriness of clothes and spending money allowed, or even for failing to bring up his children after the tried-and-true parental pattern. On the other hand, some old people, domiciled in homes of their children, develop an inferiority complex, protesting the trouble they make for their kin, lamenting every penny that must be spent in their behalf, and bewailing their ills and their worthlessness. Domiciled in rest homes or boarding in private families, aged guests are frequently fault finders. Having little to do, they find opportunity to be preoccupied with their estate and to indulge in complaining.

Dietary and Food Habits in the Aged. With the slowing down of the life processes, it is logical that there should be less food required than is needed during the vigorous working years. It is of importance, however, in the interest of reasonably good health, that the intake of food should be regulated with regard for the nutritional and maintenance needs of the body. Most elderly people consume too much carbohydrate food. A sugar- and starch-containing dietary is easy to prepare and satisfies the appetite, but it is likely to do so at the expense of needed proteins. Since carbohydrates tend, moreover, to build fatty tissue in the body, excessive carbohydrates place a burden upon the heart and digestive organs. It is a statistical fact that older people who are 25 per cent overweight have a death rate more than half again as high as people of normal weight. This circumstance should discourage excess consumption of fats and carbohydrates by older people. Protein, the great builder and repairer of tissue, is of importance in the dietary of the aged.

A calcium-rich diet is also indicated for elderly people. With the loss of calcium that normally occurs in the aging process, there may be depletion in this vitally important element unless the loss is replaced regularly by calcium-containing foods. Milk meets this requirement; so also do cheese, eggs and vegetables.

The tendency toward a mild anemia observed in older people is fairly common and typical of the last decade or two of life. Nurses and dietitians should therefore encourage their charges to eat good amounts of iron-rich foods to supply their tissues with this important element. Iodine and other minerals are needed also in small amounts and should be regularly included in the dietary.

The Financial Status of the Aged. Within the past quarter century our country, along with other progressive Western nations, has inaugurated an extensive program of old-age assistance, with the purpose that the last years of life may not be financially too difficult and discouraging for great numbers of aged people who are without adequate means of supporting themselves. In our own country, in June of 1954, Federal Old Age Assistance was being paid to 2,579,200 old people; another 296,000 were being aided by state and local assistance grants. Nearly 3 million of our aged are therefore deriving benefits from social security programs. Vast as the program already is in the United States, however, it does not yet meet adequately the needs of many aged persons. The actual amount they receive individually is slightly more than fifty dollars a month. More than half of our aged are still dependent upon their families, friends, private charities or public relief agencies. Not many more than 25 per cent of them are still able to support themselves through continuing to work. It has been estimated that one out of every five people over sixty-five years of age is the recipient of some form of pension from his former employer, enjoys some old-age protection through insurance benefits, or else is fortunate enough to have investments that yield sufficient dividends to support him. The fact remains, as we have said above, that the typical old person lacks the wherewithal to continue to be financially independent and to support himself.

Retirement: Pros and Cons. Many a person while still in his prime looks forward to a time of enjoyment and satisfaction, to the day when he can withdraw from the workaday world and retire. It is a fact often remarked, however, that many such individuals, after they have achieved their ambition and find themselves outside the ranks of gainful labor, rather steadily decline. Instead of enjoying the years of freedom from the job, they "rust out," and the records are filled with accounts of the speedy demise of men who have been unusually active and successful in the industrial or managerial world, who were lost and hopeless when retirement actually came. Perhaps it was an appreciation of this unfortunate condition of "rusting out" that led Dr. Alexis Carrel in *Man The Unknown* to exclaim: "The aging man should neither stop working nor retire. To those whose forces are declining appropriate work should be given, but not rest."

If retirement is to mean literally withdrawing from activity to sit in some chimney corner, it is about the last thing an active person ought to think of. The nurse will be called upon to minister to such individuals who find in old age nothing stimulating to do or think about. The fault lies not with the fact of retirement or with the fact of aging, but rather with the failure of the individual to have cultivated during his active years interests and avocations and hobbies to which he can now in the closing years of life turn with as much animation and anticipation as he formerly vouchsafed to his trade or profession. A planned retirement, with plenty to do, should be a true god-send to every aging person. Even if he has never taken time to build up keen interests outside his daily job, the elderly person in retirement can and ought to be guided to cultivate such lines of application and self investment. Nurses and all others who have to do with aging people ought to spend a part of their time in reassuring them that the ability of older people to learn is little inferior to that of a boy of twelve, and that there is now open before them a new world of experience which they may have in old age if they will but enter it and appropriate it for themselves.

The Problem of Housing for the Aging and Aged. It is financially impossible for great numbers of older people to retain their own homes or to maintain themselves within them as they were competent to do earlier. With less economic security, and with perhaps failing health and the mounting infirmities of age, the problem is not only one of having a roof over one's head but also of continuing to have some measure of companionship and satisfying social contacts to offset the dreadful loneliness that so often is the lot of the aged. For many, the only solution is the public institution, commonly known as the city or county home, or the poor farm. For others with restricted income but still not destitute, the solution has lain in private old people's homes, cheap lodging or boarding houses, or, if need demanded it and financial status made it possible, in nursing homes, rest homes, and the like. Too often in all these situations there is little privacy, affection and consciousness of worth as an individual, and much patronage and "bossy" handling. All of these things serve to make the individual uncomfortable, unhappy, and not infrequently querulous and testy. What he needs, after his physical status has been provided for, is a feeling of selfness, of status, of recognition as an individual, of social satisfaction and contentment.

A number of interesting movements have been projected in recent years in an effort to overcome this defect in conventional "homes" for the aged, and to make available some sort of satisfactory low-cost housing for them. It begins to look as though the small apartment house, maintained exclusively for elderly people, is the solution closest to the ideal. In making available for them privacy and a minimum of supervision, such projects where they have been undertaken are making a very interesting contribution to an increasingly difficult problem.

We shall refer here to but one of many similar efforts of this type calculated to provide housing and accommodations adequate to meet the physical and the personality needs of the aged.

Tompkins Square House, in mid-town New York, operated by the city's Community Service Society, is an excellent example of what an enlightened and understanding organization can do to make comfortable and happy the lot of older people. The house has forty-four single rooms and eight two-room apartments for couples, sisters, brothers or two congenial persons. It provides guests with kitchen facilities, including cooking and refrigeration accommodations, and bath shared with two or three others. Rental rates are on a variable basis, according to the location and type of the accommodation. A cafeteria in the building serves meals at cost. A living room and lobby on the ground floor for visitors, a delightful roof garden on the sixth floor, and a laundry equipped for washing, drying and ironing, make living agreeable and practical for everybody. A registered nurse is in charge of the house to provide supervision and the reassuring confidence that in case of illness or other emergency there is somebody within call to take an interest and render assistance.

Writing of the project in *Public Aid in Illinois*, for May, 1949, Miss Ollie Randall, Consultant on Services for the Aged, Community Service Society of New York, says:

> As applications piled up and person after person was interviewed, one fact stood out above all the others—these people did not want to enter a home for the aged but it was the only way within their means or those of the community in which they could then provide for protection and security in the future. They were apprehensive about the day when their savings would be exhausted; they were even more apprehensive about the day when they would be too ill to care for themselves and there would be no one upon whom they could call with confidence that their interests would be paramount in whatever plans were made; they were literally afraid of being the subject of one of the fairly frequent and grim news items describing older persons who die in their lonely rooms, remaining undiscovered for days, only to be buried at last in a pauper's grave. . . . We hear much today of the "aged and the chronically ill" and the need of housing them. Too seldom do we hear of any one thinking of the person still well, still going about his business, who might never require the extreme protection of a home for older people were he able to find accommodations similar to those at Tompkins Square—a small and fairly insignificant unit in the very shadow of those huge privately-

owned apartment cities, rather inappropriately called "Stuyvesant Town" and "Peter Cooper Village," and a few steps away from another large public housing project, "Jacob Riis Houses"—all for young families, with never a place for an elderly couple or a single old lady or man. If there be planning or building for tomorrow's older folks, let the thoughtful little things be done which make the difference between modest comfort and total discomfort and which compensate for the failing faculties and increasing frailties of the human frame. But above all let there be privacy and a sense of independence, for which even some physical comfort can be sacrificed, as old age itself, combined with the well-intentioned and protective attitude of others tends to rob older people of these two most priceless possessions.

New York has taken a long step ahead in promoting better care for the aged through the State requirement that all public housing financed by state and city funds must allocate 5 per cent of its accommodations to people 65 and over. This has meant a decided increase in the low cost housing accommodations for older people. Planning now goes forward to include more of this type of accommodation in limited dividend housing and in housing provided for the so-called lower middle income group.

There is growing concern on the part of both governmental and social agencies in improving standards for sheltered care for older people. There is a definite movement for cooperative effort in many states and many local communities to insure that those in charge of homes for the aged, boarding homes and nursing homes, shall work together in defining what changes need to be made in these particular types of sheltered care in order to serve best the people who are today seeking care. The amendments to the Federal Social Security Act, adopted in 1950 and effective in July 1953, require that every state shall have a standard-setting authority for those agencies which provide sheltered care.

The increase in financial benefits to persons covered under Old Age and Survivors Insurance, as well as the increase in the federal share of assistance grants, has played an important part in improving conditions for older people.

But Tompkins Square House, and others like it scattered thinly over our country, cannot begin to meet the needs of our older people. Even if we include all the homes for them philanthropically supported throughout the various states, there is a total capacity of only approximately 100,000, and all of them have long waiting lists. One third of these institutions are located in three states—Massachusetts, New York, and Pennsylvania. Everywhere in America still is to be found the spectacle of aged people being committed to mental hospitals because there are not beds for them anywhere else. A commission in New York State, appointed by Governor Dewey to investigate the situation, reported 4000 aged in that state being housed in such institutions. The overall picture of facilities in general hospitals for aged and infirm and chronically ill people is likewise disconcerting throughout the country as a whole. There is a shortage of at least 383,000 bed accommodations for the aged who need hospitalization and care, a situation which Dr. A. P. Merrill, Superintendent of St. Barnabas Hospital, in New York, denounces as "beast-like congestion." Private and semi-private nursing homes and rest homes are likewise not only short in accommodations for the aged, but they are too expensive for most old people to be able to patronize.

The Community Service Society of New York estimates that between 70 and 80 per cent of the chronically ill elderly people could continue to live and be taken care of in their own homes by auxiliary home care services if these were made generally available. Such agencies would not only relieve the crowded and inadequate facilities of the institutions, but would do much to restore to older people a sense of adequacy, security, and independence which they are so likely to lose when they pass from beneath their own roofs. Extension of hospital care into the home through visiting, housekeeping, nursing and community diet kitchens has been hailed by many old people as nothing less than a god-send. The cost of such ministrations is much less than would be the cost of hospitalization for the beneficiaries of the service. Not least among the contributions made by such extensional efforts to the psychological rehabilitation of hosts of aged persons is the effort expended to discover hidden interests, hobbies, and—very often—commercially valuable talents which need only to be discovered and directed into satisfying expression to bring new joy to the hearts of discouraged old people.

NURSING PROBLEMS

Individual Physical Hygiene Should Be Stressed. When optimum physical care is understood and practiced, the older person experiences a reassuring feeling of well-being; when omitted or ignored, the threat to comfort and health is even greater than it is in earlier years. It becomes, therefore, a primary function of the nurse who cares for elderly people to find occasional opportunity to talk with them on matters touching the conservation of their physical health. If these intimate little conversations appear to the patient to be spontaneous and casual rather than studied or planned, they will be accepted in kind and the listener will be grateful. The following represent some of the helpful topics that may be included in these conversations between patient and nurse:

The importance of periodic examination to discover defects.
Prompt remedy of defects revealed.

Nutritional needs of the individual.
Maintenance of optimum weight.
Sound information on vitamin needs.
Planned rest and exercise schedule.
Importance of baths not too hot nor too cold.
Reassurance that less sleep may be needed than was earlier required.
Importance of daytime naps.
Proper clothing for existing climate and weather.
Importance of "slowing down" in the later years.

Encouraging Sound Mental Health. Throughout this book, stress has been placed upon the importance of mental health and its practice. The nurse is in a fortunate position to carry on such educational activities incidentally with the aged patient. In the course of her ministrations, she will find it easy to bring the conversation occasionally around to such topics as the following and to encourage her patient to understand their importance, if he does not now, or to continue to observe them in his declining years:

Maintenance of normal relationships with other people.
Maintenance of individuality and self respect.
Adoption of new interests within the patient's abilities
Varied activity to keep waking hours filled with action and thought.
Planning an orderly procession of the days to come.
Time for relaxational activities.
Continuance of church and organizational activities within one's abilities
Reassurance that old age does not necessitate any drastic change in one's mode of life, but merely simple readjustment.
Continuance or initiation of some form of creative activity within one's lessened capacities.
Adopting the goal that old age can be for most individuals a happy life period.

A very important movement that has appeared in many communities in recent years has been the community planning program of activities for older folk. The idea took root originally in the awareness on the part of socially minded people that our cities number among their residents large numbers of elderly men and women who are lonely, and for whom the world passes by unheeding and indifferent. To provide community meeting places or centers where they might go to find companionship and stimulation has done no end of good for the lonely and the aged. Churches, settlement centers, clubs and societies in many of our cities have organized groups and arranged regular meeting places for them. Some of them, in addition to providing social companionship, conduct handwork classes, arrange hobby shows and exhibits for and by oldsters, and sponsor the sale of articles they have made. Libraries prepare special reading lists and regularly scheduled book reviews. Newspapers have given publicity locally and have been of much assistance in getting the necessary public interest aroused to guarantee the success of the plan. With such types of activity in behalf of the aging and the aged, the nurse should be sympathetic. She should endeavor to use her influence to induce lonely old people in her charge who are able to profit from these contacts to seek and enjoy them.

Helping the Woman Patient to Understand and Adjust to the Menopause. In the lectures on gynecology, which will probably come somewhat later in the student's program, interpretation of the changes occurring during the menopause will be included. Signs and symptoms preceding and paralleling these changes are likely to produce much anxiety and nervous tension in women undergoing this phenomenon of aging. In a conversation with an intelligent but biologically uninformed woman of forty-eight, the junior author was recently afforded a striking illustration of the unhappiness and worry suffered frequently by many women during the menopause. The women remarked, "Nurses and doctors do not help us women very much; they do not forewarn us of what we may expect or how long these changes will be in process. We hear so much about cancer that we feel scared; we become irritable and quarrelsome and we do not know where to turn for help." This does not represent an isolated case, but is fairly typical of aging women.

The nurse should not only be aware of the characteristic physical changes which are common at this period, but she needs to be on the alert to give clear explanations of the phenomenon when it becomes apparent to her that a patient is upset or troubled by the physical upheaval accompanying it. Even more important, the nurse should be ready with assistance in making the emotional and social adjustments necessary. It is desirable that she shall provide calm reassurance that this period in women is usually followed by a more comfortable interval, with increased ease in physical and emotional adaptations. While a few women are greatly disturbed both physically and emotionally during the period, there is little reason why women in general should not, if they are aided by simple advice and counsel by nurse or physician, pass through and out of the menopause without too great discomfort and be ready and competent to resume a happy and satisfying interval of ten to fifteen years before old age actually sets in. The adoption by many physicians of hormone therapy during and after the menopause is a promising means of preventing many of the unpleasant physical and emotional changes that may occur in women at this time of life.

Laying the Foundations for a Gracious Aging Process. Fundamentally, the process of growing old ought to be a gracious one. All of us have experienced the deep satisfaction of knowing elderly people who have discovered for themselves the secrets of gentle, even beautiful, aging, and to whom life is beneficent, serene, and still savors of the adventurous. Succeeding the years of vigor and achievement have come now to them years of rich harvesting. This is what age should be, and persons of happy, forward-looking dispositions find the changes of later life interesting and even intriguing. They learn with little or no guidance from others how to adjust to occasional feelings of inadequacy and insecurity. They are eager and glad to adopt programs of work, recreation and rest according to their strength and abilities.

On the other hand, persons of rebellious makeup may become impatient with their diminishing energies and come to be difficult members of a household. Aging to them is a hateful process against which they fret. For them, the aging years with their gradual physical impairments and disabilities are resented. Growing old for such individuals can hardly be a gracious process, unless they can be helped to understand the nature of the physical organism and its changes and modifications, and to accept nature's inexorable laws and learn to cooperate with them rather than to chafe against them. The nurse stands in a strategic position, in her care and ministrations to such rebellious souls, to aid them to understand their bodies and to transform their resentments and inadequacies into new hopes and new achievements within their lessening capacities. Life may thus for them become again enjoyable and satisfying.

Broader Aspects of the Nursing Profession. Finally, the nurse not only has the responsibility of being able to give adequate care to the aged and aging, but as a member of a social profession she needs also to be well informed on the related problems of aging. She will need to be ready to assist in community planning so that the potential values inherent in the thinking and occupation of old people may contribute to total community progress. So long as such a large group of our fellow men as is comprised by the aged remains insecure, afraid or apprehensive, our total welfare will be impaired. Unhappy, frightened persons, regardless of age, are never able to make their best contributions to the common good, and it is of the utmost importance that mental, emotional, spiritual and social factors receive study and joint thought in the community's care of aging members of our population. The nurse should, therefore, identify her thinking and her activities so far as she is able with social research movements and planning activities in her neighborhood and community that have as their ambition the intelligent study of old age and the setting in order of movements and institutions calculated to ameliorate it and make it a time of contentment and serenity.

THOUGHT PROBLEMS FOR THE STUDENT

1. List all the factors you can think of that have been responsible for the tremendous increase in the relative numbers of old people in our population within the past half century.
2. Try to think your way into the mental processes of some one of your aged patients who has a severe physical impairment of chronic type.
3. What experiences have you had with aged people to illustrate the fact brought out in the text that attention and memory are often fickle during the period of extreme age?
4. Make a list of some of the complaints voiced by poorly adjusted old people who smart at their incapacitation.
5. What elderly worker or workers do you know who are still productive and self-supporting? Contrast some other person or persons who are not working but who might still do so.
6. Talk for a few minutes when you have opportunity with some aged person in the hospital who is lonely, and try to understand something of the psychology of loneliness.
7. What are some of the problems commonly arising in three-generation homes where aged grandparents are living? How might these problems be agreeably resolved?
8. Prepare a week's full menu list for an aged man whose only exercise must be limited to short walks through the corridors or in the yard.
9. Familiarize yourself with the present provisions of the social security program for aging and aged people in your state. How adequate do you feel this program to be?
10. List possible occupations for full or partial self support that elderly people might engage in.
11. List other compensations of the aging process, in addition to those pointed out in the text.
12. What do you consider to be some important safeguards of retirement for any reasonably healthy individual after he has been "let go" from his job by reason of senescence?
13. Make a survey of the forms of provisions in your community for the housing and care of the aged group in the population. Include available hospital beds, rest homes, private nursing homes, as well as apartment housing, if any, designed for aged people.
14. Find out about other housing projects for the aged similar to the Tompkins Square project described in the text: for example, The Roosevelt Park Colony for the Aged, in Millville, New Jersey.
15. What are some possible developments of auxiliary home care services for the aged, community diet kitchens, and the like?
16. Make a fairly inclusive list of topics to be included in your conservations with elderly patients touching physical, emotional and adjustment problems in general.
17. Find out where there are to be found in your city planned activities for the aging and aged group, and visit or talk with some of the persons guiding such a project.
18. How can the aging process be truly a gracious one?
19. Correspond with the Social Science Research Council (230 Park Avenue, New York City), with the purpose of finding out what the Council has done and is doing in planning for better social service for the aged.

SUGGESTED READINGS

1. Brandeberry, Julia: Our responsibility to the aging. *Nursing Outlook,* January 1955, pp. 44–46.

    Nurses can be helped to recognize their responsibilities in helping the aging eventually to help themselves.

2. Clow, H. E., and Allen, E. B.: Psychiatric aspects of mental competency in the aging. *J. Am. Geriatrics Soc. 1*:30–38, 1953.

    Very good reading, especially for students interested in problems of mental effectiveness in elderly people as the psychiatrist sees them.

3. Cruze, W. W.: *Psychology in Nursing.* New York, Blakiston Division of McGraw-Hill Book Co., 1955.

    Pp. 434–449 may be read by the student with profit. Cf. especially the paragraphs on "Physical decline in old age"; "Mental decline in old age"; "Loneliness and depression"; "Needs and outlook of aged patients."

4. Havighurst, R. J., and Albrecht, R.: *Older People.* New York, Longmans, Green and Co., 1953.

    An introduction to social gerontology, this book is organized around the oldster's problems. Part 2 reports a study of the lives of older people in a small city.

5. Hildenbrand, G. C.: Psychological problems with geriatric patients. *Am. J. Occup. Therapy* 7:68, 80, 81, 1953.

    Describes the program of the New York City Home for older, dependent persons. Discusses rehabilitation and occupational therapy carried on.

6. Kirchner, W. K., and Dunnette, M. D.: Survey of union policy toward older workers. *J. Personn. Adm. Indust. Relat. 1*:156 ff., 1954.

    Finds from a survey of 18 labor unions in Minnesota that "unions have not placed emphasis on procedure designed to foster more efficient utilization of older employees on the job." None of them had a counselling program for psychological problems of retirement.

Chapter
18

The question for each man to settle is not what he would do if he had the means, time, influence and educational advantages, but what he will do with the things he has.

HAMILTON WRIGHT MABIE

NURSING THE PHYSICALLY HANDICAPPED

THE HANDICAPPED ADULT

Size of the Problem. Something of the vastness of the problem of care, nursing and training of the physically handicapped adults in the United States may be seen from the statistical fact that we have in our country at the present time 25 million persons who have been disabled from war, chronic illness and from sensory deterioration. The following figures show some significant facts that must be arresting to professional people who, like nurses, will spend time assisting and reeducating disabled or handicapped individuals. There are in the United States:

>10,000,000 people with impaired hearing;
>2,000,000 to 5,000,000 partially disabled by chronic disease;
>1,500,000 partially disabled war veterans;
>450,000 with visual impairment;
>240,000 totally blind;
>110,000 totally disabled war veterans;
>85,000 totally deaf people;
>50,000 victims of cerebral palsy (spastic patients).

In the modern day many factors have contributed to produce physical handicap and disablement. For generations we have had with us the blind person, the deaf or hard-of-hearing person, and those individuals whose vitality had been sapped by such debilitating conditions as heart disease, tuberculosis, nephritis, cancer and diabetes. We saw or heard about them in the community, but they did not seem to pose any tremendous problem.

Increasingly, however, such persons have come into prominence among us. When a nation of 160,000,000 people transforms an earlier home economy into a stepped-up factory one with its whirring machines, and its relatively minor wars to great international struggles embroiling 10 million fighting men and women armed with every modern implement of destruction in every sector of the earth as well as in the air above it and the water beneath it—the inevitable toll not only in *life* but in *limb* and *function* mounts to the figures presented in the opening paragraph of this chapter. Our population has more than doubled since 1900; we should expect to find the number of disabled to have doubled likewise within the same fifty-year period of time, provided all contributing causes had remained stabilized. The three greatest contributing causes—technological advancement, the phenomenal rise of the automobile, and the peculiarly twentieth century institution of total war—have all occurred within recent time. These three major developments in the social scene, together with the numerous offshoots of them, have caused a far greater increase in disablement. They have also brought prominently into the picture the mangled, the shell-torn and the permanently hospitalized in numbers that would have been impossible to foresee fifty years ago.

The civilian handicapped have been called by Dr. H. A. Rusk "the forgotten casualty"; they outnumber the disabled veterans seven to one. The National Safety Council estimated that in addition to 95,000 fatalities during 1953, 9,600,000 people were injured in accidents in vehicles, in their homes and at their work. This represented a total wage loss of one billion dollars. It is tragic that nearly a quarter of a million of our people annually lose an arm, leg, foot, hand, finger, or toe.

Personality Devastation Following Disablement. Only those individuals who have themselves had to endure disablement, partial or total, are in a position to comprehend fully the emotional crisis and the far-reaching personality derangements that follow loss of limb, function, or capacity. Most of us take for granted the possession of our eyes and ears, of our hands and feet, and rarely stop to imagine what life would be, at least initially, if we were to be deprived functionally of them. It is difficult at best, even for the nurse, to develop the inner ability to see through the darkened eyes, hear through the deafened ears, and walk about in imagination on the amputated stumps of men brought face to face with profound disablement.

The blinded man must henceforth move uncertainly in a black-out that is impenetrable; the deafened man must renounce every stimulus that once came through his ears and live henceforth in utter silence. The amputee, deprived of his hands, faces a world of objects that he cannot touch, feel, handle, arrange; or, deprived of his feet, a world that has suddenly shrunken to the confines of the chair or narrow bed which he occupies. The victim of incurable disease, whether cardiac or pulmonary, nephritic or cancerous, finds himself in the old familiar environment but unable longer to wrestle with it, dominate it, or bend it to his will. At least, newly disabled persons inevitably feel thus helpless and frustrated, and frequently lack the necessary courage to make the effort of attempting a comeback.

The Goal of the Disabled: Rehabilitation and Reemployment

With the exception of his misgivings and fears regarding his future personal lot and his social acceptability, the physically disabled person unquestionably suffers more anxiety and downright fright regarding his reduced economic status and his ability to earn a living for himself and his family than he does from anything else. During the early weeks following his disaster, he experiences a feeling of insecurity. With sight gone, or hearing gone, or hands gone, or feet gone, or with physical strength destroyed, he feels helpless to face life and its demands. It is only when he becomes intrigued by the reeducation or rehabilitation program initiated in his interest that he begins to become hopeful. Later, when the program begins to take shape and he can sense a dawning vocational readjustment, with reemployment and wage-earning once more in the offing, come hope and courage. If he can achieve what now seems to him to be the most desirable of all goals—reabsorption in the world of work, with the attendant economic competence and self sustenance that go with it—he will ask nothing more. In finding again a place among his fellowmen in the shop or factory, in the store or office, where he can become physically inconspicuous and vocationally successful, he anticipates the return of the contentment and peace of mind which he knew before his disablement occurred.

The Rehabilitation Program in the United States. Upward of 5 and a quarter million persons in the U. S., as of 1954, were suffering from chronic disability of some degree. Of this number, 2 millions could unquestionably benefit from the vocational rehabilitation program; 90 per cent of them, it is believed, could be rehabilitated to the point of complete economic self sufficiency. There are hundreds of thousands of others who could be made partially self-supporting by such a program.

Fortunately, authorities have already taken steps to extend greatly the role played by federal-state rehabilitation. Following the First World War, in 1920, Congress passed the original Vocational Rehabilitation Act which provided federal aid to states in reeducation of the disabled. Two types of handicapped individuals benefit by the program: first, civilians disabled in industry, accident, illness, etc.; and secondly, veterans disabled in service of their country. Operating in all the states, as well as in Hawaii, Alaska, Puerto Rico, and the Virgin Islands, the federal-state rehabilitation program rehabilitated during the year 1953 more than 60,000 disabled persons and returned them to employment. Legislation enacted in 1954 will expand this work to the rehabilitation in 1955 of 70,000, and by 1959 of 200,000 men and women. Under our present rate of annual disablement, it appears likely, then, that by 1960 80 per cent of those annually disabled will be provided for.

While the cost in dollars and cents of modern rehabilitation programs, entailing as they do the specialized training of personnel, research in methods and techniques, building programs, and essential actual placement in industry, is obviously great, it has been amply demonstrated that individuals thus removed from public assistance rolls and reabsorbed into jobs within a short period of time pay back in federal income taxes far more than the amount the government expended to rehabilitate them. It is estimated that in two years the 60,000 rehabilitated in 1953 will pay back in Federal taxes alone the entire 23 million dollars the federal government invested in them.

If the newly disabled individual can be sustained by the hopeful prospect of return in due time to a reasonably normal life of work and of economic competence, he will have a motive to endure the discouragements and the failures that will crush down upon him as he gropes his way forward to better things. The challenge presented to the nurse in keeping before her patient this prospect is strong, and the mandate clear.

It is heartening to note the change that is being effected in the status of the handicapped, both in our own country and abroad. Wider public attention to the matter has resulted not only in the enactment of federal and state legislation, but also in the conviction that eight out of ten disabled people can be reeducated and returned to gainful employment. One week during each year for the past ten years has been designated as National Employ-the-Physically-Handicapped Week. At the state level, most governors have, by proclamation and the setting up of state committees on employment of the handicapped, supported the movement actively. Voluntary organizations, civic clubs, unions, and employers have thrown in their support. Business men representing all parts of the country have organized a new Employers' Committee to promote the whole broad rehabilitation and reemployment program. Sheltered workshops have been opened in many cities, patterning after Cleveland's Rehabilitation Center and New York's Institute for the Crippled and Disabled, to help the handicapped to find their way back into gainful employment. In Kansas City, a three-year research study is going forward (1954), under the auspices of the U. S. Public Health Service, to obtain data on the costs of comprehensive rehabilitation services, on the extent to which handicapped persons can be rehabilitated, and to demonstrate to every citizen the value in dollars and cents of a community rehabilitation program. On the international level, the sixth world congress of the International Society for the Welfare of Cripples met at the Hague, in September 1954, to consider world problems of disablement and rehabilitation. Eight hundred delegates from 26 nations were in attendance, pooling their experience and wisdom in a concerted move to advance this great cause of restoration and renascence for the vast army of the handicapped and disabled.

Special Insight Needed by the Nurse. The nurse with insight, in her ministrations to patients suddenly deprived of their sense organs or appendages, will understand the bewilderment and even fright with which these persons regard their condition and their prospects. For days, and perhaps weeks or months, after the physical shock of their disablement has passed, the emotional shock will persist. Memory of past experiences adequately met and sustained is brought into sharp ideational contrast with imagined future inadequacies and frustrations in the same areas, and the resulting consternation may often border closely upon despair. The conjured-up spectacle of years of dependence upon the eyes and ears and fingers and feet of others, even upon the willingness or availability of others to lead one across a room, down a step, or to wheel one in a chair, becomes little short of a hideous nightmare. If we add to this the emotionalized attitudes in a disabled individual regarding the heavy burden which he assumes he will have to be upon his family, and resentment of the fate that has stricken him and reduced him to helplessness, we shall have some understanding of the first psychological reactions to his new condition which a suddenly incapacitated man is prone to make. Even when the nurse understands that when once the rehabilitation program has gotten under way, the future will look decidedly less black and forbidding to patients now perhaps completely immobilized, she must understand further that their minds cannot at the beginning grasp much beyond the present despair and possibly terror of tomorrow.

It becomes the clear professional duty of the nurse to take these mentally tortured individuals from where they are and guide them tactfully into eventual full conquest of themselves and their present limitations. This involves, in the first place, a conviction on her part that even the most severe disablement will usually yield to some measure of restoration; secondly, that she, together with the other workers, possesses the skill and the insight to accomplish this miracle; third, that it must be principally through her sympathetic influence that the patient can be brought to feel that his condition is not hopeless, that even in the case of serious disablement there is much to be gained through an acceptance of the condition on the victim's part and a rational adjustment to it; and finally, that through constant encouragement and assistance she can enlist the patient's best efforts to restore and rehabilitate himself, an end which depends quite as much upon a favorable mental attitude on his part as it does upon actual therapy and mechanical aids.

Indeed, without the day-by-day cultivation and growth of morale and hope for tomorrow, the cleverest therapy and the most ingenious mechanical aids will leave the disabled individual cold and passive. His eventual rehabilitation depends in large measure upon warm emotional and spiritual factors that buoy him up during the trying and difficult months and sometimes years that lie between his present reduced status and that to which he can be reeducated. Probably nobody in his environment is more essential than the nurse in carrying him through the psychological adjustments he will have to make.

A Six-Point Philosophy for Nurses of the Disabled. In caring for and encouraging the physically handicapped adult, the nurse will require a definite philosophy of optimism and faith to guide her in her salvational work. Beyond ministration to patients who are merely ill and who will shortly go back to life as it was before sickness overtook them, caring for men and women who have been crippled by some blow that will necessitate sharp and radical readjustment presents to the nurse a deeper challenge and a more intricate problem. We shall attempt in the ensuing paragraphs to sketch in the outlines of a philosophy of conduct and of optimism that nurses of disabled patients will need to cultivate in all their contacts with them.

1. *Confidence That in This Area True Miracles Occur.* It is of importance that the nurse be dominated by a warm certainty that even the devastating afflictions which these patients suffer will yield to reconditioning if both she and the victim will go at the difficult task with assurance and with the willingness to put everything they have into the conquest. The records of hospitals, clinics, and devoted families that have drawn the most seriously incapacitated individuals back to renewed joy in living and to a restored vocational and social experience are eloquent testimonials to this fact. It will be in point here to refer somewhat briefly to such a miracle of science and faith.

The case of Dr. Earl R. Carlson is a dramatic example of the human miracles that can take place in a severely handicapped individual. Earl Carlson was a spastic boy, a victim of cerebral palsy, which rendered him unable to walk, talk, or coordinate his other skeletal and voluntary muscles. But Earl Carlson had two invincible assets: wonderfully encouraging parents and a deathless determination to conquer. Aided by these unfailing resources, the boy set out on a difficult and often seemingly impossible pathway. With the determination of a heroic personality, he drove himself to attend school and high school, disciplining his protesting and wavering muscles until he could work his indomitable will upon them. In growing triumph, though still investing every ounce of his will power and determination to succeed, he matriculated at the University of Minnesota, from which he was graduated with a bachelor's degree in 1921, at the age of twenty-four. Continuing his unabating efforts, he won a Master of Science degree two years later. Determined not only to conquer his own handicap, but to devote his life to the aid of other spastic patients, he eventually graduated from medical school.

By 1932, Dr. Carlson was establishing the Department of Rehabilitation of Motor Disabilities at the New York Neurological Institute, which he directed for six years. Later on, he became an instructor in the College of Physicians and Surgeons at Columbia University. His crowning triumph came when he was able to establish two schools for spastic patients, one at East Hampton, Long Island, the other in Pompano, Florida. Both of these institutions have continued ever since to minister to and inspire hundreds of spastic individuals with the kind of heroism manifested by their founder. Dr. Carlson's professional achievements read almost like a fairy tale, when one considers the impossible start he had as a boy. Member of the American Medical Association, the New York Medical Association, the Association for Research in Nervous and Mental Diseases, and of the Society for Research in Child Development, he has lectured in almost every state in our country, and in some twenty foreign countries. Earl Carlson accomplished a miracle in his own life, and has shown legions of other unfortunates disabled like himself the way to repeated miracles of the same sort which was wrought in himself. His book, *Born That Way*, has told his story to thousands.

Science and determination, working together as partners, can achieve thrilling ends in the rehabilitation and restoration of shattered and broken bodies and the consequent reestablishment of an inner reconciliation and peace. Convinced of the achievability of such miracles of human rehabilitation, the nurse who participates in the care of physically handicapped individuals should not only be a constant believer in the potentials of such disabled people to achieve triumph in their struggles for restoration, but also ought to take real satisfaction in her own important role in the working of the miracle.

2. *The Disabled Must Be Taught to Accept and Then to Ignore Their Deficiencies.* Probably the most difficult, and certainly the first, of all the readjustments which the newly disabled person must face is that of accepting his loss. When one has been stricken by blindness, by loss of an arm, or by a severe heart attack, the emotional shock is considerable. Even with long reeducation, scientific prosthesis, and following inactive weeks and months of rest and recuperation in a hospital bed, the disabled individual can seldom hope to live the rest of his life in the old established patterns. The obvious human

reaction to the realization of this stubborn fact is resentment, tinged with fear and foreboding.

In this first crisis, the stricken man may, unless he can be given the proper spiritual regimen, adopt a self-pitying, defeatist attitude and dwell bitterly and despairingly upon his condition. Unquestionably many disabled persons fail for a long time, and indeed may never be able, to climb out of this slough of despond. Caught in such negative emotionalism, they tend to brood over the evil fate that has brought them to the present tragedy, grow morose and cynical, and end by taking refuge in some introversional mechanism that will do them no good and may bring them much psychological harm. In such an unwholesome state of mind, disfigurements and losses are magnified out of reasonable proportions and images are conjured up of a future in which the handicapped person sees himself as a helpless and abandoned derelict.

To help the newly disabled person pull out of this primary emotional despair, the understanding nurse will encourage the sufferer by every power of persuasion and reasoning that she has at her command that he will have to accept his lot, since it is a condition that exists and hence must be faced realistically.

There are various means through which she may aid him to this first victory. She will, for example, hold before him the fact that he can be in large measure restored to physical efficiency and vocational competence, the only limiting factor being his own lack of determination to cooperate to the fullest in the redemptive process already under way. She will, further, interpret and commend to him the helpful philosophy, expressed in the slogan of Possibilities Unlimited, Inc., that "It's not what you have lost but what you have left" that counts, and encourage him to forget as far as possible things as they were, and begin to envisage things as they will be later on after the work of science and psychology has been graciously accomplished. She will perceive in him the emergence of those moments of discouragement and misery which will recur during the weeks ahead, and will be ready to radiate fresh hope and cheer and to assist him to recapture the momentarily lost vision of tomorrow's victories. Throughout the period of her care of the disabled patient, she will be alert to detect changing emotional patterns. Friendliness, courage, and cheerfulness, if ever they become a nurse, are indispensable now, for it will be at first—and for a long time—only through the nurse's eyes, mind, and fancy that the patient dare look ahead to each tomorrow.

3. *The Road of Disablement Is a Hard One, but Good Efforts Yield Unbelievable Results.* The circumstance must never be lost sight of, however, as we have already pointed out, that the road ahead of the

physically disabled person is a peculiarly difficult one. To continue to live—and yet to exist upon a restricted plane—is hard for most persons to accept. The way ahead appears to be beset with hardship and frustration. To rise above the resulting despondency requires real character and dynamic motivation. It is the testimony of the rehabilitated that tremendous self discipline and determination are necessary as the long climb upward gets under way. The understanding nurse will not only appreciate the difficulty of the path ahead, but she will possess sincere inner admiration for the patients who seek to grope their way along it.

Frequent reassurance and commendation of efforts expended by the patient are in order during the earlier phase of the restoration program. When, in a thrilling moment, the nurse observes him for the time being focally oblivious of his handicap and throwing himself into a new spurt of effort, she must praise and encourage him. It may be that an amputee, emerging from a period of dread regarding his prosthesis, releases his hold on the nurse's arm, or relinquishes his cane, and takes his first unaided steps. Or it may be that a blind person is making the initial effort to learn his way hesitatingly around the ward or down the corridor, with nothing but profound attention to sounds and minute echoes from the walls around him to protect him from bruise or from a disastrous fall. Warm praise from the ever observant nurse will in many such cases hearten the afflicted individual to continue in the long pathway of reeducation and readjustment. The understanding nurse will sense also, as the skill and confidence of the patient grow, when the time has come to help the learner to regard himself as a normal individual and his efforts as being all in the day's work.

Beginnings have to be slow in the disabled person's reconquest of his world. It is essential, however, that they be made, and that they be made just as soon as the physical or surgical treatment after the accident warrants. The low morale of a newly disabled person must not be permitted to continue. The returning hope and reassurance must flow back, and it is usually the nurse who channels them into her patient's soul. With the evidence that he is beginning to stage a physical comeback, the patient will manifest new hope throughout his psychological being. Any individual who thus demonstrates the ability to emerge from his helplessness—spiritually, mentally, emotionally, and socially—as a whole personality, even though the nature of the handicap may slow down performance and sharply limit his subsequent vocational field, has the qualities of a real hero and should be so recognized and acclaimed. Often nobody but his nurse knows the background of determination and the weary weeks and often months of heartache and discouragement that have to be faced by such heroes.

Examples of the triumph of the handicapped over their disabilities abound all about us in all walks of life. Amputees play golf, drive cars, swim, dance, run business enterprises, play baseball, operate machines; frequently, moreover, nobody is the wiser regarding their impediments. Amputees, provided they have proper encouragement and training, and are willing to make the effort, are able to do most of the things which people in possession of their natural appendages can do. It was found in one survey of 300 amputees that as many as 75 per cent drive their own cars, 60 per cent bowl, 40 per cent swim, 35 per cent go fishing, 25 per cent play golf, 25 per cent dance, 15 per cent play tennis, and 10 per cent even play baseball. The disablement of these 300 individuals follows:

>   120 above-the-knee amputations (AK);
>   82 below-the-knee amputations (BK);
>   8 above-the-knee and below-the-knee amputations;
>   5 double AK amputations;
>   5 double BK amputations;
>   50 above-the-elbow amputations (AE);
>   39 below-the-elbow amputations (BE);
>   3 BK and one-arm amputations;
>   3 double BE amputations;
>   1 AE and BE amputation.

It is difficult to imagine greater resoluteness and more striking evidence of the "never-say-die" attitude than is presented by the physically maimed and disabled individuals who apply themselves without reservation to the program of rehabilitation. It is likewise difficult to estimate the part played by the nursing profession in infusing into the spirits of these unfortunate people the purpose which impels them over every barrier and every discouragement, until they win out and find new life and inspiration.

4. *Strong Faith in Self and in God Are Salvational with the Disabled.* The normal emotional reaction to severe disablement is likely to be one of despair, as we have noted. Previous values and perspectives have been distorted by one's harsh fate, and one is apt to look out upon the new world before him with profound disillusionment. Society is wrong; the world is wrong; God is wrong. In this desperate frame of mind, the victim may find it impossible to understand that society, the world, and God have not changed, but that it is he who has been changed by his hard experience.

In such circumstances, it is imperative for one's subsequent triumph that he be activated by faith to start life over again. The restoration of faith in himself will be assisted if the stricken individual can hold to his faith in God. Spiritual faith may suffer strain when physical strength and agility have been cut away, and it is not uncommon for the sufferer to cry out against God in his agony of soul. If a comeback is to be staged, the effort and hope requisite for undertaking it will have to stem from a deep faith that the power of God is unlimited and may be tapped freely by those who stand desperately in need of it. In the contemplation and acceptance of this important principle of rehabilitation, the disabled person will succeed, in his calmer and saner moments, in getting a new perspective and will be helped in reassembling his values against the struggle now before him. Victory, in the first instance, is built upon spiritual faith.

In the second instance, it is built upon reawakened faith in oneself. Following the dark hours and days of despair and frustration, when the blow has fallen that marks the end of one period of life and the beginning of another, there must come a resurgence of confidence and conviction. All is by no means lost; something, it is true, is gone, but if the patient can achieve the idea that he has within himself the power not only to rise above the handicap spiritually but also to re-educate himself and reharness his powers, he will have won his first and in many ways his greatest victory. Thereafter, all that will be required are time and practice of the new physical patterns that are imposed by his limitations. Amazing and satisfying progress will then be his experience as rehabilitation proceeds.

During these weeks of restoration and reeducation, punctuated by periods of shaking faith, the unfailing encouragement of the nurse is a vital factor in the final successful outcome of the struggle. There will be recurring hours, even days, of black defeatism that will dog the patient. Only the optimism and faith of the nurse can save the day and turn defeat into triumph. In this area of her ministry to the disabled lies the deepest challenge and perhaps the supreme contribution of the nurse. Greater than the physical care which she gives is the calm, unruffled faith which she infuses in the atmosphere surrounding the subject. There is a subtle contagion of faith and assurance from nurse to patient that fortifies him with new determination. In no phase of nursing do devotion and consecration to the profession yield more arresting results than in this outflow of the nurse's faith and confidence into the depleted spiritual channels of the crippled, the disabled and the physically circumscribed.

5. *Hobbies, Interests and Avocations Are of Major Importance.* In these days of shorter working hours and of increased amounts of leisure time for workaday people, a strong emphasis is placed by industrialists, educators and hygienists upon extravocational pursuits.

Through the appeal which hobbies and interests make, new zest in life and new horizons of understanding and challenge are brought to people after the day's work is over and the rest and relaxation hours begin. The physically impaired individual, both during the long period of readjustment to his condition and after he has returned to the vocational world, stands in even greater need of this sort of emotional and mental therapy than does the normal person.

While still in the hospital, just as promptly as his physical condition warrants, every disabled patient should be encouraged to adopt some kind of hobby, if for no other reason than to take his mind away from his physical adjustment problems. The nature of the hobby or interest is of less importance than that it actually exists. Its form will be in considerable measure determined by the nature of the disability and of the present amount of physical depletion suffered. In many cases, it may be determined on the basis of the contribution which it will make by way of increasing compensation for the loss or handicap sustained. In this regard, however, care should be taken that the activity is sufficiently interesting and absorbing to hold the attention upon it rather than upon the disablement for which it is designed to provide compensation. The therapeutic value of an interest for the physically disabled individual lies in the degree to which it diverts the mind from preoccupation with personal problems and limitations.

For the patient who still has unimpaired vision, reading is probably the greatest contributor to morale, provided of course that the material is suitably selected. Reading, because of the ease with which it can be adapted to the preferences of the individual, is probably the chief of all interests to be developed in the deaf, the patient with cardiac disease, and the leg or foot amputee. For these types also picture puzzles and crossword puzzles are excellent, as are radio, TV, and such activities as needlework or sketching. For the blinded, radio, mandolin, guitar or other instrumental playing offer possibilities of escape and of inner satisfactions.

As recuperation progresses and as active rehabilitation and related physical therapy proceed, many possibilities, depending again of course upon the nature of the handicap, enter the picture. Among them are Braille reading, lip reading, piano playing, voice culture, walking with coordination and control with artificial legs, manipulation of manual gadgets with hooks or prosthetic devices, bowling, ping-pong, billiards, cards and dancing. Possibilities Unlimited, Inc., to which reference has previously been made, has, through its magazine, through its active organization of amputees into local groups in various parts of the country, and through its inspired practice of sending a restored amputee to visit in the hospital each new accident victim of the same type of disablement, encouraged numbers of handicapped persons to adopt its prideful attitude of "possibilities unlimited" and wrought fresh miracles by giving them visions of what the disabled may yet do and become, in spite of their handicaps. The imaginative nurse, too, has "possibilities unlimited" in helping her handicapped patients to find, at first, release, and later on, hope and determination through hobbies and interests allied to their peculiar needs and condition.

6. *The Handicapped Respond Best when Treated as Normal People.* The physically depleted or disabled adult, like the physically handicapped child, thrives rather on matter-of-fact, objective treatment and handling than upon obvious sympathy or pity or upon special consideration. Sympathy, which is a common sentiment among human beings, can miscarry if it becomes saccharine. What the depleted individual wants and longs for most is to have his personality protected, and not to be singled out as an inferior or helpless person upon whom pity and compassion must be showered. He knows that he is handicapped, and he realizes that others know it. It hinders and embarrasses rather than helps and stimulates when observers and associates in a mistaken flood of pity express their concern or sorrow over his predicament. He is best helped and encouraged to forget his handicaps when they are ignored and when he observes that he is regarded no differently from his unhandicapped fellows. To have attention called, by word or by eye, to a disfigurement of any kind is bad for morale and places an extra psychological burden upon the subject. Observing, on the other hand, that his weakness of muscle and his incoordination of movement appear to be undetected by those around him, he gains new courage and struggles forward in the hope that actually he has overcome all outward evidence of his difficulties. This is a truly tonic experience, which is likely to make for redoubled effort.

NURSING PROBLEMS IN CERTAIN SPECIFIC MODERN DISEASES AND CONDITIONS

There are several modern conditions of physical impairment whose victims need particularly wise and competent nursing. While these ills of body were common in previous decades, they have increased in recent years. Many of them are of such a nature as to cause wide mental and emotional upheaval once they have attacked.

Cancer. Here is a disease which has now climbed into second place among all causes of death. We are not concerned here with etiology; rather, we wish to emphasize for the nurse the peculiar psychology of cancer victims. Once it has been diagnosed, even though treatment is prompt, the individual usually lives in fear afterwards. If early symptoms are ignored or undetected and treatment is sought too late, the patient is apt to become deeply disturbed. The possibility of spreading into other organs, with the imminence of death perhaps within a few months, presents the patient with a tremendous problem of adjustment.

Very few diseases erect such a blank wall of hopelessness before their victims as does cancer. In most other types of illness there is at least the chance of fighting the inevitable and postponing it, maybe for years; there is no postponing a malignant growth that has gotten out of hand.

Aware of the emotional state of a cancer patient, the nurse will be confronted with the need to be cheerful, to provide comforting reassurance, and to demonstrate skill and resourcefulness in keeping the patient's mind occupied with diverting thoughts and activities.

In the later stages of this disease, extreme physical suffering is not uncommon so that deep resources of character, faith, and often prayer are needed by the nurse.

To be able to watch a patient losing strength, knowing that she can not help except with supportive nursing—to accept without subjective distress the sick person's approaching death—this is an essential characteristic which the nurse at the bedside of a patient ill with cancer should strive to develop.

Cardiac Cases. While the prognosis for many diseases of the heart and circulatory system is much better than it is for cancer, it is a fact that the cardiac patient requires on the part of the nurse much guidance and encouragement. An initial attack of heart disease, regardless of its nature, ordinarily brings its victim sharply to a halt, usually necessitating not only bed but months of rest and slow recuperation. If during this long period while medical treatment is going forward he can be helped to maintain his courage and to look forward to resumption of some semblance of his former activities, he can be aided in many cases to a pleasant future. Investigations show that 75 per cent of persons who survive an initial heart attack are still alive after five years, and that as many as 70 per cent who were stricken initially by arteriosclerotic heart disease are still alive 10 years later.

In some cases, complete resumption of former work is possible after recovery; in others, the resumption has to be partial only; in still others, a complete change of employment may be indicated. Regardless of the vocational prospects before him, the cardiac patient can ordinarily be aided to make excellent recovery and gratifying adjustment to life and work.

Frequently the victims of cardiac disease are people who have been active, often strenuously so, in the physical and vocational world. Their initial emotional reaction to disablement is consequently all the more profound. It just does not seem possible to the patient who never had to stop to count the organic and physiological cost of doing anything he wanted to do that he is now a bed case with a long and entirely new road before him.

Helping her patient to confront his future sanely and sensibly and to accept the fact that after recovery his way may be more or less circumscribed, yet at the same time convincing him that it may be made satisfying and even challenging once more, becomes the nurse's mandate. Important as are her professional skills in nursing a cardiac patient, of even greater import are her personality assets which become the means through which he shortly comes to see his future not as forbidding and limited but instead as challenging and even intriguing. To help a patient to accept the trying restrictions of the present as a necessary prelude to a new day tomorrow is, in a very real way, to assist in reshaping and redirecting a temporarily baffled or actually rebellious personality.

Epilepsy. There are about one million epileptics in the U. S. While its cause is still not known, epilepsy has been found to be associated with disordered metabolism in the brain cells. It is not heritable, but susceptibility to it is believed to be. Seizures occur, as indicated by electroencephalograph, when the normal brain wave pattern becomes suddenly irregular, producing paroxysms of electrical discharges from various areas of the brain. In addition to susceptibility or predisposition, brain injuries prior to or during birth; infection in the brain resulting from such diseases as encephalitis, meningitis, etc.; brain tumors; severe head injuries; glandular dysfunction; and even emotional upsets may precipitate seizures.

The most unfortunate aspect of epilepsy is the circumstance that most epileptics possess normal health except during the brief moments when they are in the grip of seizures. Only for a few cataclysmic minutes, therefore, does the victim behave abnormally. These periodic attacks are so striking, however, that much social stigma attaches to them, and epileptics are commonly denied the privilege of working and living with other people. Epileptics cannot legally enter the U. S., are barred from marriage in many states, in many cases are denied admission to schools and colleges, and are not employable in many industries and business houses. And all this despite the fact that most epileptics under proper care and medical supervision can lead active, normal lives. Discrimination and prejudice are difficult to set aside. Fortunately, some very encouraging research in the control of epilepsy is under way.

The peculiar social shadow under which a person suffering from periodic attacks of epilepsy lives poses special problems for the nurse. In the wider sense, the nurse will use every effort to bring about in the community an improved popular attitude toward epileptics. This she can do by serving as an informed center of information locally and by constant attention as opportunity offers to sensible and sympathetic publicizing of the potentials of most epileptics to carry on vocationally and socially in the community.

In the immediately personal and professional sense, the nurse of the epileptic patient will emphasize in her daily contacts with sufferers the reassuring fact that with proper medical control epileptics may continue to carry on their usual activities and be self-supporting like other people. The comforting idea that most epileptics do not have seizures, and that those who do are no more abnormal than many a non-epileptic who manifests occasional "brain storms"—with far less real basis—will help her patient to see his infirmity in less disconcerting light than epileptics commonly do. Frequent emphasis upon such compensating traits as winsome personality, sincerity, reliability, determination, etc., is an additional aid to adjustment that the nurse is in position to render.

Neuromuscular Diseases: Cerebral Palsy, Multiple Sclerosis and Muscular Dystrophy. These three disorders of motor function have come into much prominence in recent years, thanks to increased research by such organizations as the National Society for Crippled Children and Adults (the Easter seal agency), the United Cerebral Palsy Association, the National Multiple Sclerosis Society, the National Institute of Neurological Diseases and Blindness, etc.

All three of these diseases have two things in common: first, they are the result of destruction or deterioration of the motor nerves so that the muscles of the body cannot be properly activated; and second, while destroyed motor functions cannot be restored, rehabilitation is possible for victims of these diseases, being retarded only by lack of popular understanding of them and of facilities for readjusting vocationally and socially most of those individuals who are attacked by them.

There are in the U. S. some 550,000 persons with cerebral palsy, more than one third of them under 21 years of age; 250,000 with multiple sclerosis; and another 100,000 with muscular dystrophy. Unfortunately, only a very small fraction of sufferers from these neuromuscular diseases are reached by treatment and rehabilitation programs.

Nursing of these patients should be based upon five very important considerations. In the first place, contrary to wide popular supposition, there is not necessarily any deterioration of intellect in neuromuscular victims. Society generally has supposed that because of their characteristic facial grimaces, awkward manual control, and "scissors" gait, with accompanying incoordinated and explosive speech efforts, victims of these deficiencies are mentally retarded. Such is not typically the case.

The senior author directed the education and training program of one extreme sufferer from cerebral palsy from the time when she was nine years old until she was twenty. At the outset, she was regarded both by her parents and by the primary school, to which she hitched her way daily for four years, as feeble-minded. At the age of 9 she was taken from school, placed under the charge of a young woman tutor whom the author trained specifically for the task, given a full private course in elementary subjects and later in high school subjects, drilled daily in motor coordination and speech, taught to typewrite, and sent to college where she made an excellent record. Following graduation, she was employed in a large city library for some ten years. Today she is accomplished, efficient, and has, by force of long self discipline, made herself able to speak without appreciable grimacing and to walk without conspicuous awkwardness. Unrehabilitated cerebral palsy victims are apt to be labeled mentally defective because of their very obvious inability to speak and move about normally.

In the second place, persons with this type of handicap can be aided enormously to vocational independence. While certain kinds of occupation may be out of the question for them, there are others in which they may be entirely successful. The understanding nurse will hold continually before victims of neuromuscular disease this alluring prospect and will prepare them emotionally for achieving it. Likening the daily struggle to the determined battle of good soldiers to conquer their enemy, she may triumphantly enlist them in what will be, though a long fight, a winning one in the end.

Third, the nurse will teach the patient to understand the complexity of his disablement and, while providing him with the services indicated, help him to accept limitations that will always be in some degree present and encourage him to live as full a life as he can within his physical potentials.

Fourth, since emotional disturbances tend to worsen the patient's condition, the nurse should make every effort to eliminate feelings of apprehensiveness, fear for the future, and downright discouragement over the present. She should focus his attention on the brighter and more achievable goals.

Finally, in the fifth place, the nurse needs to feel, particularly in the case of neuromuscular diseases, that they are still largely mysterious in etiology, that they are devastating and unconquered cripplers, that relatively little thus far has been done to aid their victims, and that hers is an important and strategic place in supporting and promoting locally and otherwise the promising new efforts by many agencies to bring wide public attention and help to sufferers.

Narcotic Addiction. A sharp rise in drug addiction in the U. S. within the past decade has introduced a new problem in control and therapy on behalf of upwards of 60,000 victims in our country. The number of addicts has been increasing at approximately the rate of 2,500 each year for the past five years. The four principal narcotics concerned—morphine, cocaine, heroin, and marijuana—enter the U. S. illegally; profits are so tremendous from their sale, often as high as 1000 per cent, that peddlers and "pushers" employ every device imaginable to promote their use in order to make more and more addicts.

Thousands of dope users are arrested for felonies arising either out of crimes committed in order to obtain the ever increasing amounts of narcotics needed, or as the result of physical or emotional disturbances caused by addiction. In one state alone, during 1953, the records show more than 6,000 felony arrests on narcotics charges. The months addicts spend in jail make it possible for detoxification to take place, but after release from custody the individual almost invariably reverts to drugs to satisfy his craving.

A peculiar problem is presented by juveniles who become dope users. In most cases, it appears that teen-agers who resort to narcotics are trying to escape blindly from emotional and adjustment pressures that bewilder or discourage them. Application of wise mental hygiene programs is indicated for potential adolescent dope users in home, school and community, either to prevent the habit or, once it has been formed, to build new controls and purposes for overcoming it.

A number of things have been and are being done to meet the threat of narcotics, including increased legal efforts to control the supply, obligatory group therapy programs in jails for those committed for using narcotics, placing probationers in the care of volunteer citizens after release from jail, promotion of "big brother" and "big sister" movements in their behalf, in-service training for custodial personnel on symptoms and identification of drug users, opening of infirmaries for medical treatment during the period of detoxification, and psychiatric and social case work for prisoners after detoxification.

From the standpoint of nurses called upon to assist in the therapy of addicts, whether in infirmaries or in hospitals or detentional institutions, effective professional procedures call for sympathetic understanding of the emotional bases behind resort to narcotics, in the first instance and, in the second, realization of the intense craving of every cell and tissue in the body for release through more dope. Fortified with this comprehension of the forces at work in the addict's mind and body, the nurse must display in handling the case something of the skill of a psychological counselor as well as that of a professional therapist. What the narcotics addict needs more than anything else, particularly after the early stages of detoxification have been completed, is a new point of view regarding his basal personal problems. Somehow, he must be given a new determination that it is within his power to call a halt to the unsatisfying and dangerous substitute for achieving happiness that he has been relying upon, and to set up inner controls and ideals that will free him from the grip of narcotics and restore reason and intelligence to their proper place as wiser guides for sensible living. In the advancement of this inner therapy, the nurse will guard against use of criticism or denunciation of what is past, and will focus her efforts upon encouragement for the future, upon faith in the individual's capacity to work out his goals, and upon instilling in him confidence that the realization of better days ahead is within his powers of achievement. Thus, as in all other nursing situations, a hopeful and stimulating attitude implanted in the patient represents perhaps the supreme contribution that can be made by the nurse to the reawakening of hope and new purpose in drug addicts.

Alcoholism. Alcoholism has come to be applied specifically to continuing and uncontrollable drinking that grows progressively worse. Of the 65 million persons in the U. S. who are drinkers, 4 million—one sixth of them women—are alcoholics. That is to say, these people have proceeded so far beyond the stage of so-called "social drinking" that they are now compulsive drinkers, depending upon alcohol to provide them a pseudo-comfort and a pseudo-escape from their problems.

Basally, the alcoholic's problems are personality and adjustment ones, such as overconsciousness of social inferiorities, inability to compete with fellows, family difficulties, and personal deficiencies. All these inadequacies are spirited away under the influence of alcohol, and the individual sees himself and his abilities in a more comfortable light. After the depressant's dulling of his sensibilities and self control have worn off, however, he awakens to physical torments, pain, remorse, self hate and self pity, to escape which, in a vicious circle, he returns to alcoholic excesses.

Unfortunately, there is no known cure for alcoholism; its powers can, however, be arrested through absolute abstinence which though difficult, is not impossible to achieve. While for the alcoholic who was a neurotic to begin with the chances of escape from the clutches of liquor are slim, for the individual not a victim of neurosis the chances are better. Even in his case however, the only possibility of release must arise out of full and unreserved determination to call a complete halt to indulgence.

Many public health nurses and many engaged in hospital and private practice will be called upon to assist professionally in providing nursing for alcoholics. Assuming that her patient has taken the initiative to overcome his enslavement, there are several approaches which the sympathetic nurse may make. First of all must be the assurance, repeated times without number, that escape for the alcoholic slave is possible through bulldog determination. Secondly, as the last traces of alcohol disappear from the organism and physical health begins to improve as a result, the nurse will help the individual to contrast his present feeling of returning health and emotional satisfaction with the physical suffering and the mental and emotional anguish that he knew in the old days before regeneration began. Third, she will fortify his will power by frank discussions of his need to separate himself in future from old associates, old temptations, and liquor, which will always be ready to attack him again in a weak moment. Fourth, she will aid him to develop a positive personality in which his earlier real or fancied inferiorities and deficiencies are minimized and more wholesome and promising traits are actively cultivated, so that he can begin to see himself and his potentials in a new and clearer light. Fifth, religious faith should be held up to him as a ready and staunch ally in the battle that will always lie before him. Strengthened by these means and viewpoints, the alcoholic returning to his right mind and his real sense of values will have taken a far step on the road to freedom from his former enslavement and will be basally equipped to win a decisive victory over his old enemy. As in all curative situations, the nurse will have been a powerful and beneficent agent in his restoration to mental and physical health as well as in opening up for him a new prospect for the future.

THE HANDICAPPED CHILD

Of the $33\frac{1}{2}$ million children in the United States between the ages of five and nineteen years, more than two million have physical handicaps sufficiently severe to require some special type of school service if they are to be aided to lead reasonably normal and well adjusted lives. Hardly more than $\frac{1}{10}$ of this number of physically defective children are at the present time receiving this sort of needful schooling and care. Ninety per cent of them are enrolled in the regular classes, or else they are not in school at all, either because they have passed beyond the compulsory school age or because their handicaps are of such a nature that it is impossible for them to attend school.

While no complete census of exceptional children has ever been made, the figures of the White House Conference on Child Health and Protection are believed to be reasonably correct. According to the findings of the Conference, the physically handicapped children under eighteen years of age are distributed in the following categories:

>1,000,000 totally deaf or hard of hearing;
>1,000,000 with speech defects;
>450,000 with damaged hearts;
>382,000 tubercular;
>300,000 crippled;
>50,000 partially sighted;
>15,000 blind.

Crippled Children. Crippled children are ordinarily classified as those who are unable to manipulate their bones, muscles and/or joints normally. Sometimes this condition is the result of congenital defects; sometimes, of birth injuries; sometimes, of rickets; sometimes, of cardiac disorders; sometimes, of infantile paralysis, or of tuberculosis of bones or joints; sometimes, of osteomyelitis; sometimes, of accidents.

Regardless of the causative factors of child crippling, many cripples must be transported daily to and from school, since they cannot walk, nor can they rely upon ordinary mass public transportation. Some of them cannot tolerate transportation, but must be taught either at home by special teachers assigned for this service, or in hospital classes by teachers similarly assigned. If they are able to attend school, they usually require special furniture and equipment. A considerable part of their school day must be devoted to orthopedic care; to physiotherapy, to keep their bones and muscles from deteriorating, and in some cases to bring about an improvement in them; and to occupational therapy, in order that they may be helped to prepare for self support in the years after school.

Blind Children. Psychologists believe that almost 90 per cent of our sensory impressions come through the eyes. Blind children, therefore, especially the congenitally blind or those who have never had visual patterns of perception, suffer a serious handicap. In general, blind children are classified as those who for all practical purposes have no vision, *i.e.*, they test 20/200 or less. This is another way of saying that they can barely make out at 20 feet distance what normally seeing children have no difficulty in seeing 200 feet away.

Procedures in schooling for the blind may follow either one of two plans: special teaching in the regular classroom, or residence in a special school (usually state administered). In the former, the blind pupil has the unquestioned advantage of associating with normally seeing children during the school day and of living at home. Relatively few communities, however, can maintain adequate equipment and specially trained Braille teachers for these children. In the latter plan, while the child must live away from home in the state school and can associate only with other blind children, there is likelihood that the proper equipment and teaching skills will be available, so that the progress of blind children in school work is more rapid among them than it could be if they were enrolled in undifferentiated classes in the conventional schools. Tactile methods and Braille instruction are requisite to this end. Special books, equipment and appliances are likewise indicated for schools in which blind children are enrolled.

Partially-Sighted Children. This group includes all those who test less than 20/70; *i.e.*, who can see vaguely at 20 feet only what more fortunate children can see plainly at 70 feet. Statistics indicate that approximately one in every 500 children is blind or partially-sighted to a degree serious enough to demand a special educational program. In increasing numbers of communities, the partially-sighted children are enrolled in sight-saving classes in the regular schools. The classrooms for these pupils are especially designed and equipped to promote the conservation of what vision remains, and if possible to increase it. Special lighting, desks, blackboards, books, and typewriters are provided to this end, as well as specially trained teachers. Ophthalmological services are likewise usually made available for dim-visioned children during the school years.

Regulation of the indiscriminate sale of fireworks has reduced the annual 500 eye injuries that used to mark the celebration of Independence Day. In the past forty years there has been a 90 per cent drop of ophthalmia neonatorum as a result of proper care of the eyes immediately following birth. The number of persons blind under twenty years of age is gradually decreasing. Blindness among children due to venereal diseases has dropped 50 per cent in fifteen years. Heartening as these facts are, other conditions have operated to make the picture less reassuring. There has been in recent years a 17 per cent increase in blindness from hereditary and congenital causes. Moreover, every week 420 Americans lose their eyesight, more than half of them from carelessness; 300,000 suffer preventable eye accidents in industry each year, and 800,000 are losing their sight from glaucoma.

Deaf Children. Children deaf from birth are not always recognized as being deaf until they have lived several years; often in the interim they pass as dull-witted, or even as feeble-minded, and in some cases are admitted to institutions for the feeble-minded without examination, either of hearing or of intelligence. Careful examination with the audiometer is essential for every child at the beginning of kindergarten, particularly if there is the remotest reason to suspect that his hearing is deficient. For those who are classified as deaf, that is, whose loss of hearing acuity is so extensive that they cannot be taught through their ears, special classes or special schools should be made available. As in the case of classes for the blind, few educational communities can afford to maintain their own municipal classes for the deaf, hence the feasible thing is for these children to be enrolled in state schools for the deaf, where the proper equipment and teaching techniques are available.

Hard-of-Hearing Children. These children should under no circumstances be placed in schools or classes for the deaf. If their hearing loss, though considerable, does not preclude their being taught through their ears, they should be enrolled in special classes for the hard-of-hearing, which most sizable communities now maintain. Lacking such facilities, they may remain in regular classrooms, provided electrical hearing aids are made available for them, provided they can be seated in the front of the room, and provided also they can be taught to watch people's lips and to develop skill in lip-reading. Special instruction in this last is ordinarily provided by the classroom teacher herself, by a special speech correction teacher, or in some cases by an itinerant lip-reading teacher employed by the community to go around to the various schools for this purpose. Everything possible should be done to conserve the residual hearing which each child has and to delay or prevent its greater deterioration. If, as often happens, the hard-of-hearing child becomes later the deaf adult, his earlier training in lip-reading in the school will have made it possible for him to adjust with success when his handicap becomes total. Not far from 2 per cent of all school children are deficient in hearing to the point where such special provision for them as indicated above is essential.

The Delicate Child. Delicate children include those whose vitality has been lowered by various contributing causes. These include, among others, malnutrition, with its attendant high fatigability, anemia and poor living habits; pretubercular conditions, with the low vitality and meager powers of resistance that accompany them; cardiac symptoms, with the constant danger of overstrain and the consequent necessity for a greatly circumscribed routine which must be followed by those afflicted; and a generally poor constitution, due to heredity, marked underprivilege in preschool years, or sometimes to exhausting and depleting bouts with one or more of the children's diseases and their after-effects.

These children should be enrolled in the regular classrooms if a daily regimen of good ventilation, adequate school feeding, supervision of physical expenditure, interspersed rest periods, a reduced program of studies, and attention to health and personal hygiene is followed by teachers and school health workers. Many if not most of them may emerge after the school years at least not worse off physically—and frequently much better off—than when they started.

It is obvious that those with the more serious cases of under-vitality may and should be cared for in special classes conducted by the school health service, in which a minimum of attention is devoted to formal academic study and a maximum to the improving of the precarious health condition. Transfer back to the regular class should, of course, be made for these pupils as they individually improve to the point where it will be safe for them to reengage in a full school schedule of study. The probabilities are that some 2 per cent of the children enrolled in the schools are properly classifiable as delicate children who ought to be getting special care and handling if they are to grow up conquerers of their deficiencies.

Speech Defects. Another 2 per cent of school children have faulty speech. Among these unfortunate children are the stutterers, the lispers and those who use prolonged baby talk, as well as those who have never learned to talk pleasingly and effectively. Overpitched, harsh, guttural or nasal voices are heard commonly, not only among children but among their elders as well. Various causes contribute to speech defectiveness; among them may be mentioned poor speech patterns heard at home; poor hearing, which makes it impossible for one to perceive proper patterns even though they may obtain in the environment; cleft palate or an improperly functioning soft palate; neural lesions; and a variety of other contributing causes, some of them structural, many of them emotional or psychological.

These children pass most of their time in regular classrooms where their handicaps will, unless they are relieved, tend to increase rather than to diminish, and so intensify problems of adjustment and of general mental health. Special speech correction teachers are now employed in many school systems. Where they are not available, the regular teacher can usually be of great assistance in encouraging and training those with speech defects to develop their speech or, in more serious cases, can enlist the aid of the local guidance clinic or of physicians who may be qualified to advise parents regarding the problem.

The Psychology of Handicapped Children

Two principles of primary importance emerge from study of the psychology of physically handicapped children. Each of them needs to be applied by teacher and nurse in the handling of these children.

1. **Early Attention to the Handicap Is Essential.** The personality of a child begins to develop in its individual pattern in the earliest years of life. Long before school age or even kindergarten age has been reached, the principal foundations of later personality have been laid. Any child who is burdened with a physical handicap which interferes with normal intercourse with other children will early tend to reflect this circumstance in his personality and in his self evaluation. Every added year of unaided and therefore unadjusted battling with his deficiency will make it less likely that he can be completely salvaged psychologically from the depression and perhaps the bitterness that assail him. Too much stress cannot therefore be placed upon the importance of early and prompt attention to the physical, emotional, and psychological needs of the handicapped child. To wait until he enters school at the age of five or six years is inadvisable. Alertness on the part of parents to discover developing abnormalities; cooperation on the part of family physician, district nurse and other health workers; and eagerness of teachers, school nurses, nursery and kindergarten teachers, special class teachers and all other adults concerned—these things become of the greatest importance in focusing early attention upon the diagnosis of physical handicaps.

The fact must not be lost sight of, either, that the earlier physical abnormalities are detected, the greater the likelihood that they will yield to treatment; while serious handicaps can usually not be completely removed, the chances of lessening them and of conserving and protecting the residual function are greater. It is little short of criminal, for example, to permit a low-visioned child to go either undetected or unaided until he has reduced what little vision he had to the vanishing point. This can easily happen when the symptoms are ignored by parent and school, or when the victim's retardation is ascribed to heedlessness or stupidity. Neglect of this sort not only endangers the stability of the defective organs but initiates in the personality of the victim, as we noted above, a long train of psychological complications, including discouragement, frustration, bafflement, and even delinquency.

2. **Avoidance of Oversolicitousness and Sentimental Pity.** Physically handicapped children are moved by the same motives, seek the

same satisfactions, and harbor the same feelings and emotions as do normal children. In a mistaken show of pity and oversolicitousness, many people keep crippled or otherwise handicapped children uncomfortably aware of their defects. They appear to believe that if they indicate their keen sympathy for the handicapped child and constantly make reference to his abnormality and the tragedy which he is facing, they will be encouraging the young victim to bear his lot with fortitude and grace. Nothing could be more erroneous. Handicapped children do not wish to be thought of or treated as any different from their normal fellows. Even to have their defect noted, to say nothing of being remarked upon, is distasteful to them. Most of them want to fit inconspicuously into the common group and to be treated exactly like everybody else. In this, they are not unlike the adult handicapped.

Therefore, it is desirable for every handicapped child, in so far as it is physically possible, to enter into the normal activities and the routine experiences of all children. He should be encouraged constantly in this ambition and aided by every subtle means to achieve it. Teachers and nurses and parents should refrain from helping him do things that with determination and practice he can learn to do for himself. They should by their attitudes and their expectations make it evident to such children that they are comparable with all other children. Otherwise, the handicapped easily develop apprehensions, inferiorities and lowered morale. Everything and everybody in the environment should cooperate in assuring or reassuring the handicapped, through the power of suggestion and example, not only that their deficiencies are not insuperable, but that through the combined efforts of all they may become as successful and happy as anybody else.

Such undesirable epithets as "poor little deaf child," "poor blind angel," "dear little cripple" are unwholesome and may make for morbidity and over self-consciousness in a handicapped child. Far from displaying lack of sympathy for these unfortunate children, adult teachers and health workers who refrain from such sentimental and overemotional displays are instead, by making the defect inconspicuous and by striving to create as normal an atmosphere around the victims as possible, actually building self confidence in them and enabling them to learn to react objectively and philosophically to their condition. By thus strengthening morale, they are protecting and fostering the children's mental health and adjustments.

Care and training of physically handicapped children are in sharp contrast with procedures and regimens that obtained in earlier years. It was originally deemed wise to segregate all such children in special classes or schools. Today, workers in this field are of one mind that only those with extreme defects in which the victims cannot, for physical or other reasons, be enrolled in the regular classes with normal children, need to be placed in special rooms or institutions. Many handicapped children, notably the partially seeing and hard-of-hearing, can follow the ordinary day's routine in the same classes with the non-handicapped, being withdrawn from them and segregated with other similarly handicapped pupils only at certain periods of the day or week for instruction by the special teachers provided. Thus, these children have the advantage of normal contacts and experience with normal mates during the major portion of the school day, as well as the equally important advantage of skilled part-time training by expert special teachers along the way to help them to overcome the psychological and physical impediments to their optimal growth and development.

THE NURSE IN THE SCHOOL

Regardless of whether the children in the schools are handicapped or not, school nurses have become within the past third of a century essential workers in our American educational system. Standards demanded by the National Education Association and the American Medical Association, jointly, require that communities shall employ one school nurse for every 1500 school children of elementary school age, and for not in excess of every 2500 high school students. Since the date of the appointment of the first school nurse in New York, in 1902, there has been a steady increase in school nursing services. Obviously, the smaller and more remote communities are less well provided for in this regard than are the more populous cities and larger towns. In rural areas, several thousand nurses are employed by county or district health units or by school districts. In larger towns and cities, local nurses employed by the department of public health are ordinarily assigned on a part-time basis to work in the schools. In most of the sizable cities, however, there are now separate and independent school health departments with full-time school nurses.

When school health work started, there were many more physicians than nurses employed. As the program developed, however, it was found not only that the school nurse is a more economical official than a medical man, but that because she can and does divide her time among schools, families, clinics and other agencies in the community, she is also a more effective one. By daily health inspections; by emergency treatment in the case of infection, illness or accident; by investigation of absences due to illness; by follow-up visits to the homes and consultation with parents; by cooperation with the social case worker; and by the actual teaching and demonstration of health principles, the nurse in the school has long ago proved her worth in raising the standards of child health, school attendance and general community health consciousness.

The Relationship of the Nurse to the Handicapped Child. Physically handicapped children are now enrolled in special classes or buildings in hundreds of school systems scattered over most of the states in the Union. In addition to these provisions made in the public day school system, facilities are also maintained for such children in public and private residential schools. Since nursing service is of critical importance for these unfortunate children, it is obvious that here is a field of opportunity for graduate nurses that will become increasingly extensive.

In her work as a school nurse, a public health nurse, an institutional one, or a privately employed one, the nurse will come in contact with handicapped and physically defective children. Therefore, it is important for her to understand the newer point of view regarding the handicapped child that we have been presenting in the last pages of this chapter. This philosophy may be recapitulated briefly as follows:

1. The physically handicapped child should be handled just as far as possible as though he were physically normal.

2. He should attend regular, undifferentiated classes in the schools unless the nature of his handicap precludes it.

3. If the nature of his defect is such as to make it advisable, he should spend one or more periods each week in a special class where his deficiency may be ameliorated, or at least where he may learn to conserve and make the best use of his remaining capacities.

4. If his handicap is acute, so that attendance in regular classes is impossible, he should either be enrolled in a special boarding school, or in some cases should be accorded teaching and nursing service in his own home by itinerant teachers or nurses.

5. Excessive or sentimental show of sympathy for the physically handicapped should be avoided.

6. Continuous assurance—by acts and expectations rather than by verbal glibness—that the handicap need not interfere with ultimate success and happiness and good adjustment in living should be the rule of all workers dealing with defectives.

7. Every effort should be made by all concerned to secure early wise school placement and optimal educational content for every handicapped child.

8. Maintenance of good cheer and optimism in all contacts and in planning for the future should be the underlying motive in the nurse

and in other workers whose influence is brought to bear upon handicapped children.

THOUGHT PROBLEMS FOR THE STUDENT

1. Appoint some member of your class to correspond with Possibilities Unlimited, Inc., Cleveland, Ohio, and request whatever printed matter they may have available regarding their work with amputees.
2. Try to put yourself imaginatively in the place of a recently blinded stenographer thirty-five years of age and endeavor to write down her thoughts as she faces the future.
3. Do the same in the case of a piano teacher forty years of age who last week lost both his hands in a traffic accident.
4. Read in some of the references cited in this chapter, or in any other available source, the striking autobiographical accounts given by disabled individuals regarding their struggles to adjust to their deprivation, and the eventual victories achieved.
5. List in each of two parallel columns ten things which a disabled individual should and should not do if he is to achieve readjustment: *e.g.*, he should not spend time in lamenting his lot.
6. List as many individuals as you know who have been in some way physically disabled, the nature of their handicaps, and the success or failure with which they have striven to stage a personal comeback.
7. List what you deem to be the ten most indispensable personality and character traits which nurses of physically disabled patients should possess if their ministrations are to be acceptable and beneficial.
8. Make as full lists as you can of interests and hobbies or avocations which each of the following types of disabled might well be encouraged to develop: a blind boy, a below-elbow amputee, a double below-knee amputee, a totally deaf person, a severe cardiac patient, a spastic patient.
9. What is the nurse's responsibility in the early detection of dysfunction?
10. With the nurse's opportunity for observation and assistance of handicapped persons, a rare opportunity also exists to determine the motivations which can be included in their care to bring about favorable adjustments, to lessen the time period of rejection of self, and to begin constructive rebuilding in mind as well as body. Keep running notes on your observations of these means from day to day.
11. Acquaint yourself with the signs of coming fatigue which these patients manifest before exhaustion; learn to discern also the signs of depression before complete hopelessness takes over. If you are not able to provide the necessary support, know the persons in your hospital whose resources are available to your patients.
12. What are the agencies in your community which encourage and supply new motivation for handicapped persons on the long road to rehabilitation?
13. If you saw the film, "The Best Years of Our Lives," try to recall the scenes which still remain most vividly in your memory. Did they add to your understanding of the characters portrayed? In what way?
14. Explore the progress being made in your community in assisting disabled persons to prepare for vocations in which they can achieve competence. What are the employment policies of business and industry in relation to them?

15. Arrange for the class to visit a special schoolroom or building in which training of physically handicapped children is going forward. Especially valuable experience may be had if you can visit a sight-saving or a lip-reading class, or both.
16. Write a brief case history of some delicate child whom you may know in the community.
17. Study the school medical, nursing, and general health program operating in your city. If possible, delegate one or two members of the class to confer with some official of the school health department, preferably a supervising nurse, in order to secure complete information regarding the setup of local health work.

SUGGESTED READINGS

Books
1. Gardiner, M. D.: *The Principles and Practice of Exercise Therapy*. New York, The Macmillan Co., 1954.

    Each of the methods employed in therapy and physical rehabilitation is broken down in detail to show specific effects and techniques. An excellent reference and work book for students and teachers in physiotherapy.
2. Klopsteg, P. E., and Wilson, P. D.: *Human Limbs and Their Substitutes*. New York, McGraw-Hill Book Co., 1954.

    One of the most significant and helpful books in recent years covering the field of rehabilitation.
3. Tucker, C. D.: *Betty Lee—Care of Handicapped Children*. New York, The Macmillan Company, 1954.

    This story of Betty Lee is told by the child's own mother, who knew how to meet tragedy with courage. An exceptionally valuable book for educators, nurses and doctors engaged in social work and rehabilitation.

Journals
4. Gorman, Ethel M.: It takes more than skill. *American Journal of Nursing*, May 1953, pp. 581–582.

    "Nurses need to release their sympathy and understanding in caring for the handicapped."
5. Hartigan, Helen: Nursing responsibilities in rehabilitation. *Nursing Outlook*, December 1954, pp. 649–651.

    Rehabilitation represents both opportunity and responsibility in the nurse's daily patient care plans.
6. Morrissey, A., Coe, M. H., and Gilbertson, E.: The nurse and rehabilitation. *American Journal of Nursing*, November 1954, pp. 1354–1359.

    Specific guidance is given here for nursing effectiveness in rehabilitation.
7. Neuschutz, Louise M.: I learned to hear again. *Nursing Outlook*, April 1954, pp. 203–204.

    Nurses will find of interest how the deafened may be guided to help themselves.
8. Sheppard, P. J.: Windows for the homebound. *Nursing Outlook*, February 1954, pp. 72–74.

    Red Cross Gray Ladies point the way to nurses.
9. Wilma, I. R.: As a blind nurse sees. *American Journal of Nursing*, February 1955, pp. 205–208.

    Here nurses may learn how to assist the blind in developing independence.

BIBLIOGRAPHY

The following books and journals comprise the bibliography to which constant mention is made in this volume.

1. Aldrich, C. A., and Aldrich, M. M.: Babies Are Human Beings. 2nd Ed. New York, The Macmillan Company, 1954.
2. Anastasi, A.: Psychological Testing. New York, The Macmillan Company, 1954.
3. Bernhardt, K. S.: Practical Psychology. New York, Blakiston Division of McGraw-Hill Book Company, 1955.
4. Blair, G. M., Jones, R. S., and Simpson, R. H.: Educational Psychology. New York, The Macmillan Company, 1954.
5. Bullis, H. E., and Kelly, C. W.: Human Relations in Action. New York, G. P. Putnam's Sons, 1954.
6. Carmichael, L. (editor): Manual of Child Psychology. 2nd Ed. New York, John Wiley and Sons, 1954.
7. Cole, L.: Psychology of Adolescence. 4th Ed. New York, Rinehart and Company, 1954.
8. Crow, L. D., Crow, A., and Skinner, C. E.: Psychology in Nursing Practice. New York, The Macmillan Company, 1954.
9. Cruze, W. W.: Psychology in Nursing. New York, Blakiston Division of McGraw-Hill Book Company, 1955.
10. Fidler, G. S., and Fidler, J. W., Jr.: Introduction to Psychiatric Occupational Therapy. New York, The Macmillan Company, 1954.
11. Garrison, K. C., and Gray, J. S.: Educational Psychology. New York, Appleton-Century-Crofts, 1955.
12. Gardiner, M. D.: The Principles and Practice of Exercise Therapy. New York, The Macmillan Company, 1954.

13. Gill, H. Z.: Basic Nursing. 4th Ed. New York, The Macmillan Company, 1955.
14. Goodnow, M.: Nursing History. 9th Ed. Philadelphia, W. B. Saunders Company, 1953.
15. Hall, C. S.: A Primer of Freudian Psychology. Cleveland, World Publishing Company, 1955.
16. Harmer, B., and Henderson, V.: The Principles and Practice of Nursing. 5th Ed. New York, The Macmillan Company, 1955.
17. Havighurst, R. J., and Albrecht, R.: Older People. New York, Longmans, Green and Company, 1953.
18. Jenkins, G. G., Schacter, H., and Bauer, W. M.: These Are Your Children. New and Expanded Ed. Chicago, Scott, Foresman and Company, 1953.
19. Jersild, A. T.: Child Psychology. 4th Ed. New York, Prentice-Hall, Inc., 1954.
20. Karn, H. W., and Weitz, J.: An Introduction to Psychology. New York, John Wiley and Sons, Inc., 1955.
21. Katz, B.: How to Be a Better Parent. New York, Ronald Press, 1953.
22. Kempf, F. C.: The Person as a Nurse. New York, The Macmillan Company, 1950.
23. Lehner, G., and Kube, E.: The Dynamics of Personal Adjustment. New York, Prentice-Hall, Inc., 1955.
24. Lindgren, H. C.: Mental Health in Education. New York, Henry Holt and Company, 1954.
25. Munn, N. L.: Evolution and Growth of Human Behavior. Boston, Houghton Mifflin Company, 1955.
26. Munn, N. L.: Psychology. 2nd Ed. Boston, Houghton Mifflin Company, 1954.
27. Orr, W. H.: Hormones, Health and Happiness. New York, The Macmillan Company, 1954.
28. Outler, A. C.: Psychotherapy and the Christian Message. New York, Harper and Brothers, 1954.
29. Pfeiffer, J.: The Human Brain. New York, Harper and Brothers, 1955.
30. Pitt, W. J., and Goldberg, J. A.: Psychology. New York, McGraw-Hill Book Company, 1954.
31. Rotter, J. B.: Social Learning and Clinical Psychology. New York, Prentice-Hall, Inc., 1954.
32. Ruch, F. L.: Psychology and Life. 4th Ed. Chicago, Scott, Foresman and Company, 1953.
33. Ruja, H.: Psychology for Life. New York, McGraw-Hill Book Company, 1955.
34. Shaw, F. J., and Ort, R. S.: Personal Adjustment in the American Culture. New York, Harper and Brothers, 1953.

35. Schneiders, A. A.: Personal Adjustment and Mental Health. New York, Rinehart and Company, 1955.
36. Thorndike, R. L., and Hagen, E.: Measurement and Evaluation in Psychology and Education. New York, John Wiley and Sons, 1955.
37. Travers, R. M.: Educational Measurement. New York, The Macmillan Company, 1955.
38. Thorpe, L. P.: Child Psychology and Development. 2nd ed. New York, Ronald Press, 1955.
39. Tucker, C. D.: Betty Lee—Care of Handicapped Children. New York, The Macmillan Company, 1954.

Journals

1. *American Journal of Nursing.*
2. *American Journal of Occupational Therapy.*
3. *Journal of the American Geriatrics Society.*
4. *Journal of Clinical Neurophysiology.*
5. *Journal of Personnel Administration and Industrial Relations.*
6. *Journal of Pastoral Care.*
7. *Nursing Outlook.*

INDEX

ABNORMALITY(IES), physical, 211
  of nerve function in the sick, 128
Active method in study, 64
Activities, adjusting, 81
  and interests, 6
Adequate stimulus, 17, 160, 176
Adjustment, and maladjustment, 276
  and patient, 36
  and student nurse, 2 ff.
  by attack, 278
  by flight, 282
  family, 28
  juvenile, 349
  meaning of, 276
  personal, 28
  positive, 281
  problems of, 357–404
  psychosexual, 349
  to emergency situations, 354
  to thwarting, 278
  vocational, 28, 267
Adolescence, delinquency in, 240
  early growth in, 233
  interests during, 235
Adolescents, mental health of, 347
  parents of tomorrow, 347
Adulthood, achievement of, 253–270
  conflict in, 273
Adults, as learners, 47
  handicapped, 375
Advertising, psychology of, 22
Affection, misguided, 325
Age, acting one's, 266
  in learning, 209

Age scale, 205
Aged, financial status of, 365
  mortality statistics of, 359
  physical deterioration of, 359–360
  psychology of, 358–374
Aggressiveness, in children, 344
Aging, gracious, foundations for, 371
  housing for, 366
  psychology of, 358–374
Alcohol, and learning, 212
Alcoholism, 393
American Medical Association, 401
  Psychological Association, 15
Amputees, triumphs of, 384
Anger, 292
Animal learning, 168
  as conditioning, 174
Anxiety, 226, 292
Appearance, personal, in adolescence, 236
Applied psychology, 18 ff.
Aptitude tests, 20
Aristotle, 14
Art, teaching as, 48
Assignment, essentials in, 61
Association, cortical, 125
  determiners of, 156
  importance of, 124
  law of, 155
  secondary principles of, 155
  unconscious factors in, 310
Association, free, tests of, 302
Attack, adjustment by, 278
Attention, involuntary, 145

409

Attitude(s), and the nurse, 105
  as determiners of association, 156
  of behavior, 104
  expressed in action, 5
  faulty, 104
  healthy, 259
  optimistic, in studying, 60
  problem, in study, 68
  unfortunate emotional, 228
Auditory stimuli, 117
Automatic behavior, 98
Avocations, for the disabled, 385

BASAL drive, in young child, 342
  wants of men, 78
Bassett, C., 334
Beers, C. W., 23
Behavior, automatic, 98
  compensating, dangers in, 280
  display, 92
  effective, in new situations, 5
  gregarious, 90
  habits as determiners of, 100 ff.
  learned, 97 ff.
  manipulation, 88
  reflex, 98
  rivalry, 92
Behaviorism, 17
Being needed, feeling of, in adolescence, 350
Bias, 207
Binet, A., 203
Binet-Simon tests, 203
Blindness, disablement of, 376
Bodily comfort, as basal want, 78
Bones, growth of, 234
Brain, as associative center, 124
  gateways to, 115
Bridges, K. M. B., 300

CAFFEINE, influence of in learning, 213
Cancer patient, handling of, 387
Cannon, W. B., 79
Cannon's theory of emotion, 305
Cardiac cases, nursing, 388
Care of the sick, teaching in, 45
Carlson, E. R., 380
Carrel, A., 365
Case history, 25
Cattell, J. McK., 15
'Censor,' Freudian, 310
Cerebral palsy, nursing, 390

Cerebration, rate of, in the sick, 129
Cerebrum, 125
Cheerfulness, at patient's mealtimes, 137
Chemical responses, in glands, 135
Child, growth of, 220
  guidance, 26
  handicapped, 394
    psychology of, 399
  'hard-boiled,' 328
  hard of hearing, 397
  health programs, 247
Childhood, conflict in, 272
  early, importance of, 334
  habits in, 230
  psychology of, 220 ff.
Children, as people, 41
  crippled, 395
  deaf, 397
  delicate, 397
Church interests, adolescent, 244
Circulatory changes, in pubescence, 234
Cleveland Rehabilitation Center, 378
Clinical methods in psychology, 11
  practice, 23
Closure, Gestalt, 174
Collecting interest, 106
Color, influence on the sick, 116
Comfort, bodily, as basal want, 78
Community influences, wholesome, 245
  planning, for the aged, 371
  Service Society, of New York, 367
Compensating behavior, dangers in, 280
Concave learning curves, 196
Conditioned emotional learning, 159
  and the nurse, 162
  in the home, 161
  in the school, 162
  patterns of, in the young, 342
  response, 17
Conditioning, animal, 174, 177
  early, 160
Conflict, mental, 272
  adult, 273
  in childhood, 272
  interparental, 326
  in youth, 273
Connecting processes, nervous, 124
Connectionism, in psychology, 16
'Conquering hero' mechanism, 285
Convalescing patient, 134
Convergence, of stimuli, 126
Consumer relations, 22

INDEX 411

Consultation, in therapy, 27
Continence, 349
Cortical association, 125
Courtesy, 50
Creativeness, 88
Criminology, psychology in, 29
Crippled children, 395
'Crutches' in learning, 183
Curiosity, 88
Curves, of forgetting, 152
  of learning, 191 ff.
  of normal distribution, 198

DANCING, interest in, 240
Dashiell, J. F., 224
Daydreaming, introversional, 285
Deaf children, 397
Death, causes of, in old age, 359
Deformities, 211
Delicate children, 397
Delinquency, adolescent, 240 ff.
Democracy, adolescent need for glamorizing of, 350
  to be lived, 351
Dependence, emotional, 111
Depression, in old age, 361
Deterioration, of organs and tissues in the aging, 360
Dietary, for the aged, 364
Diffusion, of nerve impulse, 127
Digit-symbol substitution, 172
Disabled, goal of, 377
  reemployment of, 377
  statistics of, in U. S., 375
  teaching to accept condition, 381
Disablement, blindness as, 376
  chronic, 377
  hard road of, 382
  personality devastation following, 376
Discipline, mental, 164
  problems of, 332
Discomfort, organic, relief from, 78
Disharmonious homes, 323
Display behavior, 92
Distractions, effects of, in learning, 214
Disuse, Thorndike's law of, 154
Divorce, effects of, on children, 329
Dominant-submissive emotional patterns, 343
'Dope' users, 392
Dream, Freudian, 311
Drives, organic, 77

Duct glands, 136
Ductless glands, 137

EFFICIENCY, as psychological factor, 21–22
  in industry, 22
Ego, Freudian, 311
Electrocardiograph, 301
Electroencephalograph, 306
Emergency, sickness as, to the organism, 133
  situations, adjustments to, 354
Emerson, H., 213
Emotional age, 255
  attitudes, unfortunate, 228
  dependence, as motive, 111
  despair, in the crippled, 382
  experience, adequate, need for in childhood, 344
  factors, unconscious, in behavior, 310
  growth, in young child, 226
  learning, conditioned, 159
  maturity, and the nurse, 112
  satisfaction, avenues for achieving, 88
  drive for, 86
  states, 291 ff.
  suppression, 347
  transfer, 313
Emotions, avoidance of, in the sick room, 138
  classic interest in, 298
  defined, 295
  education and control of, 314
  effects of, 297
  experimental methods in studying, 298
  measurement of, 301
  naïve observation of, 298
  nurse's own, 139
Employ - the - Physically - Handicapped Week, 378
Endocrine glands, 137, 210
Environment, effects on patient, 38
  relation to intelligence, 202
Epilepsy, 389
Equilibrium, in Gestalt, 174
Escaping activity, 80
Excitement, pattern of, in original emotion, 300
Exercise, and the convalescent, 134
  and the nurse, 135
  muscular, 131
  Thorndike's Law of, 154

Exhibitionism, in patient, 86
Experimental method in psychology, 10
Extinction, experimental, in conditioning, 161

FACILITATION, in nerve functioning, 126
Facing reality, 262
Failure, as motive, 108
Faith, importance of, in the disabled, 384
Family, heredity in, 201
  life, education for, 322
    need of training for, 322
  mental hygiene of, 320
Fantasy, introversional, 285
Fatigue, 181
  of illness, 134
Fear, 282
  in adults, 307
  in childhood, 309
  patterns of, 299 ff.
Federal Old Age Assistance, 365
  Social Security Act, 368
Feeling, concept of, 291
  misuse of term, 291
  of need in learning, 158
  scale, 294
  tone, 294
Fighting, 91
Figure, in Gestalt, 173
Flight, adjustment by, 282
Focal ideas, 146
Food habits, in aged, 364
  interests, in adolescents, 240
Food-seeking activity, as drive, 79
Forgetting, 151
Frank, L. K., 344
Free association tests, 302
Frequency, principle of, 155
Freud, S., 310

GALVANIC skin reflex, 302
Gang interests, 237
Gang-mindedness, 346
Gastronomic interests, of adolescents, 240
Geriatrics, 358–374
Gestalt psychology, 17
Glands, as responding organisms, 135
  duct, 136
  ductless, 137
Glandular response, 125

Goal, in learning, 177
Goddard, H., 203
Gregarious behavior, 90
Ground, in Gestalt, 173
Group tests of intelligence, 205
Growing-up process, 219–270
Growth, defined, 220
  disproportionate, in pubescence, 221
  emotional, in young child, 226
  in childhood, 223
  in early adolescence, 234
  of bones and muscles, 234
  sex differences in, 222
Guidance, child, 26
  in therapy, 25
  of health, 43
Gustatory stimuli, 120

HABIT(s), and the nurse, 102
  as determiners of behavior, 100 ff.
  importance of, in childhood, 230
  modification of, in the sick, 103
  of study and work, 4
Hall, G. S., 14, 221, 233
'Halo effect', 20
Handicapped, classification of, 375
  treatment of by nurse, 387
Handicaps, early attention to, 399
Health, and muscular exercise, 131
  child, programs, 247
  guidance of, 43
Height-weight tables, misuse of, 222
Heredity, and the patient, 138
  family, 201
  mechanics of, 199
  racial, 201
Hobbies, in rehabilitation, 385
Hollingworth, L., 231
Home, adequate, 320
  broken, 329
  disharmonious, 323
  economic condition of, effect on pubescent, 232
  ignorant, 330
  importance of, 320
  interests, 239
Homemaking, education for, 322 ff.
Hospital(s), equipment, 52
  experience, health values in, 49
  for mentally ill, 23
  organization of, 49
  psychological factors in, 53

INDEX

Hospital(s), situation, 48
  surroundings, 53
Hull, C. L., 212
'Hunches', 207
Hunger sensations, 123
Husbands, maladjusted, 323
Hypertonus, 132

IDENTIFICATION mechanism, 229, 285
Identity, as determiner of associations, 156
Illness, fatiguing nature of, 134
  of the patient, 39
Illusions, of perception, 147
Imagery, in learning, 184
  types of, 185
Inadequate stimuli, 17, 160
Infancy, mental health of, 340
  prolonged, 111
Inferiority, sources of, 345
Infirmities, of aging people, 359
Inhibition, retroactive, 154
Innate drives, 97
Innervation, reciprocal, 127
Insecurity, in childhood, 346
  in the aging, 362
Insight, 172
Institue for Propaganda Analysis, 18
Integration, 286
  faulty, in the sick, 129
  of reaction, 126
Intelligence, and environment, 202
  and sex, 202
  government by, 260
  in learning, 198
  quotient, 204
  testing of, 203 *ff.*
Intensity, principle of, 156
Interests, adolescent, 236
  and activities, 6
  as motives, 106
  church and religious, 144
  extraprofessional, need for, 108
  for the disabled, 385
  gang, 237
  gastronomic, of adolescents, 240
  home, 239
  in actors, 238
  in dancing, 240
  in food, 240
  in movies, 238
  school, 238

Interests, wide range of, 107
International Society for the Welfare of the Crippled and Disabled, 379
Introversion, mechanics of, 283 *ff.*
  nurse and, 287
Irritability, in old age, 360

JAMES, W., 15, 102, 304
James-Lange theory of emotions, 305
Jealousy, 292
Job analysis, 21

KINESTHETIC sense, 122
Koehler, W., 172
Kuhlmann, F., 204

LANGE, C., 304
Law, psychology in, 29
Learning, and insight, 172
  animal, 168 *ff.*
  curves of, 191
    characteristics of, 193
    negatively accelerated, 195
    positively accelerated, 196
    types of, 195
  day-by-day variations in, 194
  effects of tobacco and alcohol on, 212
  first stage in, 144
  human, 171, 177
  intelligence in, 198
  logical and rote, 181
  motivation of, 158
  physical factors determining, 209
  plateaus in, 194
  progression in, 191, 197
  trial and error in, 169
  whole and part methods in, 171
Lewin, K., 274
'Lie detector', 303
Libido, Freudian, 311
Limelight, passion for, 243
Lindsey, D. B., 306
Link Battery of Clerical Tests, 20
Loneliness, in old age, 363
Loyalties, adolescent, 350

MAGOUN, H. W., 306
Maladjustment, 276
Manipulative behavior, 88
Marginal ideas, 146

Marriage adjustment, 324
Mastery, 90
Maze learning, 169
Mechanical responses, in glands, 135
Medical practice, mental hygiene in, 26
Mental age, 104
　attitudes, healthy, 259
　　optimistic, in study, 60
　discipline, 164
　fatigue, in learning, 181
　growth, in the pre-school child, 225
　health, in aged, 370
　　in infancy, 340
　　in pre-school child, 340
　　in senescence, 354
　　of adolescents, 347
　　of the school child, 344 ff.
　hospitals, public, 24
　hygiene programs, 23
　　in family, 320
　　in institutions, 24
　　in medical practice, 26
　　in organizations, 24
　responses, 125
Merrill, A. P., 369
Methods, clinical, 9
　experimental, 9
　in learning, 179
　observational, 9
Miles, W. R., 213
Mind set, as determiner of association, 156
Ministry, psychology in, 32
Minnesota Mechanical Aptitude Test, 20
　Vocational Tests for Clerical Workers, 20
Misdemeanors, 240
Mnemonic devices, 183
Mood, 315
　as determiner of association, 156
Moroseness, in old age, 361
Motivation, in learning, 158
Motives, as driving force, 342
　importance of, 77
Motor development and growth, in childhood, 223
Movies, interest in, 238
Muscle tonus, 130
　modification of, in the sick, 131
Muscles, growth of, 234
　role of, 130

Muscular exercise, 131
　responding processes, 130

NARCOTIC addiction, 392
National Committee for Mental Hygiene, 23, 230
　on Visiting Teachers, 330
　Council on Family Relations, 323
　on Parent Education, 323
　Education Association, 401
　Institute of Neurological Diseases and Blindness, 390
　Multiple Sclerosis Society, 390
　Safety Council, 376
　Society for Crippled Children and Adults, 390
Need, feeling of, in learning, 158
Nerve function, abnormality of, in the sick, 128
Nervous processes, 124
Neuromuscular diseases, 390
New York Institute for the Crippled and Disabled, 378
Noise, abatement of, 118
　and the sick, 119
　nuisance of, 118
Non-verbal tests of intelligence, 206
Normal distribution curve, 198
Notebooks, 62
Note taking, 61 ff.
Nurse, and adjustment, 281
　and conditioning, 162
　and emotional maturity, 112
　and feeling tone, 294
　and introversion, 287
　and organic drives of the patient, 82
　as learner, 187
　as thinker, 208
　attitudes of, 105
　effective, 2
　Freudian psychology and, 312
　handling of modern diseases and conditions by, 387
　in the school, 401
　physical well-being of, 3
　relationship to the family of patient, 335
　special insight needed by, in care of disabled, 379, 402
　student, 2
　success and, 110
　trial and error and, 186

INDEX

Nursing, and motivation of patient's behavior, 93
and olfaction, 119
and perception, 149
and transference in learning, 165
applicants for, as a profession, 131, 135, 137
of the addict, 392
of the alcoholic, 393
of the aged, 358 ff.
of the physically handicapped, 375 ff.
of the sick child, 249
practice of mental hygiene in, 26
Nutrition, adequate, 211

OBJECTIVES, essential to maturity, 257
unobtained, 275
Observation, method of, in psychology, 15
untrustworthiness of, 299
O'Connor Finger Dexterity Test, 20
Ocular discomfort and aberration, in the sick, 117
Old Age and Survivor Insurance, 368
Olfactory stimuli, 119
Optical illusions, 149
Organic comfort and discomfort, as drives, 78
function, disturbance of, in sick, 98
senses, 122
tensions, 77
Overlearning, 153
Oversolicitousness, 228, 377

PAMPERING, 324
Parents, adequate, 321
incompatible, 328
of tomorrow, 47
Patient, adjustment of, 36
and family, 54
appearance of, 38
approach to, 36
care of, 36
nurse's first concern, 35
Pavlov, J. P., 174
Peevishness, in old age, 360
Perception, 147
and the nurse, 149
Performance tests, 206
Peripheral theories of emotion, 305

Personality, dominating, in the parent, 325
effect of disablement upon, 376
of prolonged infancy upon, 111
types of, 343
Personnel, selection of, 19
Physical programs, adequate, in adolescence, 349
surroundings, in study, 69, 215
well-being of the nurse, 3
Physiological factors in learning, 209
limit, in learning, 195
Pity of the handicapped, avoidance of, 399
Plateaus, in learning, 194
Play, 88
Pleasantness-unpleasantness scale, 293
Pneumograph, 301
Point scales, 205
Policies, institutional, 51
Polygraph, 304
Possession, 90
Practice periods, 178
Preoccupation with self, in senescence, 363
Prepotence of stimuli, 126
Previously learned materials, use of, in studying, 59
Problem attitude, in studying, 68
box, 168
child, 230
Progress, knowledge of, in learning, 178
Pseudo-fatigue, 182
Psychiatry, 27
Psychoanalysis, 310 ff.
Psychogalvanic reflex, 302
Psychogalvanometer, 302
Psychological changes in aging, 360
services in detentional and correctional institutions, 31
weaning, 253, 348
Psychology, and adjustment of nurse, 2
applied, 18
contemporaneous schools of, 16
early history of, 14
fields of, 15
in business and industry, 19
in clinical practice, 23
in law and testimony, 30
in ministry, 32
in propaganda, 18
in testimony, 30

Psychosexual adjustment, 349
Puberty, onset of, 231 ff.
 changes in, 231
Pure Food and Drugs Administration, 22

RACIAL heredity, 201
Rage, patterns of, 299
Randall, O., 367
Rating scales, 20
Rationalization, 285
Reading, with discrimination, 67
Reality, facing of, by adult, 262
Reasoning, 163
Recall, 155
Recency, 155
Reciprocal innervation, 127
Recognition, in learning, 157
Recreational programs, adequate, in adolescence, 349
Reemployment, of disabled, 377
Reflex behavior, 98
 intensified in the sick, 129
Rehabilitation, of disabled, 377
 programs in U. S., 377
Religious interests, in adolescence, 244
Remarshalling, in study, 66
Responding organs, 130
 glands as, 135
Retention of ideas, 151
Retirement, pros and cons, 365
Retroactive inhibition, 154
Reynolds, B. C., 322
Rising curves of learning, 193
Rivalry behavior, 92
Rote learning, 181
Rusk, H. A., 376

SAFETY, supervision for, 43
Sanford, E. C., 221
Satisfaction, drive for, 86
School interests, 238
 nursing, 401
Schools of psychology, 16
Searching for essentials, in study, 61
Security, feeling of, in student nurse, 3
Self guidance in study, 58
Self reliance, adult, 255
 need for, in childhood, 340
 spiritual, 3
 through self realization, 353
 wider meaning of, 341
Senescence, mental health of, 354

Sensations, organic, 293
Sense organs, as gateways to the brain, 115
 deteriorating, in the aged, 360
 efficient, in learning, 209
 vestibular, 121
 visceral, 122
Sensory stimuli, overintense, 81
Separation, parental, 329
Sex, capacity in old age, 361
 differences in growth rate, 222
 in intelligence, 202
 urge, in disease, 85
Sherman, M., 299
'Showing off,' 92
Sickness, as emergency, 133
Similarity, as determiner of association, 156
Simon, T., 203
Skills, 187
Skin reflexes, 302
Sleep rhythm, disturbance of in the sick, 84
Snider, R. S., 306
Social adjustment, in adults, 264
 experience, need for adequate, 344
Speech, defects of, 398
Sports, in adolescence, 237
S-shaped curves, 196
Standardized tests, 20
Stanford Revision of the Binet Scale, 203
Static sense, 121
Status, 353
Stimulus, adequate, 17, 160, 176
Stimulus-response psychology, 16
Study, active method in, 64
 advance remarshalling in, 66
 habits, 4
 making summaries in, 67
 physical surroundings in, 69
 promptness in starting, 59
 self guidance in, 58
 wider meaning of, 71
Sublimation, of sex, 349
Subvocal images, 185
Success, and the nurse, 110
 as motive, 108
 awareness of, in goal seeking, 345
'Suffering hero' mechanism, 286
Summaries, in study, 67
Summation of stimuli, 126

Supervision, for safety, 43
Symbols, in learning, 184

TEACHING, as art and science, 48
  effective, principles of, 44
  in health guidance, 45
  methods of, 44
  nursing as, 43
Teen-agers, fundamental needs of, 348
Temperament, 315
Tension reducing, in learning, 158
Tensions, organic, 77
  emotional, 291 ff.
Terman, L. M., 203
Testimony, psychology of, 30
Testing, of intelligence, 203 ff.
Tests, aptitude, 20
  vocational, 20
Thinking, defined, 206
  poor, 207
  wishful, 208
Thirst sensations, 123
Thorndike, E. L., 15, 16, 154
Thurstone Clerical Tests, 20
Thwarting, adjustment in, 278
Tissues, deteriorating, in the aging, 360
Tobacco, and learning, 212
Tompkins Square House Settlement, 367
Topological concept, Lewin's, 274
Transfer, and the nurse, 165, 186
  emotional, 313
  in learning, 163
Trial and error learning, 169

UNEMPLOYABILITY, in the aging, 362
United Cerebral Palsy Association, 390
United States Public Health Service, 379
Unlearned behavior, 97

VALENCES, topological, 274
Vestibular sense, 121
Visceral senses, 122
Visual experience, 116
Vocalization, 88
Vocational adjustment, 28, 267
  counselling, 28
  Rehabilitation Act, 377

WADA, T., 80
Wanderlust, 92
Wants, basal, of man, 78
Watson, J. B., 159, 176, 298
'Weaning,' psychological, 253, 348
Wechsler-Bellevue Tests, 205
White House Conference, 223, 315
Whole method in learning, 179
Wishful thinking, 208
Wives, maladjusted, 323
Work, excessive, in childhood, 232
Workers, aging, 362
Worry, 292
Wundt, W., 14

Y.M.C.A., 28
Young, patterns of self-care in, 46
Youth, conflict in, 273

ZIEGLER Rate of Manipulation Test, 20